West Point's Scientific 200: Celebration of the Bicentennial Biographies of 200 of West Point's Most Successful and Influential Mathematicians, Scientists, Engineers, and Technologists

by

Chris Arney

The College of Saint Rose

Albany, NY

Palmetto Bookworks
P.O. Box 2105
Lexington, SC 29071

First Edition
First Edition run: 1,000 copies

Published
by:

Palmetto Bookworks
P.O. Box 2105
Lexington, SC 29071

ISBN 1-887301-15-1

West Point's Scientific 200: Celebration of the Bicentennial Biographies of 200 of West Point's Most Successful and Influential Mathematicians, Scientists, Engineers, and Technologists

by Chris Arney

The College of Saint Rose

Albany, NY

Chris Arney retired from 30 years of Army service as a brigadier general in 2001 and serves as the dean of the School of Mathematics and Sciences at The College of Saint Rose in Albany, NY. He is the author or editor of 15 technical books (mathematics texts, educational monographs, and a web-based text supplement) and over 100 journal articles, written under his given name David C. Arney. He recently co-authored a historical book on West Point's mathematics book collection. Writing under the penname Alan Firstone, Chris wrote a historical novel, *Son of the Silvery Waters*, and annotated a previously published biography. He directs an international mathematics contest and edits several mathematics journals.

Chris earned his Ph.D. from Rensselaer Polytechnic Institute and recently received a national undergraduate teaching award. As a 1971 graduate of USMA and a mathematics faculty member at the Academy for 18 years, Chris has experienced first-hand the science program at the Academy, which advanced his interest in the history of American science education. Writing his first work under the sobriquet of Chris, he celebrates USMA's Bicentennial with the publication of *West Point's Scientific 200*.

Date of Publication: 16 March 2002

(200th anniversary of the founding of the United States Military Academy)

Table of Contents

Photograph and Art Credits

I am grateful to the following for granting photograph and art permissions and access to photography and art for this volume:

West Point Museum Collection, United States Military Academy:
> Artwork of the following people: Bailey, Bass, Bowman, Church, Courtenay, Davies, DeRussy, Echols, Edgerton, Partridge, J. Swift, Thayer, Whistler.

West Point Library Special Collections and Archives, United States Military Academy:
> Class Album photographs (1857-1915),
> *Howitzer* photographs (1910-1965),
> Stockbridge Collection,

with cooperation of Directorate of Information Management for photographs on page 247 (frontispiece from Villeneuve 1740) and page xi (engraving from Bonnycastle 1818).

Association of Graduates Publications
> Annual Reunions (1860-1923)

Jeff Skalicky for his collection of pictures of Civil War Generals on the internet.

Sue Arney for her original artwork for the cover of this volume.

Preface

As the United States Military Academy (USMA) celebrates its bicentennial in 2002, there is a natural interest in its history, traditions, heritage, roles, evolution, and impact. This work is a result of my interest in USMA's roles in science and science education. The Academy's first Superintendent Jonathan Williams called West Point "a station favorable to the pursuits of science."[1] Not only was Williams' assessment accurate nearly 200 years ago, but as evidenced by the outstanding accomplishments made in science by the 200 Academy graduates portrayed in this volume, it has been an accurate assessment for West Point's entire 200-year existence. This is the first component of the underlying story in this book.

Williams' definition of science was quite broad, including mathematics and virtually all of the applied quantitative fields except those in business and finance. If anything, my definition for this book is even broader because of the many new science-based disciplines and technologies that have emerged over the past 200 years. So for the interest of this volume, science broadly includes all the mathematical sciences (statistics, operations research, applied mathematics, etc.), all varieties of the natural sciences (physical, life, earth, environmental, geographical, etc.), all varieties of engineering (civil, electrical, mechanical, nuclear, industrial, systems, topographical, etc), and all applied technologies (industrial, computational, military, surveying, ordnance, etc.). West Point graduates are first and foremost generalists, even in the sciences, and the versatility of those profiled is also a significant component of the story being told.

As a member of the Department of Mathematical Sciences at USMA for over 18 years, I had the great fortune of seeing how West Point developed its cadets and produced successful graduates, ready for military service and technically capable of solving complex problems and leading soldiers using state-of-the-art technology. It takes tremendous energy and dedication to accomplish such a mission. One recent reflection on the Academy's program explains that the generation of such energy and dedication is possible because "the Academy is a tightly bound and highly interconnected campus with tremendous espirit-de-corps that has been molded over almost two centuries."[2] Another modern assessment indicates that the West Point program is "likely to have more impact – for better or for worse – on students than almost any other kind of institution" because it has "an uncommon concentration of the characteristics that have been shown in the research of the past 30 years to have an impact on students."[3] There is no doubt that West Point has impact on its students. This is another part of this book's message.

In 1802, the United States was weak in science, but as soon as West Point graduates began their work, the country began building its scientific strength. It was "the time when

---

[1]   This quote is from a letter to William Franklin (Ben Franklin's son) dated October 22, 1807. This quote was also used in the title of a book about the mathematics books in the West Point library co-authored by the author of this work (see the References section).

[2]   John Dossey in the Mathematical Association of America book, *Confronting the Core Curriculum*, 1998, p. ix.

[3]   K. Patricia Cross, Professor of Higher Education, Berkeley, and Past President of the American Association of Higher Education, in an address at a conference held at West Point.

American science got its start."[4] Fortunately, the Academy developed a plan "to unite the scientific discussions of the French, with the practical methods of the English: that theory and practice, science and art, may mutually aid and illustrate each other."[5] The plan worked to perfection as Academy graduates forged the country's new scientific culture, established America's technical education system, and built the nation's infrastructure. Secretary of War Peter Porter explained in 1828 that West Point's legacy of "scattering the fruits of science not merely to the rest of the Army, but to the youth of our country generally, and the interchange of theoretic science … with the practical skill and judgment of our civilian engineers, … will soon furnish every part of the country with the most accomplished professors in every branch of civil engineering." [6] It was not long before West Point did all this, and America became the world's leader in science with West Point graduates leading the effort and contributing to its success. This is the remaining component of the underlying story.

To tell this story, I have included biographies of 200 of the most scientific of deceased West Point graduates. They were all important figures and contributors in their day, but it was not easy to make the evaluations and decisions of whom to include and whom to leave off this list. Even more difficult was my evaluation and ranking of the top 25 of these people. I did this, not to raise controversy, but to highlight a group for their special accomplishments and examples as West Point scientific graduates. In addition to the biographies, I also include in the volume an introduction on the historical impact of West Point graduates, short historical stories of several relevant science-based organizations and programs, and tables of information about the 200 scientists. One can't help but wonder, "What if?" these people weren't so productive. How would our lives be different today?

While others have expertly chronicled the Academy's contributions in military affairs and in general areas of human endeavor, I believe this volume is the first to concentrate solely in science, using biography as the major format. I hope through this biography you get to know the "flesh and blood" human beings who did this work and made sacrifices for the benefits of mankind. As historian James Morrison stated in 1986, "It is no exaggeration to say that an understanding of the military academy is essential to a full appreciation of the history of the United States."[7] Other authors and scholars have expertly analyzed the history of American science. So while I have included some historical essays, this book is better described as a celebration than a scholarly analysis. I've tried to be accurate, but I have not investigated all the facets of the issues raised.

And so, we begin our journey through two centuries of science and 200 distinguished graduates of West Point. The scientific accomplishments described in the volume, as dated as some are, still retain a special vitality and significance, since they helped America prosper. These 200 people, even though they lived in earlier eras, are remembered and celebrated for

---

[4] George Daniels, *American Science in the Age of Jackson*, 1968.
[5] Charles Davies, *Elements of Algebra*, 1835.
[6] Porter's quotation is found in James Endler, *Other Leaders, Other Heroes*, 1998, p. 11.
[7] James Morrison, *The Best School in the World*, 1986, (p. ix of Preface)

their versatility, dedication, and productivity. I hope you will be as amazed and excited as I am by the abundant and meaningful accomplishments and activities of this special group of the *Long Gray Line* – **THE SCIENTIFIC 200**. I also hope you will celebrate with me both the Bicentennial of the United States Military Academy and its important role in developing the nation that it has faithfully served.

Acknowledgements

Many people helped on this project. My inspiration and mentoring came from historians of mathematics and friends, Fred Rickey and Joe Albree, who co-authored an earlier book about West Point history with me, and gave me the background and confidence to attempt a project like this. Others indirectly inspired my work: Joe Arkin, George Rosenstein, Dick Jardine, Amy Shell, and Jim Tattersall. Some of the members of this group were involved in the Conference on the History of Undergraduate Mathematics in America, held at West Point in the summer of 2001. The excitement generated by that gathering gave me the energy to pursue the final stages of this work. A final boost was given by fellow mathematician Brian Winkel, who both offered help in editing and encouraged me to continue my work towards publication.

During my last years at the Academy, I had the pleasure of serving on the Academic Board, a committee of department heads and other academic leaders at USMA. Many predecessors of the group that I served with are members of **THE SCIENTIFIC 200**. I give special thanks to those department heads in mathematics-science-engineering departments for enlightening me as to the flavor and essence of these disciplines. My appreciation to engineers Kip Nygren, Dan Litynsky, Andre Sayles, Jack Grubbs, Chris King, Jim Kays, and Mike McGinnis and scientists Dave Allbee and Ray Winkel. Additional thanks to social and behavioral scientists Casey Brower, Barney Forsythe, and Dan Kaufman.

I recently retired from the Army after nearly 30 years of service and left my position as Head of the Department of Mathematical Sciences. My predecessor in that position, Frank Giordano, and my successor, Gary Krahn, have always been supportive friends and models of the West Point ideal as dedicated scientists and educators. I thank them for all they have done to build upon the legacy that is chronicled in this volume. Similarly, the support I received in my new position as Dean of the School of Mathematics and Sciences at The College of Saint Rose in Albany, NY was necessary for the completion of this project. The Vice President for Academic Affairs, Bill Lowe, and the President of the College, Mark Sullivan, have been both supportive in my efforts and tremendous leaders and mentors in my transition from the military profession to civilian life and an academic profession.

The people who helped this project most directly are the librarians. At West Point, Alan Aimone of the Special Collections Division and an expert in the Academy's history among other subjects, was extremely helpful in supporting my work with references and answering my research questions. Likewise, Suzanne Christoff, the Associate Library Director for Special Collections and Archives, was supportive in locating photographs and helping with my research. Alicia Maudlin, Archive Technician, was also helpful. David Reel, Art Curator at the West Point Museum, helped me to find the relevant artwork in their splendid collection. At The College of Saint Rose, I also found an expert library staff and numerous resources to support my work. Head Librarian Pete Koonz and his colleague Steve Black were both supportive and obliging. Whenever or wherever I needed assistance, I found the right people willing to lend a hand. Way back in the 1980s, when I first started thinking about the history of the Department of Mathematics at West Point, Army instructors like Marty Vozzo volunteered to assemble information and write preliminary studies on the people and programs. Thanks to Marty and the many others who participated in that work over the years. They taught me and motivated my work in this area. Recently, David Greene came on board to help support my general efforts in the history of science, specifically working on the history of American technical education.

Another special group in which I am proud to be a member is that of the *Long Gray Line* of Academy graduates. During my writing of the book, I celebrated my 30th graduation reunion with my USMA class of 1971. Just seeing these friends and knowing that the members of *THE SCIENTIFIC 200* were much like them made my task all the more exciting. As part of our reunion activities, we cruised the Hudson River from West Point to New York City to see the harbor and skyline shortly after the 11 September 2001 terrorist attack. This was a moving experience, and it gave me pause to reflect on the many West Point graduates, who, as construction engineers, designed and built the infrastructure of this great city. In discussions with my classmates who were working in the Pentagon on that fateful day, I gained further respect for the special effort made in the construction of America's military headquarters. West Point graduate Leslie Groves supervised this immense and miraculous work that took just 16 months to complete in 1941 and 60 years later stood tough to an attack and saved many lives. This is yet another example of the many lasting contributions made by members of *THE SCIENTIFIC 200.* I wish all Academy graduates continued success as they pursue their own service. I also give special thanks to the Association of Graduates for their support of my efforts and all they do for Academy graduates.

In researching this book, I read considerable American science history. I found three books so fascinating and helpful that I must recommend them to readers who are interested in science history in America. They gave me an appreciation for this subject that as a mathematician had I never developed before. Two volumes on American science are Robert Bruce's *Launching of Modern American Science, 1846-1876* and Hugh Slotten's *Patronage, Practice, and the Culture of American Science: Alexander Dallas Bache and the U. S. Coast Survey* (see the References section). Similarly, James Endler's recent work *Other Leaders, Other Heroes* gave me a clearer picture of the scope of the contributions of West Point graduates in all areas of human endeavor.

As a result of my retirement and taking on a new position, my family and I moved to Duanesburg, NY in the middle of the research work. This is a rural area, but even here, much like everywhere in America, West Pointers have affected change and improved the area. It was with great glee that I discovered the scientific life of West Point graduate James Duane, a member of *THE SCIENTIFIC 200*, who grew up in Duanesburg and whose grandfather first settled the area where I now live. I expect every reader will find connections to their own areas and life by members of *THE SCIENTIFIC 200*. I also hope this volume will motivate readers to conduct further research and investigation into the lives of West Point graduates.

I wish to acknowledge the support of my family, who encouraged me and helped me. Sue helped with the typing, Dan and Kristin proofread, and Katie and Lisa made us all happy. Sue's parents, Bob and Betty Skopek, helped with the editing as well. None of this would be possible without them.

Finally, I thank the members of *THE SCIENTIFIC 200*. They make this work a story of people (West Point graduates), who made a difference in America. We all owe them our gratitude and respect, because they gave to the United States and the world the lasting and meaningful gifts of knowledge and prosperity.

I know there are errors in this volume, but I do not know where they are. I take full responsibility for what is incorrect, wrongfully included, and wrongfully left out. I hope that any errors do not distract from the message and content in the book. In meeting the deadline of the bicentennial celebration of the Academy, many parts of this book were parallel processed, which expedited publication. I thank the publisher, Gary Baker of Palmetto Bookworks, and his staff who helped put this together for all of us to enjoy.

DUANESBURG, NY AND WEST POINT, NY
November 2001

Introduction

In celebration of the bicentennial of the United States Military Academy (USMA) in 2002, this book biographs 200 West Point graduates who have made significant contribution to and impact upon America's scientific professions (mathematicians, scientists, engineers, technologists). The biographies emphasize the professional aspects of their lives, while highlighting noteworthy accomplishments such as military service, political service, humanitarian deeds, business success, and personal adventure. Many photographs and portraits of the honorees are included. USMA's primary mission is to develop leaders for America's military, but as America's first science-based engineering college, West Point's impact on the technical and educational cultures of America has been significant and noteworthy. West Point's leader development system, which has creditably produced America's military leaders for two centuries, also developed numerous technical leaders, who have greatly impacted American history. This book provides insights and highlights on 200 of the most significant of these people. This group is referred to as *The Scientific 200* (or *The 200*) in this volume. Of the nearly 58,500 West Point graduates (as of June 2001), thousands have served in technical positions or as technical educators (both in and out of the military). These 200 are exemplary representatives of the numerous successful graduates, who have contributed to America's technological achievements.

The Contents

In addition to the 200 biographies and this introduction, this volume contains short accounts of several relevant science-based professional organizations. The organizations include: Technical Education Community in America, USMA's Mathematics-Science-Engineering (MSE) Program, Army Corps of Engineers, Corps of Topographical Engineers, Ordnance Corps, U.S. Coast Survey, American Association for the Advancement of Science, National Academy of Sciences, American Philosophical Society, and U.S. Military Philosophical Society.

As West Point celebrates its bicentennial, it seems appropriate to take stock of its overall role in American society. As President Theodore Roosevelt stated on the Academy's Centennial Celebration, June 11, 1902, "no other educational institution in the land has contributed as many names as West Point has contributed to the honor roll of the nation's greatest citizens."[8] This study of the technical/educational role of the Academy demonstrates just one aspect of the profound influence this highly visible and world-renown institution has made on society. Certainly, looking at the Academy's contributions in its major mission area of training men and women for military service, it is hard to find a conflict or military event where the graduates of the Academy were not influential. The same can be said in technical education. USMA graduates contributed greatly to America's technology and profoundly influenced America's educational culture. Analysis shows that the Academy's academic program and leader development system had direct effects on setting high standards and making scholarly contributions in the form of the *militarization* of science and technical education.

---

[8] *Centennial*, p. 20.

The Selection

How were the 200 selected? Naturally, all are West Point graduates. Secondly, they are deceased, therefore, eliminating many currently active or recently retired professionals and educators from eligibility. This requirement reduces the potential pool of candidates from the 58,500 total graduates to less than 16,000 deceased West Point graduates. Therefore, this list of *THE 200* includes over 1% of the eligible candidates. This requirement also makes all members on this list men, since the Academy graduated women for only the last 22 years. Thirdly, a balance of educators and other professionals was sought, along with diversity in their positions and disciplines of studies. While many graduated from West Point early in the 19th century when Academy graduates had relatively few competitors or colleagues in the technical professions, the list was balanced with graduates of the late 1800s and early 1900s. Overall, there are 149 entries of 19th century graduates and 51 of the 20th century. The period 1827 to 1851 dominates the other quarter centuries with 59 selectees in *THE 200*.

All of *THE 200* are classified into one of four broad technical disciplines – mathematician, scientist, engineer, or technologist. In many cases, this was a difficult decision; West Point graduates are often versatile and multi-talented, working in varied aspects of technical and leadership positions. This is possible because of the breadth of the required technical courses in USMA's curriculum. The historical essay of USMA's MSE (technical) program contained in this volume describes some of the subjects and course content of the program over the years. Some of the members of *THE SCIENTIFIC 200* performed duties in two, three, or even all four of the disciplinary categories. However, a primary classification was made in order to see the overall nature of the technical work performed by these 200 West Point graduates. This categorization produced 89 engineers, 48 mathematicians, 45 scientists, and 18 technologists. Along with the primary classification, the other technical professions and disciplines of the person are listed. To better visualize some of the attributes of *THE 200*, tables and listings of various characteristics for the 200 members are provided in the Appendix.

West Point graduates, for the most part, have careers that begin with military service. The military has always been a highly technical profession because of the sophisticated weapons, equipment, and support systems used for its mission. Much of what Army officers do can be called military science. The modern military is even more technically advanced, with many military careers engendering scientific accomplishments and technical expertise. So it is not surprising that some of *THE SCIENTIFIC 200* spent most, if not all, of their professional lives in the military (primarily Army, but some were in the Air Force). Others of *THE 200* performed their science outside of military service. There was no attempt to include more of either kind of technical service in assembling *THE 200*. However, it is evident that most of the scientists in this list are *doers* – people who were not satisfied with only learning or studying science, but used their science to accomplish something for society or build a product for use in the world. The involvement, expertise, and leadership of these 200 graduates were used in the development and utilization of the emerging technologies of their eras.

The members of the list had academic talent in addition to their dedication. Most showed their talent during their cadet years by high academic achievement, although some struggled a bit in academics. Using class rank as a gage, members of *THE SCIENTIFIC 200* outperformed their classmates. Exactly 50% of the 200 honorees finished in the top 10% of their class, and 26% were valedictorians or salutatorians. See the Appendix for further statistics.

It is evident that most of the professional work of these 200 (and West Point graduates in general) was based in the mathematical or physical sciences. This is not surprising given the historical needs of the military and the civil, mechanical, electrical, and systems engineering focus of the West Point program. There are some exceptions of undertakings in the biological sciences, but often those efforts were in addition to assigned duties in the physical sciences or completely separate from their West Point education or military profession.

Twenty-five biographies are highlighted as foremost examples of the West Point graduate as a technical professional. These 25 graduates have made significant contributions as scholars or are well known as West Point graduates and, therefore, spark special interest. These *Top 25* are given in order of their influence as judged by the author, followed by the remaining 175 entries in graduation order.

As in any selection, there were many difficult choices on who to include in the list. There are many more West Point graduates who are deserving of inclusion in *THE SCIENTIFIC 200*. Therefore, an extra entry entitled Honorable Mentions is provided at the end of the biographies. This entry mentions hsome of the others of note – essentially those that could have been included. Also in this section are people who were West Point cadets that did considerable scientific work, but did not graduate from the Academy, and West Point faculty members whose scientific contributions were substantial, but again were not graduates of the Academy.

Technical Details

Details about the entries are as follows. Each West Point graduate is assigned a Cullum number (named after **George Cullum (USMA 1833)** [9] who first assigned these numbers), which provides the graduation order. Each entry contains this *Graduate #*. From 1818 until 1978, these numbers were assigned by class rank order. Before 1818, there was no class rank, but there were various dates of graduation which provided the assigned Cullum order. After 1978, Cullum numbers were assigned alphabetically in each graduating class. The graduation date listed for the 200 entries is usually the year of graduation, unless there were more than one class graduation in a year. For instance, during World War I and World War II classes graduated after 2 or 3 years. During the Civil War, the program lasted four years instead of the normal five years. Therefore, some years contain two graduating classes, listed by both month and year. There are classes of May 1861, June 1861, April 1917, August 1917, June 1918, November 1918, 13 June 1922, 14 June 1922, January 1943, and June 1943. There were no graduates in 1810 and 1816, and only one graduate in 1813. Each entry also contains the specific class rank, when applicable, and the dates and places of birth and

---

[9] The bold font for Cullum and Holden (on the next page) indicate that they are members of The 200. Whenever the name of one of The Scientific 200 appears in this volume (except in his own biography or repeated in the same section), the name and graduation year are highlighted in bold-face type.

death, when known. Some of this basic information, along with some assignments, awards, and promotions, can be found in the *Registrar of Graduates and Former Cadets of the United States Military Academy,* published annually by the West Point Association of Graduates. The additional information in each entry was consolidated from several sources. The major ones being published biographies, such as:

DAB   *Dictionary of American Biography*

ANB   *American National Biography*

ACAB   *Appleton's Cyclopaedia of American Biography*

NCAB   *National Cyclopedia of American Biography*

DSB   *Dictionary of Scientific Biography*

BDAS   *Biographic Dictionary of American Science.*

Obituaries for West Point graduates, published by the Association of Graduates, found in either:

AR   *Annual Reunions* until 1941

AS   *Assembly* magazine after 1941.

Some biographies of the early graduates of the Academy also appeared in George Washington Cullum's five volumes, *Biographical Register of the Officers and Graduates of the U.S. Military Academy,* (the first three volumes were edited by Cullum, the fourth by **Edward Holden (USMA 1870)**, and the fifth by Charles Braden (USMA 1869)) and its supplements. See the Reference Section for citations to these works and the others used for general reference. When the written biography includes information from these sources, it is indicated with the codes listed after the disciplines and professions of the person. Other general sources are listed in the references section at the end of the volume. Specific references, in addition to the ones listed above, for an individual entry are listed at the end of the entry.

Summary of the *Top 25*

The characteristics that seem to distinguish the *Top 25* are opportunity for scientific service and intense passion for their technical work. For them, science and scholarship were their calling, often demanding sacrifice in other areas of life (sometimes military careers and advancements) to maintain their scientific progress. Their production and leadership in science were significant. Their entries outline the credentials and contributions of these noteworthy leaders in American science. The impact of their work on society and the obstacles they overcame to achieve their successes are also presented. For the most part, these 25 were professional scientists, who directly contributed to teaching, research, leading, and problem solving in their discipline. Some were authors of books, articles, and monographs. Others were expert users of their subject to solve problems that benefited society or were formidable leaders of major scientific or technical projects. Through the historic lens, we see several roles played by these talented people. Several were truly *Captains* of American science – pioneers in the development and spread of science across society and leaders of departments, programs, schools, or government organizations. Some were well-known *Celebrities*, known for their scientific contributions or possibly their military or political exploits. Others were relatively unknown *Sentinels*, making significant contributions in the hidden background of science, scouting out solutions and reporting their findings, but whose influence was substantial and lasting. All were scientific trailblazers in one form or another. In total, their collective impact on science in America has been significant. In the ***Top 25*** of ***The Scientific 200***, eight are *Captains* of science, nine are *Celebrities* of science, and eight are *Sentinels* of science.

The ***Top 25***, in order, are shown in the following list along with their graduation year, Cullum number, discipline, and the author's classification of their role in science:

	Name	Grad Yr	Cullum #	Discipline	Classification
1	Alexander D. Bache	1825	392	Scientist	Captain
2	Sylvanus Thayer	1808	33	Mathematician	Captain
3	Jacob W. Bailey	1832	666	Scientist	Sentinel
4	Charles Davies	1815	157	Mathematician	Celebrity
5	Edward Courtenay	1821	262	Mathematician	Sentinel
6	George W. Goethals	1880	2828	Engineer	Celebrity
7	Leslie R. Groves	1918	6032	Engineer	Celebrity
8	Ormsby M. Mitchel	1829	555	Mathematician	Celebrity
9	A. A. Humphreys	1831	641	Engineer	Captain
10	Thomas H. Johnson	1965	25511	Scientist	Sentinel
11	John G. Barnard	1833	708	Engineer	Captain
12	Kenneth D. Nichols	1929	8491	Engineer	Sentinel
13	Edward S. Holden	1870	2314	Scientist	Celebrity
14	William P. Trowbridge	1848	1369	Scientist	Captain
15	Alden Partridge	1806	15	Mathematician	Celebrity
16	Andrew Talcott	1818	181	Engineer	Celebrity
17	Richard Delafield	1818	180	Engineer	Celebrity
18	Boyd W. Bartlett	1919	6258	Scientist	Sentinel
19	Wirt Robinson	1887	3182	Scientist	Sentinel
20	Dennis H. Mahan	1824	361	Engineer	Captain
21	William H. C. Bartlett	1826	429	Scientist	Captain
22	Albert E. Church	1828	508	Mathematician	Captain
23	William Norton	1831	635	Scientist	Sentinel
24	Roscoe C. Wilson	1928	8273	Technologist	Celebrity
25	Henry Abbot	1854	1632	Engineer	Sentinel

The first two on this list, Bache and Thayer, were intimately involved in the significant activities of science development and in the vanguard of American science. Bache has been called the "Father of American Science," and Thayer, in addition to his designation as "Father of the Military Academy," has been titled "Father of American Technical Education." The three long-term, 19th century MSE professors, Mahan, Bartlett, and Church, taught nearly half the members of the 200 and indirectly influenced many more. Adding to the particulars in their biographical entries, information on their roles in various organizations is contained in several of the historic essays.

Professors of Renown

The leaders of academic programs at America's colleges were the Professors (of the disciplines). There was typically one Professor in each department with several assistants and possibly some associates. West Point was no exception, except that its technical curriculum in mathematics, science, and engineering (MSE) disciplines was so large, it had more assistant professors than most colleges. The MSE Professors at USMA played the additional roles of faculty mentor and developer, since most, if not all of the assistant professors, were woefully inexperienced, filling short military tours of three to five years teaching cadets before returning to field duty. The Professors were the academic leaders and the most experienced educators at USMA (and in some cases in all of America). The following are the USMA Professors who appear in *THE 200*:

- In the Department of Mathematics: **Alden Partridge (USMA 1806)**, **Charles Davies (1815)**, **Albert Church (USMA 1828)**, **Edgar Bass (USMA 1868)**, **Wright Edgerton (USMA 1874)**, **Charles Echols (USMA 1917)**, **William Bessell (USMA 1920)**, and **Charles Nicholas (USMA 1925)**.

- In the Department of Natural and Experimental Philosophy: **Edward Courtenay (USMA 1821)**, **William Bartlett (USMA 1826)**, **Peter Michie (USMA 1863)**, **William Gordon (USMA 1877)**, and **Clifton Carter (USMA 1899)**.

- In the Department of Engineering (Civil and Military, 1823-1942) (Military Art and Engineering 1942-1969): **Dennis Mahan (USMA 1824)**, **James Mercur (USMA 1866)**, **Gustav Fiebeger (USMA 1879)**, and **William Mitchell (USMA 1902)**.

Science section room (from Howitzer)

- In the Department of Chemistry (Chemistry and Mineralogy, 1820-1837, Chemistry, Mineralogy, and Geology, 1837-1943, Chemistry and Electricity, 1943-1967, Physics and Chemistry, 1946-1967): **William Hopkins (USMA 1825)**, **Jacob Bailey (USMA 1832)**, **Henry Kendrick (USMA 1835)**, **Samuel Tillman (USMA 1869)**, **Wirt Robinson (USMA 1887)**, **Chauncey Fenton (USMA 1904)**, **Boyd Bartlett (USMA 1919)**, **Gerald Counts (USMA August 1917)**, **Edward Gillette (USMA 1920)**, and **John Jannarone (USMA 1938)**.

- In the Department of Drawing (Earth, Space, and Graphics, 1960-1979): **Lawrence Schick (USMA 1920)**.

- In the Department of Ordnance and Gunnery: **Stephen Benét (USMA 1849)**, **Alfred Mordecai (USMA June 1861)**, **Henry Metcalf (USMA 1868)**, **Colden Ruggles (USMA 1890)**, and **John Billingsley (USMA 1928)**.

- In the Department of Practical Military Engineering: **George Cullum (USMA 1833)**, **Alexander Bowman (USMA 1825)**, **John Barnard (USMA 1833)**, **James Duane (USMA 1848)**, **Oswald Ernst (USMA 1964)**, **Henry Robert (USMA 1857)**, and **George Goethals (USMA 1880)**.

USMA graduates became founders and leaders of many of the technical programs at new American technical schools and large universities during the middle of the 19th century.

Professors of distinction serving at other colleges and universities include: **Horace Webster (USMA 1818)** at Hobart College, NY and City College of New York; **Albert Bledsoe (USMA 1830)** at University of Virginia; **William Norton (USMA 1831)** at Yale University, CT; **Benjamin Ewell (USMA 1832)** at William and Mary College, VA; **Francis H. Smith (USMA 1833)** at Virginia Military Institute; **Henry Eustis (USMA 1842)** at Harvard University, MA; **Issac Quinby (USMA 1843)** at University of Rochester, NY; **William Peck (USMA 1844)** at Columbia University, NY; **William Trowbridge (USMA 1848)** at Yale University, CT; **Frank Soulé (USMA 1866)** at University of California at Berkeley; **Robert Fletcher (USMA 1868)** at Dartmouth College, NH; and **Frederic Hinrichs (USMA 1902)** at California Institute of Technology.

There were many others who were involved in the spread of USMA's academic program to schools across the country. The history of the USMA's mathematics-science-engineering program given later in this volume provides more details of this expansion of USMA's influence.

Military Technologists and Engineers

Military service in the technical branches (engineers and ordnance and to some extent signal corps and artillery) could take on many flavors. West Point graduates were often the administrative leaders with just enough knowledge to understand how to use the technical aspects of the branch to accomplish the military mission. However, some Academy graduates took their technical duties a step or two beyond just knowing enough to do the job. These are the type who appear in *THE 200*. For instance the Chiefs of Army Engineers who appear on the list are: **Joseph Swift (USMA 1802), Joseph Totten (USMA 1805), Richard Delafield (USMA 1818), Andrew Humphreys (USMA 1831), Horatio Wright (USMA 1841), John Newton (USMA 1842), James Duane (USMA 1848), Thomas Casey (USMA 1852), Henry Robert (USMA 1857), John Wilson (USMA 1860), John Barlow (USMA May 1861), George Gillespie (USMA 1862), William Marshall (USMA 1868), Raymond Wheeler (USMA 1911),** and **William Gribble (USMA 1941)**.

Some of the other engineers of distinction in *THE 200* are: **Rene DeRussy (USMA 1812), William McNeill (USMA 1817), Andrew Talcott (USMA 1818), G. W. Whistler (USMA 1819), John Barnard (USMA 1833), Montgomery Meigs (USMA 1836), Quincy Gillmore (USMA 1849), Henry Abbot (USMA 1854), William Merrill (USMA 1825), Eugene Griffin (1875), George Goethals (USMA 1880), Hiram Chittenden (USMA 1884),** and **William Kaula (USMA 1948)**.

Engineers who performed topographical work were prevalent in the 19th century. Well-known topographic engineers in *THE 200* are: **John Abert (USMA 1811), Hartman Bache (USMA 1818), William Turnbull (USMA 1819), William Swift (USMA 1819), William Williams (USMA 1824), Thomas Cram (USMA 1826), Robert E. Lee (USMA 1829), Thomas Jefferson Lee (USMA 1830), William Emory (USMA 1831), E. Parker Scammon (USMA 1837), William Franklin (USMA 1843), William Peck (USMA 1844),** and **Gouverneur K. Warren (USMA 1850)**.

Ordnance officers were involved in all areas of MSE and technology. Some of the most distinguished and productive, who appear in *THE 200* are: **George Bomford (USMA 1805), James Ripley (USMA 1814), Alfred Mordecai (USMA 1823), Robert Parrott (USMA 1824), Josiah Gorgas (USMA 1841), Thomas Rodman (USMA 1841), William Crozier (USMA 1876),** and **John Thompson (USMA 1882)**.

Research Scientists

While most of the USMA graduates in science were users of scientific knowledge and skills to solve problems, some were researchers, who discovered new theories or created new results. Therefore, some of *THE 200* had the opportunity to develop new science as classical researchers and theorists. Some of these scientists include: **Ormsby M. Mitchel (USMA 1829), Roswell Park (USMA 1831), Jacob Bailey (USMA 1832), Edward Holden (USMA 1870), Wirt Robinson (USMA 1887), Boyd Bartlett (USMA 1919), Kenneth Nichols (USMA 1929), Alfred Haussman (USMA 1946), John Kallfelz (USMA 1956),** and **Thomas Johnson (USMA 1965)**.

Librarians

The West Point Library has been a valuable resource to both cadets and faculty over its 200 years of service to the Academy. There were several members of *THE 200* who served as head librarians, among them are: **Absalom Baird (USMA 1849), Oliver Howard (USMA 1854), Stephen Benét (USMA 1849), Edward Boynton (USMA 1846), Edgar Bass (USMA 1868), Quincy Gillmore (USMA 1849), Peter Michie (USMA 1863), Samuel Tillman (USMA 1869),** and **Edward Holden (USMA 1870)**.

Military Leaders

Many of *THE 200* served in combat, and several in multiple wars (as many as four). The Civil War involved the most at 74 of the 200 honorees. Several times in the Civil War, the two field commanders (both Union and Confederate) of major battles were members of the *THE 200.* As was stated earlier, West Point graduates are often very versatile. Some of *THE 200* were so versatile they were able to accomplish tremendous amounts in science while, or in addition to, successfully pursuing their military careers as leaders of soldiers. Some of *THE 200* that fit this mold are: **Robert E. Lee (USMA 1829), Henry Halleck (USMA 1839), John Schofield (USMA 1853), Douglas MacArthur (USMA 1903), Henry Arnold (USMA 1907), Omar Bradley (USMA 1915),** and **Dwight Eisenhower (USMA 1915)**. Additionally, people like **Benjamin Alvord (USMA 1833)** had to overcome the hardships of constant field duty to perform his science while living and working on the frontier.

THE SCIENTIFIC 200

This table lists all 200 of the members of West Point's **SCIENTIFIC 200** in graduation order. The bold type indicates inclusion in the **TOP 25**. Because of the limited space in this table only some affiliations are listed and many abbreviations are used. Refer to the Index for alphabetical look up and listings of other entries.

Name	Pg. #	Grad year	Grad #	Discip-line	Position	School/organization	Combat Service
Joseph G. Swift	43	1802	1	Engineer	Sup't	USMA	1812
George Bomford	44	1805	8	Tech.	Engineer Inventor	Fortifications Cannon	1812
Joseph G. Totten	45	1805	10	Engineer	Supervisor Regent Member	NY Harbor Smithsonian Nat'l Acad Science	1812 Mex. C.W.
Alden Partridge	**26**	1806	15	Math.	Sup't Founder	USMA Norwich	
John Anderson	46	1807	28	Engineer	Surveyor	Lake Champlain	1812
Sylvanus Thayer	**4**	1808	33	Math.	Sup't	USMA	1812
John J. Abert	47	1811	71	Engineer	Surveyor		1812
Rene DeRussy	48	1812	89	Engineer	Sup't Inventor	USMA Gun Carriage	1812 1812
James Wolfe Ripley	49	1814	102	Tech.	Sup't Chief	Springfield Armory Army Ordnance	1812 Sem. Mex. C.W.
Charles Davies	**7**	1815	157	Math.	Dept Head Professor Professor	USMA Columbia Trinity	
William G. McNeill	50	1817	172	Engineer	Engineer	Railroads	Sem.
Richard Delafield	**29**	1818	180	Engineer	Engineer Sup't Regent	Fortifications USMA Smithsonian	C.W.
Andrew Talcott	**28**	1818	181	Engineer	Engineer	Fortifications	
Horace Webster	51	1818	183	Math.	Professor Professor President	USMA Geneva College CCNY	
Hartman Bache	52	1818	198	Engineer	Topograph	Harbors	C.W.
Henry Brewerton	53	1819	207	Engineer	Sup't Engineer	USMA Fortifications	
William Turnbull	54	1819	211	Engineer	Engineer	Lighthouses	Mex.
George W. Whistler	54	1819	214	Engineer	Engineer	Railroads (in Russia)	
William H. Swift	55	1819	231	Engineer	Surveyor	Coast Survey	
Thomas E. Sudler	56	1820	234	Math.	Professor Professor	St. Johns' College Dickinson College	
Edward Courtenay	**9**	1821	262	Math.	Professor Professor	USMA U of VA	
Edward Ross	57	1821	268	Math.	Professor	Kenyon College	Sem.
Alfred Mordecai	58	1823	326	Scientist	Professor	USMA	Mex.
George S. Greene	59	1823	327	Engineer	Professor Engineer	USMA Aqueducts/RRs	C.W.
Dennis H. Mahan	**34**	1824	361	Engineer	Dept Head	USMA	

Robert P. Parrott	61	1824	363	Scientist	Inventor	Cannon	Indian Mex.
William Williams	62	1824	375	Engineer	Surveyor	Great Lakes	
Alexander Bache	**1**	1825	392	Scientist	Sup't	US Coast Survey	
					1st Pres	Nat'l Acad Sciences	
					Professor	U of Pennsylvania	
Alexander Bowman	63	1825	394	Engineer	Sup't	USMA	
William F. Hopkins	64	1825	402	Scientist	Professor	USMA	
					Professor	USNA	
William Bartlett	**36**	1826	429	Scientist	Dept Head	USMA	
Thomas J. Cram	65	1826	432	Engineer	Professor	USMA	C.W.
John Childe	66	1827	471	Engineer	Constr Eng	Railroads	
Gabriel James Rains	66	1827	482	Scientist	Inventor	Landmines	Sem.
						Torpedoes	Mex. C.W.
Albert Church	**38**	1828	508	Math.	Dept Head	USMA	
William W. Mather	68	1828	522	Scientist	Professor	Ohio University	
Robert E. Lee	69	1829	542	Engineer	Sup't	USMA	Mex.
					President	Washington College	C.W.
Cath. Buckingham	70	1829	546	Math.	Professor	Kenyon College	C.W.
Charles Hackley	71	1829	549	Math.	Professor	Columbia College	
O. M. Mitchel	**15**	1829	555	Math.	Professor	Cincinnati College	C.W.
James Clark	72	1829	574	Math.	Professor	Georgetown	
					President	Holy Cross	
Thomas J. Lee	73	1830	593	Engineer	Topograph	Boundaries	
Albert T. Bledsoe	74	1830	602	Math.	Professor	Kenyon College	C.W.
					Professor	Miami University	
					Professor	U of Virginia	
Roswell Park	75	1831	629	Scientist	Professor	U of Pennsylvania	
					President	Racine College	
William Norton	**39**	1831	635	Scientist	Professor	Delaware College	
					Professor	Yale	
					Member	Nat'l Academy Sci	
Jacob Ammen	76	1831	640	Math.	Professor	USMA	C.W.
					Professor	Transylvania College	
					Professor	Indiana University	
A. A. Humphreys	**16**	1831	641	Engineer	Surveyor	Coast Survey	Sem. C.W.
William H. Emory	77	1831	642	Scientist	Surveyor	Boundaries	Indian Mex. C.W.
Charles Whittlesey	79	1831	660	Scientist	Surveyor	Ohio Geology Survey	C.W.
Benjamin S. Ewell	80	1832	664	Math.	Professor	Hampden Sydney	C.W.
					Professor	Washington College	
					President	William & Mary	
George W. Cass	81	1832	665	Engineer	Engineer	Roads	
Jacob W. Bailey	**6**	1832	666	Scientist	Professor	USMA	
					Professor	Princeton	
					President	AAAS	
John G. Barnard	**19**	1833	708	Engineer	Sup't	USMA	Mex.
						Nat'l Acad Sciences	C.W.
George W. Cullum	82	1833	709	Engineer	Sup't	USMA	Mex.
						American Geo Soc	C.W.
Francis H. Smith	83	1833	711	Math.	Professor	Hampden Sydney	C.W.

Benjamin Alvord	84	1833	728	Math.	Professor	USMA Nat'l Acad Sciences	Sem. Mex. C.W.
Richard S. Smith	85	1834	779	Scientist	Professor President	USNA Girard College	C.W.
Henry L. Kendrick	86	1835	801	Scientist	Professor	USMA	Mex.
Herman Haupt	87	1835	816	Engineer	Professor Inventor	Pennsylvania College Pneumatic Drill	C.W.
Joseph R. Anderson	88	1836	845	Tech.			C.W.
Montgomery Meigs	89	1836	846	Engineer	Engineer Fellow Regent	Construction Projects Nat'l Acad Sciences Smithsonian Museum	C.W.
Henry Lockwood	90	1836	863	Math.	Professor	USNA	Sem. C.W.
Henry W. Benham	91	1837	891	Engineer	Scientist	Coast Survey	Mex. C.W.
Alexander B. Dyer	92	1837	896	Tech.	Chief	Army Ordnance	Sem. Mex. C.W.
E. Parker Scammon	93	1837	899	Math.	Professor President	Seton Hall Polytechnic College	Sem. Mex. C.W.
Pierre Beauregard	94	1838	942	Engineer	Sup't	USMA	Mex. C.W.
Isaac I. Stevens	96	1839	986	Engineer	Assistant	Coast Survey	Mex. C.W.
Henry Halleck	97	1839	988	Engineer	Cmdr	Union Army	C.W.
Zealous B. Tower	98	1841	1059	Engineer	Sup't	USMA	Mex. C.W.
Horatio G. Wright	99	1841	1060	Engineer	Professor	USMA	C.W.
Josiah Gorgas	100	1841	1064	Tech.	President	U of Alabama	Mex. C.W.
Thomas J. Rodman	101	1841	1065	Scientist	Inventor	Cannon	Mex. C.W.
Claudius Sears	102	1841	1089	Math.	Professor Professor	U of Louisiana U of Mississippi	Sem. C.W.
Henry Eustis	103	1842	1111	Engineer	Professor Dean	USMA Harvard	C.W.
John Newton	104	1842	1112	Engineer	Professor	USMA	C.W.
George W. Rains	105	1842	1113	Scientist	Inventor Professor Dean	Steam Engines USMA Georgia Med College	Sem. Mex. C.W.
Alexander Stewart	106	1842	1122	Math.	Professor Chancellor	Nashville University U of Mississippi	C.W.
Daniel H. Hill	107	1842	1138	Math.	Professor Professor President	Washington College Davidson College U of Arkansas	Mex. C.W.
William B. Franklin	108	1843	1167	Engineer	Professor	USMA	C.W.
Isaac F. Quinby	110	1843	1172	Math.	Professor	U of Rochester	Mex. C.W.
William Peck	111	1844	1206	Math.	Professor Professor	USMA Columbia	Mex.
Edward B. Hunt	111	1845	1232	Engineer	Professor	USMA	C.W.
William F. Smith	112	1845	1234	Math.	Professor President	USMA Int'l Telegraph Co.	C.W.

Ed. Kirby-Smith	114	1845	1255	Math.	Professor	USMA	Mex.
					Professor	U of the South	C.W.
					Chancellor	U of Nashville	
Edward C. Boynton	115	1846	1283	Scientist	Professor	USMA	Mex.
					Professor	U of Mississippi	Sem.
W. Trowbridge	**24**	1848	1369	Scientist	Researcher	US Coast Survey	C.W.
					Professor	Yale	
					Member	Nat'l Acad Sciences	
James C. Duane	116	1848	1371	Engineer	Professor	USMA	C.W.
					Chief	Army Engineers	
Quincy A. Gillmore	117	1849	1407	Engineer	Professor	USMA	C.W.
					1st Pres	Mississippi R Com	
Stephen V. Benét	118	1849	1409	Tech.	Professor	USMA	
Absalom Baird	119	1849	1415	Math.	Professor	USMA	Sem.
							C.W.
							Indian
Gouverneur Warren	120	1850	1451	Engineer	Professor	USMA	C.W.
Thomas L. Casey	121	1852	1536	Engineer	Professor	USMA	C.W.
					Engineer	Washington Mon	
William Boggs	122	1853	1582	Tech.	Professor	Virginia A&M	C.W.
John M. Schofield	123	1853	1585	Scientist	Professor	USMA	C.W.
					Sup't	USMA	
					Professor	Washington U	
G. W. Custis Lee	124	1854	1631	Engineer	Professor	VMI	C.W.
					President	Washington & Lee	
Henry L. Abbot	**41**	1854	1632	Engineer	Professor	Army Engr School	C.W.
					Professor	Geo Washington U	
Oliver O. Howard	125	1854	1634	Math.	Professor	USMA	C.W.
					Sup't	USMA	Indian
Junius Wheeler	127	1855	1681	Engineer	Professor	USMA	C.W.
Alexander S. Webb	128	1855	1689	Math.	Professor	USMA	Indian
					President	CCNY	C.W.
Edward Alexander	129	1857	1762	Engineer	Professor	U of South Carolina	C.W.
Henry M. Robert	130	1857	1763	Engineer	Chief	Army Engineers	C.W.
William E. Merrill	131	1859	1825	Engineer	Engineer	Corps of Engrs	C.W.
Samuel H. Lockett	132	1859	1826	Engineer	Professor	USMA	C.W.
					President	Calhoun College	
Horace Porter	133	1860	1849	Engineer	Engineer	Railroads	C.W.
Benjamin F. Sloan	134	1860	1853	Scientist	Professor	U of South Carolina	C.W.
					President	U of South Carolina	
John M. Wilson	135	1860	1858	Engineer	Sup't	USMA	C.W.
John W. Barlow	136	May 1861	1901	Engineer	Professor	USMA	C.W.
					Surveyor	Yellowstone Park	
Alfred Mordecai	137	June 1861	1941	Math.	Professor	USMA	C.W.
George L. Gillespie	138	1862	1968	Engineer	Engineers	Rivers and Harbors	C.W.
Peter S. Michie	139	1863	1996	Scientist	Professor	USMA	C.W.
William R. King	141	1863	1999	Engineer	Professor	Army Engineer School	C.W.
William Benyaurd	141	1863	2000	Engineer	Professor	USMA	C.W.
Oswald H. Ernst	142	1864	2025	Engineer	Professor	USMA	C.W.
					Sup't	USMA	Sp-Am
Charles Raymond	143	1865	2047	Engineer	Professor	USMA	
James Mercur	145	1866	2116	Engineer	Professor	USMA	
Frank Soulé, Jr	146	1866	2125	Engineer	Professor	U of CA (Berkeley)	

Hiero B. Herr	147	1866	2129	Engineer	Professor	USMA	
					Professor	Lehigh	
Henry Dunwoody	148	1866	2133	Scientist	Inventor	Radio receiver	Sp-Am
Lewis M. Haupt	149	1867	2162	Engineer	Professor	U of Pennsylvania	
John G. D. Knight	150	1868	2220	Math.	Professor	USMA	WW I
Edgar W. Bass	151	1868	2222	Math.	Dept Head	USMA	Indian
William L. Marshall	152	1868	2225	Engineer	Professor	USMA	C.W.
Henry Metcalf	153	1868	2227	Scientist	Professor	USMA	
					Inventor	Detachable magazine	
Robert Fletcher	154	1868	2230	Engineer	Professor	Dartmouth	
					Director	Thayer Engr School	
Samuel E. Tillman	155	1869	2275	Scientist	Professor	USMA	
					Sup't	USMA	
Arthur S. Hardy	156	1869	2282	Math.	Professor	Dartmouth	
David A. Lyle	157	1869	2284	Scientist	Professor	USMA	Sp-Am
Winfield S. Chaplin	158	1870	2313	Engineer	Professor	Harvard	
					Professor	Union College	
					Chancellor	Washington U	
Edward S. Holden	**22**	1870	2314	Scientist	Professor	USMA	
					Astronom'r	U of Wisconsin	
					President	U of CA	
William Bixby	159	1873	2468	Engineer	Professor	USMA	
John P. Wisser	160	1874	2517	Tech.	Professor	USMA	WW I
Wright P. Edgerton	161	1874	2522	Math.	Dept Head	USMA	Sp-Am
Eugene Griffin	162	1875	2552	Engineer	Professor	USMA	Sp-Am
					Researcher	General Electric	
William Crozier	163	1876	2597	Tech.	Professor	USMA	Phil.
					Inventor	Heavy cannon	WW I
Henry H. Ludlow	165	1876	2598	Math.	Professor	USMA	Phil.
William B. Gordon	166	1877	2646	Scientist	Professor	USMA	Indian
					Inventor	Gun carriage	WW I
Henry O. Flipper	167	1877	2690	Engineer	Engineer	AK Engr Commission	
Gustav Fiebeger	168	1879	2764	Engineer	Professor	USMA	Indian
George Goethals	**11**	1880	2828	Engineer	Professor	USMA	
					Director	Panama Canal	
Lyman Hall	169	1881	2917	Math.	President	Georgia Tech	
John T. Thompson	170	1882	2942	Tech.	Professor	USMA	Sp-Am
					Inventor	Machine Gun	WW I
Hiram Chittenden	171	1884	3023	Engineer	Surveyor	Yellowstone Park	Sp-Am
Wirt Robinson	**33**	1887	3182	Scientist	Professor	USMA	
Edgar Jadwin	173	1890	3331	Engineer	Engineer	Panama Canal	Sp-Am WW I
Colden Ruggles	174	1890	3335	Scientist	Professor	USMA	WW I
Charles P. Echols	175	1891	3387	Math.	Professor	USMA	WW I
James P. Jervey	176	1892	3451	Math.	Professor	U of the South	WW I
					Engineer	Panama Canal	
Clifton Carter	177	1899	3888	Scientist	Professor	USMA	Sp-Am WW I
George Pillsbury	179	1900	3940	Engineer	Engineer	Great Lakes	WW I
William Mitchell	180	1902	4068	Engineer	Professor	USMA	WW I
Frederic Hinrichs	180	1902	4077	Scientist	Professor	U of Rochester	WW I
					Professor	CA Tech	
					Dean	CA Tech	
William Williams	181	1902	4089	Scientist	Professor	U of CA (Berkeley)	

Name	No.	Year	No.	Field	Role	Institution	Wars
Douglas MacArthur	182	1903	4122	Tech.	Sup't	USMA	WW I WW II Korean
Thomas E. Selfridge	184	1903	4152	Tech.	Inventor	Aviation	
Charles R. Pettis	185	1904	4215	Scientist	Professor Professor	USMA Mississippi State	WW I
Chauncey L. Fenton	186	1904	4229	Scientist	Professor	USMA	WW I
Richard R. Somers	187	1907	4538	Math.	Professor Professor Professor	USMA UNH Dartmouth	
Henry Arnold	188	1907	4596	Tech.	Chief	Army Air Corps	WW II
Raymond Wheeler	190	1911	4940	Engineer	Chief	Army Engineers	WW I WW II
Allen P. Cowgill	191	1914	5216	Math.	Professor	Syracuse U	
Omar Bradley	192	1915	5356	Math.	Professor ORAnalyst	USMA War Dept	WW II
Dwight Eisenhower	194	1915	5373	Math.	ORAnalyst President	War Dept Columbia	WW II
Harris Jones	195	Apr 1917	5602	Math.	Professor Dean	USMA USMA	WW I
Gerald Counts	196	Aug 1917	5742	Scientist	Dean	USMA	WW I WW II
Bartley Harloe	198	Aug 1917	5748	Engineer	Professor	U of Hawaii	WW I WW II
Leslie R. Groves	13	Nov 1918	6032	Engineer	Engineer Cmdr VP	Pentagon Manhattan Project Sperry Rand	WW I
Boyd W. Bartlett	31	1919	6258	Scientist	Professor Dept Head	Bowdoin College USMA	
William Bessell	199	1920	6545	Math.	Dept Head Dean	USMA USMA	WW II
Edward C. Gillette	200	1920	6635	Scientist	Dept Head	USMA	WW II
Lawrence E. Schick	202	1920	6674	Tech.	Dept Head	USMA	WW I WW II
Kenner F. Hertford	203	1923	6964	Scientist	Dep Cdr	Sandia Base, NM	
Leslie E. Simon	204	1924	7292	Tech.	Director	Ballistic Res Lab	WW II
Charles P. Nicholas	205	1925	7670	Math.	Dept Head	USMA	
Holger Toftoy	206	1926	7923	Tech.	Director	Explorer I	WW II
Theodore Weyher	207	1927	8027	Engineer	Dean	U of Miami, FL	WW II
James W. Green, Jr	208	1927	8063	Engineer	Professor	USMA	WW II
James L. Green	209	1928	8227	Engineer	Professor	Princeton	WW II
Roscoe C. Wilson	40	1928	8273	Engineer	Designer Professor Researcher	Combat Aircraft USMA Manhattan Project	
John D. Billingsley	210	1928	8341	Engineer	Professor	USMA	WW II Korean
Kenneth Nichols	21	1929	8491	Engineer	Professor Director Chief	USMA Special Weapons Proj Army R&D	
John H. Dudley	211	1930	8813	Engineer	Professor Researcher	CA State-Long Beach Manhattan Project	WW II
Howard M. Parker	212	1931	9041	Math.	Professor	U of Iowa	WW II
Ellis E. Wilhoyt	213	1937	10760	Scientist	Researcher	Manhattan Project	WW II
John Jannarone	214	1938	11034	Scientist	Professor Dean	USMA USMA	WW II

Name	#	Year	ID	Field	Title	Institution	Wars
Nicholas Paraska	215	1939	11362	Engineer	Professor	Youngstown State	WWII
John Graf	216	1940	11795	Engineer	Professor	Tech Inst Memphis	WW II Korean
William Gribble	217	1941	12250	Engineer	Chief	Res & Develop	WW II
Joseph I. Gurfein	218	1941	12289	Engineer	Dean	U of District of Columbia	WW II Korean
					Professor	George Mason	Vietnam
William McMaster	219	1946	15308	Scientist	Director	U of CA Rad Lab	
					Director	Special Weapons Proj	
Alfred Haussman	220	1946	15688	Scientist	Ass't Director	Lawrence Livermore Lab	
Gerald W. Medsger	221	1948	16477	Engineer	Professor	USMA	
					Res Dir	USMA	
					Dean	USMAPS	
William M. Kaula	222	1948	16486	Engineer	Scientist	NASA	
					Chief	National Geo Survey	
					Member	Nat'l Acad Sciences	
John H. Saxon, Jr	223	1949	17267	Math.	Professor	Rose State College	WW II Korean Vietnam
					Writer	Math Textbooks	
Monty D. Coffin	224	1950	17351	Math.	Professor	USMA	Korean
					Dept Head	USAFA	
					Director	AF Missile Lab	
Robert S. Tickle	225	1952	18614	Scientist	Professor	U of Michigan	
Edward H. White II	226	1952	18619	Tech.	Astronaut	NASA	
Robert L. LaFrenz	227	1955	20242	Scientist	Professor	USMA	Vietnam
					Researcher	Livermore Labs	
John M. Kallfelz	228	1956	20678	Engineer	Professor	Georgia Tech	
					Researcher	Switzerland Institute	
John P. Porter	229	1959	22676	Tech.	Director	NAVSTAR GPS	Vietnam
Thomas Johnson	**18**	1965	25511	Scientist	Professor	USMA	
					Director	White House Science Council	

USMA 1825 | Alexander Dallas Bache | Scientist

19 July 1806 (Philadelphia, PA) – 17 February 1867 (Washington, DC)
Graduate # 392 (1ˢᵗ out of 37), listed in *DAB, ANB, NCAB, DSB, BDAS*

Military Service:
1827-1829: Construction engineer for Fort Adams, RI

Professional Service:
1826-1827: Assistant Professor of Engineering, USMA
1829-1836: Professor of Natural Philosophy and Chemistry, University of Pennsylvania
1829: Elected to the American Philosophical Society
1836-1840: President of Girard College
1841-1842: Superintendent of Philadelphia public schools
1842-1843: Professor of Natural Philosophy and Chemistry, University of Pennsylvania
1843-1863: Superintendent of the United States Coast Survey
1863-1867: President, National Academy of Sciences

A. D. BACHE was the great-grandson of Benjamin Franklin and received his school education at a preparatory school in Philadelphia. At age 15, he entered the U.S. Military Academy. Bache distinguished himself as a student, graduating first in his class, serving as a mathematics instructor during his junior year and teaching chemistry during his senior year. His scientific abilities were needed at West Point, so upon graduation he was assigned as an Assistant Professor in the Department of Engineering. After a year of teaching, he moved to Newport, RI to assist in the construction of Fort Adams. Bache was only 20 years old, but already had three years of college-level teaching. While stationed at Newport, Bache continued his study of physics and chemistry and contributed several articles to mathematics journals. Bache resigned his commission in 1829 and became the Professor of Natural Philosophy and Chemistry at the University of Pennsylvania. Bache was an excellent teacher and a superb scientist. While at the University of Pennsylvania in 1833, he published a revision of David Brewster's *Treatise on Optics*. His academic interests were in chemistry, physics, meteorology, and astronomy, and he published regularly in all these areas. As early as 1830, Bache studied terrestrial magnetism. In his second year on the faculty, he was elected Secretary of the Faculty and became involved with the establishment of the Franklin Institute where he helped edit the Institute's journal and investigated the causes of explosions in steam boilers. Demonstrating a broad range of interests, he continued to write papers on chemistry and physics, along with special works in ice flows, mineralogy, meteorology, and solar eclipses. He established the first permanent magnetic observatory in the United States in the garden next to his house, studied the motion of winds in tornadoes, and investigated the measurement of rainfall as related to wind direction. His scientific works and achievements earned him recognition in the academic and scientific communities. In 1836, Bache was named President of Girard College. The college was funded from the estate of Stephen Girard and was in the process of being established. Before assuming his duties, Bache traveled throughout Europe for two years to examine educational systems. He visited over 200 institutions – gathering books and scientific instruments, talking with educators, and analyzing educational methods. Upon return to the United States, he published *Report on Education in Europe,* which had a positive effect on the educational methods used in America. In addition to his work as an educator, he continued his research in the physical sciences.

Bache's contributions as an educator were recognized, and he was appointed as the Principal of the Central High School in Philadelphia in 1839. This was the first public high school in the United States outside of New England. Based on his knowledge of the educational system in Europe and his own technical education at USMA, he reorganized Central High School – establishing a school library and restructuring the curriculum to include applied science. This school became the model for many other new public and private high schools and colleges. The school was equipped with an astronomical observatory, and Bache hired excellent teachers of science to utilize the facilities and motivate the students. His work with the Central High School was so well received that he was appointed the Superintendent of the Philadelphia school system in 1841.

In 1842, Bache was re-appointed Professor of Natural Philosophy and Chemistry at the University of Pennsylvania. During the academic year of 1843, he was selected by the President of the United States as the Superintendent of the United States Coast Survey succeeding Ferdinand Hassler (see the essay on the Coast Survey). The Survey made tremendous progress under his guidance, and Bache was able to gain the support of Congress, an accomplishment that Hassler was never able to achieve. He increased the scope of the Survey to include the Pacific Coast and introduced studies of tides, astronomy, seismology, and geomagnetism into the Survey. He also made use of new technologies such as the telegraph and photography to aid the work of the Survey. Bache's experience as an administrator helped him establish the Survey as a distinguished scientific agency and the largest employer of scientists in America. Bache's contributions were not limited to the Coast Survey. In 1843, he simultaneously became Superintendent of Weights and Measures of the United States. Later, he served on the national commission responsible for designing and building America's lighthouse system. Bache was appointed a regent of the Smithsonian Institution in 1846 and was active and influential in the American Philosophical Society and the American Association for the Advancement of Science. He was elected President of these organizations in 1856 and 1850, respectively. In 1863, the Secretary of the Navy appointed him to a scientific committee called the Permanent Commission, which he helped evolve into the National Academy of Sciences. He served as the National Academy of Science's first president from 1863 to 1867. Bache continued with the Coast Survey until the Civil War, when the Survey's work was suspended. Bache's military engineering talents were then employed in organizing the defense plan for the city of Philadelphia. Bache's work was honored and recognized by many scientific societies around the world. During his life, he received dozens of honorary degrees. He was a member of the Bologna Academy of Sciences; Bohemian Industrial Society, Statistical Society of London, Royal Academy of Turin, Mathematical Society of Hamburg, Geographical Society of Berlin, Royal Astronomical Society, Institute of France, Royal Irish Academy, Royal

Geographical Society of Vienna, Royal Society of Edinburg, Royal Society of London, American Philosophical Society, Permanent Commission on the Sciences, American Association for the Advancement of Science, and the National Academy of Sciences.

Bache was one of the great scientists and educators of the nineteenth century and is considered one of the premier developers of the American scientific community. An American born and educated scientist, his work enriched the science and educational system of his country for many years. Possessing leadership attributes and expertise most conducive to the success of public technical agencies, he advocated for and was involved in the use of science by the government for the resolution of important social issues and the solution of pressing national problems. As a stellar *Captain* of American science, he influenced many federal policies, programs, and agencies as America faced the technological and educational challenges of industrialization and expansion during the 19th century.

Quotations:
By Bache in 1851: "While science is without organization, it is without power."

About Bache by Jefferson Davis: "An American has been found, who has not only been able to discharge the duties of his office, who has not only been able to keep pace with science, but who has been foremost in some of the most difficult investigations, and has attained results for highly useful application to the necessity of commerce and the perfection of the work with which he is charged; often passing before, never falling behind, the improvements of the age, he has elevated our scientific reputation abroad, and is at home justly the object of American pride."

About Bache by Benjamin Gould: "... the greatest of all his mental gifts or attainments were his marvelous knowledge of human nature and his unrivaled skill in using it. He had studied men, as he once expressed it to me, as he would study physical phenomena."

References:

Guralnick, Stanley, *Science and the American College, 1828-1860*, Ph.D. Dissertation, University of Pennsylvania, Philadelphia, 1975.

Henry, Joseph, *Eulogy on Professor Alexander Dallas Bache*, Report of the Smithsonian Institute, Government Printing Office, Washington, 1872.

Odgers, Merle M., *Alexander Dallas Bache, Scientist and Educator*, University of Pennsylvania Press, Philadelphia, 1947.

Slotten, Hugh R., *Patronage, Practice, and the Culture of American Science: Alexander Dallas Bache and the U. S. Coast Survey*, Cambridge University Press, Cambridge, MA, 1994.

USMA 1808 — Sylvanus Thayer — Mathematician

9 June 1785 (Braintree, MA) – 7 September 1872 (Braintree, MA)
Graduate # 33, (educator), listed in *DAB, ANB, AR* (1873)

Military Service:
1808-1809: Inspector of coastal fortifications in New England
1811-1812: Engineer and ordnance duty in New York City
1812-1815: Engineer duty in the War of 1812

Professional Service:
1809-1811: Assistant Professor of Mathematics, USMA
1815-1817: Visited military and technical schools in France and England (purchased over 1000 books
            for USMA Library)
1817-1833: Superintendent, USMA
1833-1843: Engineer for construction of Ft. Warren and Ft. Independence, MA and various
            New England harbors
1838:   Elected to the American Philosophical Society
1843-1846: Visited Europe
1846-1857: Resident engineer at Ft. Warren, MA
1867-1871: Founder of Thayer School of Engineering, Dartmouth College, NH

S. THAYER graduated from Dartmouth College in 1807 and then went to West Point for less than a year before graduating in 1808. After completing his first commissioned duties as an inspector of fortifications, Thayer returned to West Point to teach mathematics. During the War of 1812, he was engaged in duties in upper New York State and Norfolk, VA. In 1815, Thayer had the opportunity to visit the technical military schools in Europe to investigate their educational methods, curricula, and programs and to purchase books for use at West Point. He brought back a model development program based on the École polytechnique in Paris and over 1000 volumes of books in military science, mathematics, science, and engineering. When Thayer returned from Europe, he was appointed the Superintendent of the Academy; however, his predecessor **Alden Partridge (USMA 1806)** did not leave his post quietly. After a messy court-martial, Partridge finally left West Point. Thayer went to work establishing a rigorous, demanding engineering program, which earned him the title "Father of the Military Academy." Through his strong will and technical expertise, Thayer found the resources to improve the academics and to obtain right people to design, teach, and administer his program. Thayer continued to purchase books, adding to the library's collection. Besides the new curriculum, Thayer's academic reforms included implementing new teaching methods, establishing sections based on ability, having cadets tested daily, instituting a highly competitive class rank system, and using the blackboard for practice and feedback. Cadets spent at least three hours per day on mathematics for the first two years and three hours per day on science and engineering their last two years. As America's first engineering school, setting the proper standards and finding the right staff were tremendous challenges. Thayer had to develop the faculty he needed, since America did not have the quality mathematicians, scientists, and engineers to meet the requirements of a top-notch engineering school. However, in less than a decade, he had established the Academy as one of the premier educational programs in the world. Thayer and his staff had completely changed mathematics education from a liberal art into a language of science and physical science into the bridge to engineering. Thayer's West Point graduates knew how to build products as engineers and improve them as scientists and mathematicians. Through his own development by working with the faculty, Thayer became competent in mathematics, science, engineering, military science, leadership, and education. In short, he was one of the first of America's technologists and a leader of America's growing scientific community. After his Superintendent duties were completed in 1833, Thayer remained in the Army as a fortification engineer in New England. In 1867, he donated $40,000 to Dartmouth to establish a School of Architecture and Civil Engineering. In 1871, the Thayer School at Dartmouth College opened its doors becoming a top-notch program in civil engineering. Thayer selected **Robert Fletcher (USMA 1868)** as the School's first Professor of Engineering, and Fletcher directed the School for 47 years. Thayer used his vast experience in designing the innovative program. The original engineering program was a 2-year graduate program, which followed 4 years of undergraduate education. Thus, the Thayer School offered the first graduate-level professional engineering program in the United States. It was Thayer's belief that engineers ought to be educated thoroughly in the basic sciences, mathematics, and liberal arts, as well as the technical skills of their profession. He felt that an

understanding of the economic, cultural, historical, and political environment in which the technology would be developed and applied was necessary for quality engineering. Because of Thayer's immense contributions to America's beginnings in technology and technical education, he is sometimes referred to the "Father of Technical Education in America." Thayer received numerous tributes and honorary degrees and was memorialized in the Hall of Fame of Great Americans.

Reference:
Dupuy, R. E., *Sylvanus Thayer: Father of Technology in the United States*, USMA, 1958.

USMA 1832 | **Jacob Whitman Bailey** | **Scientist**

29 April 1811 (Ward, MA) -- 27 February 1857 (West Point, NY)
Graduate # 666 (5th out of 45), (Botanist, Geologist), listed in *DAB, ANB, NCAB*

Military Service:
1832-1834:   Artillery duty in Charleston, SC (during the nullification revolt) and at Bellona Arsenal, VA

Professional Service:
1834-1835:   Assistant Professor of Chemistry, Mineralogy, and Geology, USMA
1835-1857:   Professor of Chemistry, Mineralogy, and Geology, USMA
1852:   Elected to the American Philosophical Society
1857:   President, American Association for the Advancement of Science

J. W. BAILEY was one of the premier botanists in America. He developed an interest in biology by collecting shells and insects as a young boy and working in a library where he had access to scientific books. After graduating from West Point in 1832, he served two years in artillery duty before returning to the Academy. Back at West Point, he taught a mixture of science subjects as the Assistant Professor of Chemistry, Mineralogy, and Geology. While he was knowledgeable and published articles in these fields, his real passion and area of research was botany. Just a year later, Bailey was selected to the position of Professor and Department Head. He was the first to permanently fill this professorship at the Academy, in the new science department that Superintendent **Sylvanus Thayer (USMA 1808)** had lobbied to establish at the Academy. His work as department head and researcher was impacted by a fire in 1838 that destroyed the Academy's library and chemistry laboratories. He lost many specimens and notes from his research work. He rebuilt the science laboratories in a new building and re-established his research. Later in his career, he saved his research collection from a hotel fire. Bailey's botany knowledge grew as he began using microscopes to investigate algae and other organisms. He was a pioneer in the use of the microscope in such studies and quickly became the foremost expert in the world in the study of microscopic plants, as part of the general field of micro-paleontology. His sketches alone filled 450 pages, containing over 3000 drawings. Bailey's substantial talents in drawing were evidenced when he took drawing as a cadet. Diligent in his work, he completed more than 550 specimen slides of 3000 objects, each with reference to his classification system called Bailey's Indicator. He corresponded with scientists from around the world. Many of whom sent him specimens or asked for his advice and help. Bailey wrote many technical papers in addition to his volumes of research notes and personal correspondence. One of his close colleagues was anatomist Henry Gray. Among the subjects of his works are fossil studies, deep-sea life forms (specimens sent to him by the Coast Survey), and detailed explanations of plants found in coal ash. He also is credited with designing and building substantial improvements in the power and accuracy of microscopes. Many of Bailey's fifty technical papers appeared in the *American Journal of Science* (*"Silliman's Journal"*) and the *Journal of Microscopic Science*. Bailey was given the title of "Father of Micro-Geology in America," since his work contributed so much to the understanding of geology and the physical history of earth. Bailey served as President of the American Association for the Advancement of Science in 1857. Suffering through several personal hardships, he lost his wife and daughter in a steamboat accident on the Hudson River, while narrowly saving himself and young invalid son. He died at age 46 at West Point after suffering from a long illness. Bailey was a modest, quiet, somewhat feeble man, whose energies and passions were consumed in science and teaching. While he had an international reputation as a scholar and naturalist, he was always first concerned with the development of cadets as students of science. Among his many tributes were an honorary degree from the College of New Jersey (Princeton) and membership in several international societies of science.

Quotation: By A. Gould about Bailey: "He may be styled the Ehrenberg of America, and has won for himself a place by the side of the most eminent microscopists and algologists of the Old World. He will always stand as the father, in this country, of those Branches of Natural History that relate to the world of atoms."

USMA 1815   **Charles Davies**   **Mathematician**

22 January 1798 (Washington, CT) – 17 September 1876 (Fishkill, NY)
Graduate # 157, (author), listed in *ACAB, NCAB, AR* (1877)

Military Service:
1815-1816: Garrison duty in New England
1841-1846: Paymaster and Treasurer, USMA

Professional Service:
1816-1821: Assistant Professor of Mathematics, USMA
1821-1823: Assistant Professor of Natural and Experimental Philosophy, USMA
1823-1837: Professor of Mathematics, USMA
1826:   Fellow, American Academy of Arts and Sciences
1839-1841: Professor of Mathematics, Trinity College, CT
1848-1849: Professor of Mathematics, University of the City of New York
1856-1857: Professor of Mathematics, Normal School at Albany, NY
1857-1865: Professor of Higher Mathematics, Columbia College, NY

C. Davies was appointed to the Academy through the influence of **Joseph Swift (USMA 1802)**, the Academy's first graduate. Davies had earned praise by helping Swift's unit during the War of 1812. After two years of successful studies at West Point, Davies graduated and served in garrison for one year before becoming an Assistant Professor of Mathematics at West Point, serving as the principal assistant under Department Heads Andrew Ellicott and David Douglass. From 1821 to 1823, he was an Assistant Professor of Natural and Experimental Philosophy. In 1823, Davies returned to the Department of Mathematics as Professor and Department Head and stayed in that position until 1837. As a dedicated teacher and a prolific author of essays and textbooks, he made significant impact on America's educational system, just as its foundation was being developed. He was the first successful text writer in America and a major player in mathematics education during the 19th century. His textbooks on mathematics from elementary arithmetic to college-level calculus, which were used in schools, academies, and colleges of America, directly influenced millions of students and several generations of Americans. The Superintendent during Davies' tenure at USMA was **Sylvanus Thayer (USMA 1808)**, who had brought to the Academy the influence of the French military academy, École polytechnique. Under Davies and Thayer, the mathematics curriculum grew from basic problem solving and simple skills to a rigorous, calculus-based engineering program. Davies orchestrated this curriculum expansion and advanced the methods of instruction in the classroom. His series of textbooks were so thorough and complete that by 1839 all the mathematics textbooks used at the Academy were authored by Davies. The title of his undergraduate book series was the "West Point Course." Davies' first textbook was in descriptive geometry, the foundation for civil engineering at the time. He then went on to writing and translating books in geometry and algebra. His book on surveying, published in 1830, was used both as a textbook and also as a reference for professional surveyors. His books were so successful and in such great demand around the country that he decided to devote his efforts to full-time text writing. In 1837, after spending a year in Europe, he resigned from West Point. In all, Davies prepared more than 45 different mathematics books, with hundreds of editions and printings, and sold over 5 million copies of his works. He was by far the most successful textbook author of his time, and as such became a well–known *Celebrity* in American science. Davies' publications show the span of his work from lower-level school mathematics to advanced college-level mathematics and science. Some of his works are: *First Lessons in Arithmetic, Grammar of Arithmetic, Practical Mathematics, Primary Arithmetic, Descriptive Geometry* (1826), *Elements of Surveying* (1830), *Differential and Integral Calculus* (1836), *Logic and Utility of Mathematics* (1850), *Shades and Shadows and Linear Perspective* (1851), and *Metric System* (1871).

From 1839 until 1841, Davies was Professor of Mathematics at Trinity College in Hartford, CT. While serving in this capacity, he formed a business connection with A. S. Barnes for the exclusive publication of his books. In 1841, Davies was re-appointed in the Army as paymaster and served as Treasurer of the Academy until 1846. In 1848, he became the Professor of Mathematics and Philosophy at the University of the City of New York. He retired from that position a year later one again so that he could devote time to writing. Davies returned to the classroom, teaching briefly at the Normal School in Albany and then at Columbia College in New York City for eight years. He was a prolific speaker, often invited to present his philosophy of teaching to mathematics teachers around the country. He used these opportunities to speak out against converting to the metric system, which his strong influence helped prevent. While not a research mathematician, he did author one paper for the *American Journal of Science*. Among his many honors was a LL.D. degree from Geneva College (later Hobart) in 1840. Davies continued to write his mathematics books after his retirement as a professor in 1865 until his death in 1876.

Quotations:

By Davies at his inauguration at Columbia College, NY: "The great problem of the present age is the education of the young. Although the struggle may be long, and the progress of truth, justice and intelligence occasionally impeded, they must and will ultimately triumph."

By Davies at the National Meeting of Teachers, MI: "Teach one thing at a time – teach that thing thoroughly – and as far as possible, teach all its connections with other things."

References:

Ackerberg-Hastings, Amy, "Charles Davies, Mathematical Businessman", *Proceedings of the History of Undergraduate Mathematics in America*, 2001.

Hoskins, Keith, "Textbooks and the mathematisation of American reality: the role of Charles Davies and the U.S. Military Academy at West Point," *Paradigm*, May 1994 (11-41).

USMA 1821 **Edward Henry Courtenay** **Mathematician**

19 November 1803 (Baltimore, MD) – 21 December 1853 (Charlottesville, VA)
Graduate # 262 (1st out of 24), listed in *DAB, NCAB*

Military Service:
1821-1834: Primarily served in technical positions
   during his military service
1826-1828: Administrative duties as the Assistant Chief of Army
   Engineers, Washington, DC

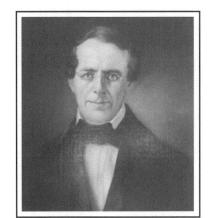

Professional Service:
1821-1822: Assistant Professor of Natural and Experimental
   Philosophy, USMA 1822-1824: Assistant Professor of
   Engineering, USMA
1824-1826: Construction engineer at Ft. Adams, RI
1828-1834: Professor of Natural and Experimental Philosophy,
   USMA
1834-1836: Professor of Mathematics, University of Pennsylvania
1835: Elected to the American Philosophical Society
1836-1837: Railroad construction engineer

1837-1842:   Construction engineer for Fort Independence,
             Boston, MA and Naval Dry Dock in Brooklyn, NY
1842-1853:   Professor of Mathematics, University of Virginia

---

Entering West Point at the young age of 15, **E. H. COURTENAY** was so impressive on his entrance examinations that he was immediately labeled as a bright, well-prepared cadet. He graduated first in his class after just three years of study. After graduation, he was assigned to teach at the Academy, and during the next three years held assistant professorships in engineering and natural and experimental philosophy. From 1824 to 1826, Courtenay was an assistant engineer under **Joseph Totten (USMA 1805)**, constructing Fort Adams, RI. His next assignment was two years of administrative duty at the Office of the Chief Engineer in Washington, DC. He then became Department Head and Professor of Natural and Experimental Philosophy at the Academy in 1829, while only 25 years old. He had already established a fine reputation as a technical educator and as early as 1827 James Monroe had tried unsuccessfully to hire Courtenay for the University of Virginia. Courtenay was one of Superintendent **Sylvanus Thayer's (USMA 1808)** expert educators, who was expected to build up the technical programs by raising standards and increasing the technical content in the academic program. The natural and experimental philosophy position was important because it involved teaching mechanics and physics as the bridge from mathematics to engineering. In 1833, Courtenay published his first textbook, which was a translation of a French work, entitled *An Elementary Treatise on Mechanics*. Since the only textbooks at the proper level and academic nature of cadet instruction were in French, the cadets had to study French to read their technical textbooks. Therefore, this translation as a new English-language textbook was an important step in the development of America's technical educational system. In 1834, Courtenay resigned from the Army and moved to the Professor of Mathematics position at the University of Pennsylvania, where **Alexander Bache (USMA 1825)** was the science professor. After just two years, Courtenay turned to construction engineering for railroads and then building an Army post at Fort Independence, Boston in order to increase his income. He also served briefly as an engineer for the construction of the Navy Dry Dock in Brooklyn. Returning to academics in 1842, he accepted the Professor of Mathematics position at the University of Virginia, which had been just vacated by the departure of famous European mathematician J. J. Sylvester. Courtenay was a successful professor, full of energy and practical insights that motivated his students. He taught three levels of pure mathematics and a section of applied mathematics. He added descriptive geometry to the curriculum, probably from his West Point background, using **Charles Davies' (USMA 1815)** textbook. His students at Virginia, like those he had taught previously at West Point and Pennsylvania, learned well and enjoyed their professor's clear lectures and patience. He kept busy as a textbook author, writing *A Treatise on the Differential and Integral Calculus, and on the Calculus of Variations*, which was published in 1855 (after Courtenay had died) through the help of Courtenay's old mathematics professor and colleague at West Point, Charles Davies. This book was both commercially and technically successful and had several editions published over many years. It was considered an outstanding book and most comprehensive work on this mathematical subject written in America at that time. Courtenay, like many other West Pointers, was a versatile scholar, mostly concerned with the practical application of his subject. He was a highly capable expert in a range of technical subjects – mathematics, science, mechanics, and engineering. He taught all these subjects, published in these areas, and was one of the premier academic leaders in America when he died in 1853.

Quotations: About Courtenay by Charles Davies:
"He never by look, act, word, or emphasis disparaged the efforts or undervalued the acquirements of his pupils. His pleasant smile and kind voice, when he would say, 'Is that answer *perfectly* correct?' gave hope to many minds struggling with science."

"The intellectual faculties of Professor Courtenay were blended in such just proportions that each seem to aid and strengthen all the others. ... He possessed in an eminent degree that marked characteristic of a great mind, the power of a just and profound generalization."

Reference:
Despeaux, Sloan; Martini, Laura; Parshall, Karen Hunger; and Rice, Adrian; "The University of Virginia, 1825-1900: A Case Study in the Institutionalization of Mathematics in the United States," *Proceedings of the History of Undergraduate Mathematics in America*, 2001.

USMA 1880   **George Washington Goethals**   **Engineer**

29 June 1858 (Brooklyn, NY) – 21 January 1928 (New York, NY)
Graduate # 2828 (2nd out of 52), listed in *DAB, ANB, NCAB, AR* (1928)

Military Service:
1894-1898: Assistant to the Chief of Army Engineers, Washington, DC
1903-1907: Engineer staff work on General Staff in Washington, DC
1917-1918: Recalled to active duty as staff officer for World War I

Professional Service:
1880-1881: Assistant Professor of Practical Engineering, USMA
1881-1882: Graduate study at the Engineer School of Application, Willet's Point, NY
1882-1884: Surveying and bridge construction duty, Spokane, WA
1884-1885: Engineer improving navigation on Ohio River
1885-1889: Assistant Professor, Civil and Military Engineering, USMA
1889-1894: Engineer improving navigation on Cumberland and Tennessee
            Rivers (built locks on Muscle Shoals Canal)
1898-1900: Assistant Professor of Civil and Military Engineering, USMA
1900-1903: Engineer duty for fortification construction and harbor improvements in RI
1907-1914: Leader of the construction of the Panama Canal
1913:   Elected to the American Philosophical Society
1916-1926: Consulting engineer for various civic projects

G. W. GOETHALS put himself through three years of study at the College of the City of New York and then came to West Point to study engineering. After graduating and entering the Corps of Engineers, Goethals combined engineer field duty in Spokane, WA and OH with a tour of graduate engineering study at Willets Point before teaching at West Point. He had the privilege of working with **William Merrill (USMA 1859)** on the navigational improvements for the Ohio River. After teaching cadets for four years, Goethals returned to civil works projects. In his engineering work, he built dams, bridges, levees, and locks on the Tennessee and Cumberland Rivers working with fellow engineer **John Barlow (USMA May 1861)**. His undertaking of building a lock with a 26-foot lift was controversial and set the stage for others to build high-lift locks. Through this success, Goethals became known as both an expert engineer and an inspiring leader. After duty as the assistant to the Chief of Army Engineers **Thomas Casey (USMA 1852)**, Goethals returned to West Point for two more years of teaching. After constructing fortifications in RI, he was back on the engineering staff in Washington, DC. He first visited the Panama Isthmus during this staff tour in 1905 to study the area in order to plan fortifications. His previous engineering experience of building numerous locks and dams qualified him for the important work on the Canal. Having studied and taught at West Point, he understood the demands of major construction projects and that gave him confidence in performing the type of work the canal required. When President Theodore Roosevelt appointed Goethals as chairman and chief engineer of the Isthmian Canal Commission in 1907, he was ready for the responsibility. Two other men had previously failed this mission and resigned their positions, so there was tremendous pressure not to fail or fall behind schedule. Once in Panama, Goethals divided his time between his office and the construction and digging sites. He often inspected and toured the canal zone and construction sites by rail car. Goethals recognized that the administrative issues were as big a challenge as were the technical issues. On Sundays he held informal court sessions, listening to complaints and settling disputes. He assembled an expert staff of capable engineers, many West Point graduates, and pushed them to succeed in their assigned missions. By driving himself, his staff, and his workers to their full potential, the canal was completed six months ahead of schedule and under budget. The building of the Panama Canal was an enormous engineering feat. For seven years, Goethals and his 50,000 workers dug through mud, sand, and rock. The size of the project was immense: 3,500 buildings and 15 hotels in 7 towns, 24 schools for the workers' children, 63 huge steam shovels, 300 locomotives with 2,700 railroad cars. A total of 262 million cubic yards of dirt was excavated. His workforce built locks and railroads, cut channels and lakes, and eventually joined the Atlantic and Pacific Oceans. The police system, courts, post

offices, and fire departments were all his responsibility. The Canal opened for traffic in 1914, and Goethals became a popular public figure and a *Celebrity* of American Science. In the eyes of many Americans, he had accomplished the impossible. He was awarded the Cullum Medal (endowed to the American Geographical Society by **George Cullum (USMA 1833)**) in 1917, the National Institute of Social Science Gold Medal, and the John Fritz Medal, which is sponsored by six technical societies for outstanding scientific contributions. Goethals remained in Panama as governor of the Canal Zone for two more years, retiring as a Major General in 1916. During World War I, he was recalled to active duty and served as the quartermaster general, before retiring again in 1918. For the remainder of his life, he served as a consulting engineer on projects including the construction of new shipping facilities in New York Harbor. After his canal success, these other projects seemed so minor that Goethals often became frustrated with his duties, yearning for the excitement of a major engineering challenge.

References:

Bishop, Joseph Bucklin and Bishop, Garnham, *Goethals, Genius of the Panama Canal; A Biography*, Harper & Brothers, New York, 1930.

Goethals, George, *Panama Canal: An Engineering Treatise*, 2 vols. McGraw Hill, New York, 1916.

McCullough, David, *The Path Between the Seas: The Creation of the Panama Canal, 1870-1914,* Simon and Schuster, New York, 1977.

USMA November 1918 | **Leslie Richard Groves** | **Engineer**

17 August 1896 (Albany, NY) – 13 July 1970 (Washington, DC)
Graduate # 6032 (4th out of 227), listed in *DAB, ANB, AS* (June 1973)

Military Service:
1918:   Brief combat duty in World War I
1919-1931: Engineering duty at CA, HI, DE, and Nicaragua
1931-1935: Assistant Chief of Engineers, Washington, DC
1939-1941: Army General Staff, Washington, DC

Professional Service:
1941-1942: Construction engineer in charge of building the Pentagon, Washington, DC
1942-1947: Command, Manhattan Engineer Project
1947-1948: Chief, Army Special Weapons Project (Lieutenant General)
1948-1961: Consultant and Vice President, Sperry Rand

L. R. GROVES attended Massachusetts Institute of Technology for two years before entering West Point. Because of World War I, Groves and his classmates graduated after only two and a half years of academics at the Academy. Groves and his classmates were rushed to France for service in World War I, which ended shortly after their arrival. Groves served as a construction engineer for the next decade, as he took on duties in CA, HI, and DE. His foreign service was in Nicaragua conducting more engineering-related work. In 1931, he began a series of staff assignments and schooling. First he worked

in the Office of the Chief of Engineers in Washington, DC and in 1939 served with the Army General Staff. In 1941, he supervised the construction of the Pentagon, which was an immense engineering effort. His leadership and technical expertise were critical in the rapid and efficient construction of the extensive building, which was finished in just 16 months. In 1942, he was placed in charge of the Manhattan Project with the secret mission to develop the atomic bomb. Groves took on this mission with tremendous determination. While he did not know all the science or perform the research, he had to communicate and understand the needs of the scientists and the best means to manage the project. He arranged for the best team of scientists that he could find and the proper facilities to get the job done. His decision to have Robert Oppenheimer direct the scientific effort was bold and risky, because it created jealously and concern by several of the top scientists. However, the selection proved to be brilliant. Groves was a forceful and effective leader and at times upset his scientists with bold, steadfast decisions. Facilities at Oak Ridge, TN; Hanford, WA; and Los Alamos, NM were his top priorities. Groves was blessed with the help of **Kenneth Nichols (USMA 1929)** to keep the scientists focused on the tasks while fulfilling U.S. Army requirements. At its peak, over 200,000 workers were under Groves control, many not knowing the secret mission of the project. The first bomb was tested less than three years after Groves, Nichols, and Oppenheimer began their work. Groves remained with the atomic bomb project after the war, and finally in 1948, he left military service. His last dozen years as a technological leader were spent as Vice President of Sperry Rand Corporation.

References:

Groves, L. R. *Now it can be Told: The Story of the Manhattan Project*, Harper, New York, 1962.

Lawren, William, *General and the Bomb: A Biography of General Leslie R. Groves, Director of the Manhattan Project*, Dodd, Mead, New York, 1988.

USMA 1829 | Ormsby McKnight Mitchel | Mathematician

28 July 1809 (Morganfield, KY) -- 30 October 1862 (Beaufort, SC))
Graduate # 555 (15th out of 46), (astronomer), listed in *DAB, ANB, NCAB, ACAB*

Military Service:

1831-1832: Garrison duty in Florida

1861-1862: Combat duty in Civil War (raids in AL) and in command
of Department of the South (Major General)

Professional Service:

1829-1831: Assistant Professor of Mathematics, USMA

1834-1844: Professor of Mathematics, Philosophy, and Astronomy,
Cincinnati College, OH

1836-1837: Construction engineer for railroad company

1842: Visit to Europe

1843-1859: Director, Cincinnati Observatory

1848-1853: Construction engineer working on Mississippi and Ohio Rivers

1840's: Public lecturer on Astronomy throughout the United States

1846-1848: Editor of *Sidereal Messenger*

1850: Elected to the Royal Astronomical Society

1853: Elected to the American Philosophical Society

1859-1861: Director of Dudley Observatory, Albany, NY

1848-1863: Author of three astronomy books

O. M. MITCHEL was a child prodigy in mathematics and continued his interest in the subject while a cadet and an assistant professor of the subject for two years after graduation. In 1832, after a non-technical assignment in FL, he resigned his commission and became a lawyer. However, Mitchel soon realized his love was in mathematics and science. He taught for 10 years at Cincinnati College as the Professor of Mathematics, Philosophy, and Astronomy. As he developed his interest in astronomy, he helped to establish the Cincinnati Observatory, which at that time held the second largest telescope in the world. Mitchel became an immensely popular astronomer and lectured across the country before large audiences. He ignited an explosion in the popularity of and interest in astronomy. Adding to this effort was his work as editor of the popular magazine *Sidereal Messenger*. He worked with astronomers from around the world, including George Airy of the Royal Observatory in England. He also supported **Alexander Bache (USMA 1825)** and the Coast Survey in the astronomical work for the geodetic survey. Together they developed Mitchel's automatic clock register, which Mitchel regarded as his most significant work. Enjoying his fame as a gifted and powerful lecturer, he declined an offer of the Rumford Professorship at Harvard to continue his lecturing. Off and on for many years, he found time to work as a mathematician, engineer, and surveyor for railroad companies and as a government engineer on the navigation of the Mississippi and Ohio Rivers. Mitchel was controversial and opinionated and soon found himself at odds with Bache on several issues. One such occasion involved the standing committees of the American Association for the Advancement of Sciences. Another occasion involved the directorship and organization of the Dudley Observatory in Albany, NY. This squabble between the premier scientists in America was reported in newspapers across the country. When Mitchel's wife fell ill in 1857, he was completely involved in her care until she died in 1861. At the outbreak of the Civil War, Mitchel was quick to seek his commission as a commanding general and led a combat raid all the way into Alabama. He was assigned to command the Department of the South, but, just a year into the War, he contracted yellow fever and died. Mitchel had been an astronomer for only 20 years, but during that time he accomplished many amazing results – authored three books, invented several important instruments, lectured throughout America and in England, helped build and establish two of the largest research observatories in the world, and led a surge of interest in the general population in the subject of astronomy. Through his immense energy and perseverance, he made contributions that were beyond anyone's expectations in the areas of astronomy and surveying. As a popularizer and well–known *Celebrity* of American science, Mitchel was a contributor to America's development as a technological nation. He was an eminent scientist and a gifted orator. Through his strong personality, Mitchel came to fore just when the scientific community in the United States needed such a person to give it visibility and character. Among his numerous tributes were honorary degrees from Harvard College, MA and Washington College, PA.

Quotation: About Mitchel's popularity: "In New York, the music hall is thronged night after night to hear his impassioned eloquence poured in an unbroken flow of thoughts that breathe and words that burn on the excited thousands."

Reference:

Warner, Deborah, "Astronomy in Antebellum America," *The Sciences in the American Context: New Perspectives*, Reingold, Nathan, editor, Smithsonian Institution Press, Washington, 1979.

| USMA 1831 | **Andrew Atkinson Humphreys** | Engineer |

2 November 1810 (Philadelphia, PA) – 27 December 1883 (Washington, DC)
Graduate #641 (13th out of 33), listed in *DAB, NCAB, AR* (1884)

Military Service:

1831-1835: Topographic engineering duties (surveying, chart making) in GA, SC, OK, FL
1835-1836: Combat action in Seminole War, FL
1840-1844: Assistant engineer in Topographic Bureau, Washington, DC
1861-1866: Commander and high-level staff officer in Civil War (Antietam, Fredericksburg, Chancellorsville. Gettysburg, Sailor's Creek)
1866-1879: Chief of Engineers, U.S. Army

Professional Service:

1831-1835: Topographic engineering duties (surveying, chart making) in GA, SC, OK, FL
1836-1838: Construction engineer, DE

1838-1840: Harbor construction, IL, NY
1844-1849: Assistant Director, Coast Survey office, Washington, DC
1849-1861: Surveying in MS, LA
1854-1855: Surveyor and designer of routes for western railroads
1860:   Advisor on new curriculum at USMA
1863:   Corporator of National Academy of Sciences

A. A. HUMPHREYS was the son and grandson of two famous chiefs of naval construction. His grandfather designed *Old Ironsides.* Young Humphreys graduated from the Military Academy in 1831 and served as an artillery officer in Florida during the Seminole War. He resigned from the Army in 1836 and went to work as a civilian engineer for the Army Corps of Engineers. Working for **Alexander Bache (USMA 1825)**, he designed lighthouse and breakwaters for Delaware Bay. He re-entered the Army by accepting  an appointment as first lieutenant in the newly formed Corps of Topographical Engineers in 1838 and worked in various field and garrison duties as a topographic engineer for six years. In 1844, Humphreys had the opportunity to work for the Coast Survey under the direction of Bache. His next assignment in 1850 brought him to study the Mississippi River navigation system. His work was affected by severe sunstroke and a trip to Europe to recover and study the European river systems. From 1854 to 1861, Humphreys headed the Office of Pacific Railroad Explorations and Surveys, charting possible railroad routes from the Mississippi River to the Pacific Ocean. His report proved to be valuable to the future construction of western railroads. His Mississippi River report, written with **Henry Abbot (USMA 1854)** and published in 1861, contained valuable practical information along with tremendous scholarship in the study of hydrology. It was translated into several languages and became a classic in hydraulics literature. Humphreys, after distinguishing himself with brilliant leadership as a Civil War corps commander, became the Chief of Army Engineers in 1866. He established the Engineer School of Application at Willet's Point and oversaw a substantial expansion of the Corps' river and harbor work. During his thirteen years in that position, he contributed to numerous reconstruction projects and the revitalization of America's civil works. During that period, Humphreys obtained a Harvard degree and published Civil War histories. Humphreys was a tremendous contributor to the scholarly and professional components of topographic engineering. A first-rate scientist and engineer, along with being a talented military leader and administrator, Humphreys was one of the founders of the National Academy of Science and a member of the American Philosophical Society (1857) and American Academy of Arts and Sciences (1863).

Reference:

Abbot, Henry Larcom. "Memoir of Andrew Atkinson Humphreys, 1810-1883," *National Academy of Sciences: Biographical Memoirs*, vol. 2. Washington: National Academy of Sciences 1886.

USMA 1965 | **Thomas Hawkins Johnson** | **Scientist**

11 November 1943 (Boston, MA) – 26 June 1990 (Washington, DC)
Graduate #25,511 (26th out of 596), (physicist, poet), listed in *AS* (Nov 1991)

Military Service:
1965-1990: Various technical duties in Air Force and Army

Professional Service:
1965-1967: Research duties at Air Force Weapons Laboratory, Defense Nuclear Agency, CA
1967-1968: Graduate studies in physics (MS) at University of California at Davis
1968-1972: Research duties at Defense Nuclear Agency, CA
1972-1974: Graduate studies in physics (Ph.D.) at University of California at Davis
1975-1977: Research duties in physics and Chief of section at Air Force Weapons Laboratory, CA
1977-1980: Professor of English, USMA (taught physics and mathematics courses as well)
1980-1990: Professor of Physics, USMA
1981-1983: Special duty as Assistant to Presidential Science Advisor and executive director of
                 White House Science Council
1983-1990: Director, Science Research Laboratory, USMA
1980-1985: Adjunct Professor in Political Science, Columbia University, NY

T. H. JOHNSON was a gifted and multi-dimensional student as a cadet. He was particularly skilled in both scientific thinking and creative writing. Entering West Point as a National Merit Scholar, Johnson continued to excel by graduating in the top 5% of his class. Classmates in his stellar USMA class of 1965 included Daniel Christman (former Superintendent of USMA), James Golden (former Head of Social Sciences), Robert Doughty (Head of History), and Paul Bucha (Medal of Honor recipient). Johnson entered the Air Force to explore its   opportunities in science and advanced education. For his first twelve years of service, he either worked in physics research for the Air Force Weapons Laboratory as part of the Defense Nuclear Agency or attended the University of California at Davis. In 1974, he earned his Ph.D. in Physics. His research work was superb and soon had made major contributions in applied plasma physics. Johnson also had developed his other interests, poetry and creative writing, to such an extent that he was offered a teaching position in the Department of English at West Point. He was a professor for several disciplines as he taught courses in poetry, physics, mathematics, mechanics, and engineering at the Academy. Johnson transferred to an Army commission in 1980 to accept a professorship in

physics at West Point. He was also made Director of the Science Research Laboratory and the Associate Dean for Research. Johnson found time to adjunct teach at Columbia University in Political Science and to give seminars on arms control and science policy at Harvard, Princeton, Stanford, Cornell, and Yale. From 1981 to 1983, Johnson served as an assistant to the President's Science Advisor and the Executive Director of the White House

Science Council. In these roles, he influenced the highest levels of government policies on strategic defense, fusion energy, lasers, satellite communications, nuclear weapons, biomedical issues, and general science. He often visited the national laboratories (Lawrence Livermore and Los Alamos) to advise researchers and policy makers. Johnson was a prolific writer of both science articles and poetry, publishing both his technical and literary work in prestigious journals. Johnson received numerous awards and commendations for his tremendous contributions to science and national policy. In 1986, his review article on electronics received the prize for best publication of the year by the Institute of Electrical and Electronic Engineers. Johnson was one of America's finest scientists and policy advisors and a tremendously creative writer. While he died at the young age of 46 years, his contributions will be felt by many generations of Americans.

USMA 1833 | **John Gross Barnard** | **Engineer**

19 May 1815 (Sheffield, MA) – 4 May 1882 (Detroit, MI)
Graduate # 708 (2nd out of 43), (mathematician, physicist), listed in *DAB, NCAB, AR* (1882)

Military Service:
1833-1834: Assistant to the Engineer Board, Newport, RI
1846-1848: Combat engineering duty in Mexican War
1861-1865: Construction engineer for defenses of Washington, DC
          during Civil War
1861-1862: Combat engineer duty for Union Army
          (Bull Run, Yorktown, Gaines Mill)
1864-1865: Chief Engineer of Union Field Armies (Brigadier General)

Professional Service:
1834-1835: Construction engineering duty on coastal defenses and
          fortifications in NY and FL
1835-1846: Civil engineering duties on river and harbor improvements in
          FL, LA and AL
1848-1850: Civil engineering on the Mississippi River navigation
1850-1852: Construction engineer and surveyor for railroad work in Mexico
1852-1855: Construction engineering in ME and CA
1855-1856: Superintendent, USMA
1856-1861: Construction engineer in New York Harbor
1863-1865: Member of Permanent Commission and corporator of National Academy of Sciences
1867-1881: Leader of Boards of Engineers and Commissions for Fortifications, Rivers, Canals, Harbors,
          Mississippi River, Lighthouses, the use of iron in armaments, and removal of obstructions
1870-1871: Visited Europe to investigate military use of iron

J. G. BARNARD was a talented military and construction engineer and a devoted physical scientist and mathematician. After his graduation from West Point at the young age of 18, he worked on constructing coastal defenses and fortifications, improving navigation in rivers and harbors, and building America's infrastructure. He had the opportunity to work on the important ports of Portland, ME; New York; Mobile, AL; New Orleans, LA; and San Francisco, CA. Barnard was the most capable of the Army's engineers and was utilized in critical situations. He was assigned to help educate future engineers as Superintendent of West Point in 1855. However, his talents were soon needed in the field, as it was realized that the coastal fortifications were inadequate to defend against the new armored naval vessels with rifled cannons. Once the Civil War started, his first duty was to insure that the defenses of Washington, DC were sound. His next assignment took him into the field in support of the Army of the Potomac. In 1864, he was made chief engineer of the Union armies in the field, working directly for Ulysses Grant (USMA 1843). After the war, Barnard resumed the study and challenge of coastal defense in the light of new technologies. In 1870, he visited Europe to further investigate the latest scientific developments in this area. Barnard's expertise was next utilized in the navigation improvements at the mouth of the Mississippi River. He served on numerous commissions and boards as a leader and advisor to many engineering projects across the country. Barnard had always maintained an active scholarly interest in mathematics and physics. He was an avid reader of science and an articulate spokesman for the scientific aspects of military developments. In addition to writing numerous Corps of Engineer reports, Barnard published several technical reports on his mathematics and science in Smithsonian Institute publications. His writings for Johnson's *Universal New Cyclopedia* showed his versatility and capabilities. His 70 articles included many of his areas of technical interest: gyroscopes, pendulums, tides, bridges, harbors, jetties, lighthouses, aeronautics, differential equations, calculus, biographies, and histories. Barnard retired from the Army in 1881 and died one year later. Despite his partial deafness, Barnard was truly a leader of technical and engineering research and development. He was able both to study the deepest theories of science and also work on the practical problems of engineering in the field. He was one of the corporators of the National Academy of Sciences and a valuable contributor to the advancement of science in the U.S. Among his numerous honors were degrees from Yale College and University of Alabama.

Quotation: About Barnard by the Chief of Army Engineers: "Modest and retiring in disposition, considerate and courteous, … [Barnard] will be missed as few are missed, and his name will be held as one of the foremost names in the Corps of Engineers."

USMA 1929 | **Kenneth David Nichols** | **Engineer**

13 May 1907 (Cleveland, OH) -- 21 February 2000 (Bethesda, MD)
Graduate # 8491 (5th out of 299), (scientist, mechanist), listed in *AS* (Sep 2000)

Military Service:
1929-1931: Engineer duty in Nicaragua
1941-1942: Construction engineer, Rome Air Depot, Rome, NY

Professional Service:

1931-1932: MS in engineering from Cornell University
1933-1934: Assistant Director, U.S. Waterways Experiment Station,
            Vicksburg, MS
1934-1935: Graduate study in science, Berlin
1935-1937: Ph.D. in engineering from Iowa State
1937-1941: Instructor and Assistant Professor, Civil and Military
            Engineering, USMA
1942-1947: Scientific and leadership duties with the Manhattan Project
1947-1948: Professor of Mechanics, USMA
1948-1950: Chief, Armed Forces Special Weapons Project
1950-1952: Deputy Director, Guided Missile Division
1952-1953: Chief of Army Research and Development
1953-1955: General Manager, Atomic Energy Commission

Upon graduation from West Point, **K. D. NICHOLS** was assigned to Nicaragua for survey duty and technical work on the proposed Nicaraguan inter-oceanic canal. Later, for his efforts during and after the Managua earthquake in March 1931, he was awarded the Nicaraguan Medal of Merit. Following his attendance at Cornell University, where he received a master's degree in Civil Engineering, he became the assistant director of the Waterways Experiment Station in Vicksburg, MS. Nichols then went to the Technische Hochschule in Germany under a fellowship from the Institute of International Education to study hydraulics. Upon his return to the States, he taught in the Department of Civil and Military Engineering at West Point for four years. At the beginning of World War II, he was given a critical assignment in the secret organization established to develop and produce the atomic bomb – the Manhattan Project. In this special position, he reported directly to **Leslie Groves (USMA November 1918)**, the Commanding General of the Project. Nichols supervised the research, development, and production related to the design, construction, and operation of the facilities for the production of weapons-grade plutonium and uranium for the first atomic bombs. Part of his duties was to construct the towns of Oak Ridge, TN and Richland, WA. His role in the success of the Manhattan Project was significant, as both his technical and managerial skills were utilized at the most critical stages of the work. After completing his duties on the Manhattan Project, Nichols was appointed Professor of Mechanics at USMA in 1947; however, it was soon evident that his expertise in atomic energy was needed by the United Nations Atomic Energy Commission and the United States Atomic Energy Commission. Therefore, he left West Point to become the Chief of the Armed Forces Special Weapons Project and given responsibility for atomic weapons logistics and training. He commanded this joint Army-Navy-Air Force organization for three years, while also serving as the Deputy Director of Atomic Energy Matters, for the Army Staff. He next served as Deputy Director of the Guided Missiles Project, where he refocused his science and used his technical leadership to build a successful organization. Nichols retired from the Army in 1953, but continued to serve in high-level technical positions. President Eisenhower appointed him General Manager of the Atomic Energy Commission with the special duty to develop the means to produce commercial electric power using atomic energy. Immediately successful in this important effort, he retired from government service in 1955. Nichols received numerous awards for his contributions and was elected a member of the National Academy of Engineering and a Fellow of the American Nuclear Society. Nichols published an account of his personal perspective of America's nuclear policies in the book *The Road to Trinity*. Throughout his service as a technical leader of America's development of the atomic bomb and nuclear energy, Nichols made invaluable contributions to the national security and industrialization of the United States during a critical period of world war and the tensions of the cold war.

USMA 1870   **Edward Singleton Holden**   **Scientist**

5 November 1846 (St. Louis, MO) -- 16 March 1914 (West Point, NY)
Graduate # 2314 (3rd out of 58), (astronomer, mathematician), listed in *DAB, ANB, NCAB DSB, BDAS, AR* (1915)

Military Service:
1870-1871: Artillery duty in North Carolina

Professional Service:
1871-1872: Assistant Professor of Natural & Experimental Philosophy, USMA
1872-1873: Assistant Professor of Practical Military Engineering, USMA
1873-1879: Astronomer, U.S. Naval Observatory, Washington, DC
1879-1881: Librarian, U.S. Naval Observatory, Washington, DC
1881-1885: Director, Washburn Observatory, University of Wisconsin
1883:   Led a National Academy of Sciences expedition to observe a solar eclipse
1885:   Elected to the National Academy of Sciences
1885-1888: President, University of California at Berkeley
1885-1897: Director, Lick Observatory, University of California at Berkeley
1889:   Founder of the Astronomy Society of the Pacific
1897:   Elected to the American Philosophical Society
1901-1914: Librarian, USMA

E. S. HOLDEN developed an interest in astronomy at a young age. As a child, he made frequent visits to the Harvard Observatory. Holden attended Washington University in St. Louis and graduated in 1866 at the age of 19. He went immediately to West Point and graduated from the Academy in 1870. After graduation he served one year in an artillery unit before returning to West Point to teach courses in mechanics, astronomy, acoustics, optics, and engineering during his two-year tour. In 1873, Holden left the Army to fulfill a lifelong dream to become an astronomer at the U.S. Naval Observatory in Washington, DC. There

West Point Library (from Howitzer)

he assisted the eminent astronomer Simon Newcomb, who was using the world's largest refracting telescope to make observations and develop new scientific theories. Holden published several articles and wrote an astronomy textbook with Newcomb. In 1881, Holden became the director of the Washburn Observatory at the University of Wisconsin. While there, he led an expedition organized by the National Academy of Sciences to study an eclipse. Next, he worked with Newcomb to design the Lick Observatory for the University of California at Berkeley. Holden was the principal advisor and designer of the world's largest (36-inch) observatory refractor that was built at the observatory. In 1886, Holden filled the Presidency of the University of California at Berkley with the condition of becoming the Director of the Lick Observatory when it was completed. In 1888, the move was made, and Holden became the director of the world's most powerful telescope and a *Celebrity* in American science. To his credit, he assembled an excellent

research staff. Holden's talents were in the organizational and financial matters of the observatory. He built a superb library and obtained the finest equipment possible. His personal research mostly involved photography of features of the moon. He founded the Astronomy Society of the Pacific during his tenure as director. Unfortunately, his leadership style and research talents were not acceptable to his colleagues and staff. Holden was unpopular and considered to be a dictator by the staff. After a revolt by the staff, Holden was forced to resign. Returning to New York City in 1897, he wrote many articles and books on various subjects, both technical and expository, during the next four years. He tendered his services to the War Department at the outbreak of the Spanish-American War, but at age 52, he was not accepted. In 1901, Holden was appointed the USMA Librarian, serving in that position

until his death in 1914. As Librarian, he helped compile and write the one of the supplements of Cullum's *Register of USMA Graduates* and authored several articles in the *Centennial of the United States Military Academy*. Some of his technical publications were, "The Bastion System of Fortification" (1872), *Central Parts of the Nebula of Orion* (1882), *Astronomy for*

High Schools and Colleges (1879, with S. Newcomb), *Publications of the Washburn Observatory*, and *Publications of the Lick Observatory*. He also wrote about education at the Military Academy in a chapter for the *Report of Bureau of Education* (1891-1892). He was elected to the National Academy of Sciences, the Royal Astronomical Society, Astronomical Society of France, and the American Association for the Advancement of Sciences. Among his many tributes were honorary degrees from University of Wisconsin, University of the Pacific, and Columbia College.

References:

Campbell, W. Wallace, "Edward Singleton Holden," *National Academy of Sciences Biographical Memoirs*, vol. 8 (1919) pp. 347-372.

Osterbrock, Donald, "The Rise and Fall of Edward S. Holden," *Journal for the History of Astronomy*, 1984, (Part 1) pp. 80-127, (Part 2) pp. 151-176.

USMA 1848 | **William Petit Trowbridge** | **Scientist**

25 May 1828 (Troy, NY) – 12 August 1892 (New Haven, CT)
Graduate # 1369 (1st out of 38), (mathematician), listed in *DAB, NCAB, BDAS, AR* (1893)

Military Service:
1861-1865: Engineer duties in support of fortifications & defenses of New York City during the Civil War

Professional Service:
1848-1851: Research scientist at West Point Observatory
1850-1851: Engineer duty at West Point
1851-1853: Topographic duties in ME and VA working for Coast Survey
1853-1856: Scientific duty on Pacific Coast for Coast Survey
1856-1857: Professor of Mathematics, University of Michigan
1857-1861: Chief Scientist, Coast Survey
1861: Hydrographic Survey of Narragancett Bay, RI
1870-1877: Professor of Dynamical Engineering, Sheffield Scientific School, Yale College, CT
1872: Elected to the American Philosophical Society
1877-1892: Professor of Engineering School of Mines, Columbia College, NY
1888-1892: Mathematician analyzing statistics of 1890 census

W. P. TROWBRIDGE entered the United States Military Academy at the age of 16 and graduated first in his class of 1848. He taught chemistry during his last year at the Academy. Having so impressed his science professor, **William Bartlett (USMA 1826)**, as a studious and brilliant cadet, Trowbridge had the unique opportunity to perform research at the Academy's observatory for two years after graduation. This was good preparation for his next assignment with the United States Coast Survey. His first surveys were along the Atlantic Coast, in particular the rugged Maine coast and the Appomattox and James Rivers in VA. From 1853 to 1856, he was positioned on the Pacific Coast, conducting astronomical, tidal, meteorological, and magnetic investigations from San Diego to Puget Sound. Trowbridge was comfortable in both field work and laboratory science. While out West, he participated in the Williamson and Abbot expedition of Pacific Railroad surveys. He resigned from the Army in 1856 taking a professorship in mathematics at the University of Michigan. Just a year later, he had the opportunity to return to the Coast Survey as Superintendent Bache's assistant and the Survey's chief scientist, which afforded him numerous opportunities to lead and perform scientific research and engineering activities. While involved in Coast Survey work, he devised an instrument for determining ocean depths and obtaining specimens from the ocean bottom, investigated the wind patterns along the Pacific Coast, collected and analyzed temperature data on the Gulf Stream, investigated measurement techniques for deep sea soundings, and studied fluctuations in magnetic readings at Key West, FL. He wrote numerous articles for the annual reports published by the Coast Survey. In preparation for the Civil War, he produced detailed descriptions of southern harbors for the Navy. During the Civil War, he assumed responsibility for the engineering unit supplying materials for Union fortifications and supervised construction of the fortification at Willet's Point and other coastal defenses near New York City. After the war, he became the vice-president of Novelty Iron Works in New York City. From 1871 to 1877, he taught some of the nation's brightest engineering students at Yale University. Using his vast experience and knowledge, Trowbridge was a successful motivator and lecturer, while serving as Professor of Dynamic Engineering at Yale. He accepted a new position in 1877 until his death in 1892 as Professor of Engineering in the School of Mines at Columbia College, NY. As a teacher he emphasized the strong theoretical science and mathematical basis for engineering, realizing that the applications of those subjects better served the engineer as the nature and needs of engineering changed over the years. An active member of many engineering commissions to construct buildings and harbor facilities, he was an expert on cantilever bridges, steam generators, and electric motors. Among his design works were the Capitol Buildings of the states of CT and NY. He was an active member and leader of the New York Academy of Sciences, the American Association for the Advancement of Science, and the National Academy of Sciences. His publications were numerous and varied. In addition to the many articles that he authored in science and engineering, he published treatises on power production using heat and turbine wheels. Trowbridge also contributed a significant collection of fish to the Smithsonian Institute, which added over 50 new species to the museum collection. Two varieties of Pacific Coast fish were named after Trowbridge. Trowbridge was such a multi-talented person it is difficult to label him as a mathematician, scientist, engineer, inventor, explorer, educator, or technologist. At various times, he was one of America's experts in all these areas and more. He made tremendous contributions to all areas of American science, much like his mentor **Alexander Bache (USMA 1825)**; therefore, he is best remembered as a successful leader of science and a technical innovator.

USMA 1806 — Alden Partridge — Mathematician

12 February 1785 (Norwich, VT) – 17 January 1854 (Norwich, VT)
Graduate # 15, listed in *DAB, ANB, NCAB, ACAB*

Military Service:
1806-1818: Army service in technical duties

Professional Service:
1806-1813: Assistant Professor of Mathematics, USMA
1813:   Professor of Mathematics, Head of the Department, USMA
1813-1816: Professor of Civil and Military Engineering, USMA
1814-1817: Acting Superintendent of USMA
1819-1843: Founder and President of American Literary, Scientific
                     and Military Academy at Norwich, VT
1822-1823: Surveyor General of VT

A. PARTRIDGE went to Dartmouth College for three years, but left before graduating to attend West Point in 1805. Just a few months later in 1806, Partridge graduated from USMA and was commissioned in the Corps of Engineers. Partridge was stationed at West Point for his entire Army career. He was assigned to teach mathematics and for seven years developed cadets using many new ideas and innovative teaching methods. During this time, he presented papers to the United States Military Philosophical Society (see the essay on USMPS), which was located at West Point. Partridge performed some of his investigations in collaboration with President Thomas Jefferson. In 1813, Partridge was elevated to the position of Professor of Mathematics and Head of the Mathematics Department, serving only a few months in that position before being selected as Professor of Engineering. In establishing this new engineering department, Partridge was the first to fill such a position in the United States. Since Joseph Swift was away from the Academy, Partridge was the acting superintendent for nearly four years. When Thayer was appointed the new Superintendent, Partridge refused to relinquish command and was dismissed from the Army for his actions in 1818. This action made Partridge a controversial figure. Historian Lester Webb called Partridge "the greatest educator developed by the United States Military Academy." Others take the other side, as Ernest Dupuy wrote that Partridge was an "arrogant, insubordinate, martinet."

Partridge spent some time surveying the northern boundary of the United States before returning to his passion of undergraduate military and technical education. Partridge believed that a large standing army was a menace to the country and urged the training of citizen soldiers in the art of war. In 1820, Partridge opened the American Literary, Scientific and Military Academy at Norwich, VT, the first technical and military school for training and educating citizen soldiers in the world. The Academy had an initial enrollment of 100 cadets. His military school developed a reputation for having an excellent academic program embodied in a tough, disciplined military environment. Partridge was an innovative teacher, who used practical exercises and examples, laboratory work, and field exercises to consolidate and motivate student learning. He was also innovative in his own research in various areas of mathematics, science, and engineering. Partridge taught the applications of mathematics and science to engineering and was able to develop outstanding engineers with a strong conceptual background. Some of his publications were: "Observations Relative to the Calculation of the Altitude of Mountains, etc, by the Use of the Barometer" (1812), "Method of Determining the Initial Velocity of Projectiles" (1812), "Newton's Binomial Theorem" (1814), "Meteorological Tables" (1810-1814), "A General Plan for the Establishment of Military Academies" (1815), and "Lectures on National Defense" (1821-1827). His school at Norwich moved to CT for a short time before returning to VT and being renamed Norwich University. As part of his plan of training citizen soldiers, he founded several more military schools including Virginia Literary, Scientific and Military Academy at Portsmouth, VA (1839-1846), Pennsylvania Literary, Scientific, and Military Academy at Bristol, PA (1842-1845), Pennsylvania Military Institute at Harrisburg, PA (1845-1848), Wilmington Literary, Scientific and Military Academy at Wilmington, DE (1846-1848), the Scientific and Military Collegiate Institute at Reading, PA (1850-1854), Gymnasium and Military Institute at Pembroke, NH (1850-1853), and the National Scientific and Military Academy at Brandywine Springs, DE. For the most part, these schools were administered by and staffed with Norwich University graduates. Partridge is regarded as the founder of the system of military preparatory academies for school-age children and his ideas were the precursor to ROTC. He had influence on his neighbor, Congressman Justin Morrill, who later authored the Morrill Act of 1862, which established funding for land-grant institutions throughout the United States. In addition to his educational and technical work, Partridge was a politician and orator, having served as Surveyor-General of Vermont and in the Vermont legislature. He lectured extensively on military, scientific, engineering, and educational subjects.

References:

Baker, Dean, *Partridge Connection: Alden Partridge and Southern Military Education,* University of North Carolina, Chapel Hill, 1986.

Dupuy, Ernest, "Mutiny at West Point, " *American Heritage*, Vol. 7, pp. 22-27.

Forman, Sidney, "The United States Military Philosophical Society, 1802-1813: Scientia in Bello Pax," *William and Mary Quarterly*, July 1945, pp. 273-285.

Jardine, Dick, *Alden Partridge: Educational Innovator,* Proceedings of the History of Undergraduate Mathematics in America, West Point, 2001.

Lord, Gary, "Alden Partridge's Proposal for a National System of Education: A Model for the Morrill Land-Grant Act," *History of Higher Education Annual*, 1998.

Webb, Lester, *Captain Alden Partridge and the United States Military Academy,* American Southern, Northport, AL, 1965.

USMA 1818 | **Andrew Talcott** | **Engineer**

20 April 1797 (Glastonbury, CT) -- 22 April 1883 (Norfolk, VA)
Graduate # 181 (2nd out of 23), (topographer, surveyor, astronomer), listed in *DAB, NCAB, AR* (1883)

Military Service:
1820-1821: Aide-de-camp for General Atkinson during expedition along Missouri and Yellowstone Rivers
1818-1836: In military service as topographic engineer.

Professional Service:
1818-1819: Construction engineer for fortification at Rouse's Point, NY
1821-1824: Construction engineer for defenses at Hampton Roads, VA
1824-1835: Construction engineer for various forts in RI, NY, DE, VA
1832-1836: Construction engineer for improvements of Hudson River navigation
1836-1837: Construction engineer for railroad company
1836: Elected to the American Philosophical Society
1837-1839: Engineer for navigation and improvement of Mississippi River delta
1840-1843: Surveyor of the northeast boundary of United States
1844-1845: Engineer for Naval docks
1848-1857: Construction engineer for railroad companies
1852-1853: Astronomer and surveyor for northern boundary of Iowa
1855-1856: Construction engineer of U.S. Mint Building
1859-1867: Construction engineer for railroad across Mexico

A. TALCOTT finished second in the West Point class of 1818 behind **Richard Delafield**. His first assignment in the Corps of Engineers was for one year to assist the engineers at Rouse's Point in building a fortification on the northern end of Lake Champlain. He then became the aide-de-camp for General Atkinson on a one-year expedition to survey lands and to build fortifications along the Missouri and Yellowstone Rivers. For the next 11 years, Talcott continued construction engineering work on fortifications in several East Coast states. He was considered one of the best military construction engineers. In 1826, he superintended the canal construction through Dismal Swamp in VA and then the construction of Ft. Monroe and Ft. Calhoun, VA. In 1832 to 1834, he surveyed the border between Ohio and

Michigan. In 1836, Talcott resigned from the Army to profit from his skills as a construction engineer. His first job was with a railroad company locating track and designing railroad bridges, but soon he was working on improvements on the delta of the Mississippi River for the federal government. His next endeavor was so successful that it established a national reputation for Talcott as an expert scientist and surveyor. He worked on the difficult and challenging survey of the northern border of the United States for three years, performing astronomical observations and supervising the survey teams. In 1843, Talcott was one of the prime candidates for the newly vacated and prestigious position of Superintendent of the Coast Survey. Although Talcott was not selected, it marked him as one of the leaders of American technology. Talcott went on to further construction engineering duties on Navy yards, buildings, and railroads. In 1852, he was hired back into surveying on the boundary line of Iowa. Talcott perfected his method for latitude determination that he established in 1838 using precise astronomical observations. His method had achieved international acclaim over the years. In 1857, Talcott began his last, most challenging and substantial project, building a railroad across Mexico. By the time of his retirement from professional work in 1867, the amazing project was nearly complete. Talcott authored several technical reports, and the Talcott Method of latitude determination was first described in the *Journal of the Franklin Institute* in 1838. The Coast Survey and the Army Corps of Engineers utilized this method, along with other survey innovations discovered by Talcott, in their numerous surveys. As a brilliant surveyor, scientist, engineer, mathematician, and astronomer, Talcott was honored through his election to the American Philosophical Society.

USMA 1818 | **Richard Delafield** | **Engineer**

1 September 1798 (New York, NY) -- 5 November 1873 (Washington, DC)
Graduate # 180 (1st out of 23), listed in *DAB, ANB, NCAB, AR* (1874)

Military Service:
1855:   Observer of Crimean War
1861-1864:   Supervisor of coast defenses, NY harbor during Civil War (MG)

Professional Service:
1818-1819:   Astronomer and draftsman for survey of U.S. - Canada border
1819-1824:   Fortification engineer in Hampton Roads, VA
1824-1832:   Fortification engineer for New Orleans area and navigation engineer for Mississippi River
1832-1838:   Supervisor of construction of Cumberland Road
1838-1845:   Superintendent, USMA
1845-1855:   Fortification engineer for New York Harbor
1856-1861:   Superintendent, USMA
1866:   Regent of the Smithsonian Institute

R. DELAFIELD attended West Point during its transition from a fledgling academic program to Thayer's more rigorous technical curriculum. He underwent a four-year curriculum, taking courses in applied mathematics and science with textbooks from the British Military Academy at Woolrich, authored by Hutton and Simson. His coursework consisted of algebra, geometry, logarithms, conic sections, trigonometry, surveying, mensuration, natural philosophy, and the rudiments of engineering. He was the first graduate of the Military Academy to receive a merit class standing under **Sylvanus Thayer's (USMA 1808)** new competitive system, ranking first in the class of 1818. It was obvious during his studies that Delafield was a gifted draftsman and had the talents of a superb fortification engineer. The Army recognized these talents and assigned him to work on the team surveying the border between Canada and the United States in the aftermath of the War of 1812 and the Treaty of Ghent. After just one year of this survey duty, Delafield moved south to Hampton Roads, VA, where he designed fortifications for seacoast defenses as a consequence of the security concerns after the War of 1812. After six years in VA, his engineering talents were needed for the design and construction work of defenses in New Orleans and for navigation improvements on the Mississippi and Ohio Rivers. His contributions to improvements of America's major north-south transportation system were considerable. He was recognized by the Army Corps of Engineers as its most capable draftsman and most effective civil engineer. His next project was back on the East Coast where he worked on one of the nation's most pressing needs, the construction of a reliable route from the East Coast westward to the Plains. Delafield worked diligently for six years on the construction of the eastern portion of the Cumberland Road, which cut through the Appalachian Mountains from Baltimore, MD, through Hagerstown and Zanesville, and westward to Vandalia, IL. The route was essentially complete when Delafield left this project in 1838. As part of this effort, he designed and built the first cast-iron tubular-arch bridge in the United States. By 1838, Delafield's engineering talents were needed to produce the next generation of Army engineers, so he was sent to West Point to serve as Superintendent of the Academy. Over his seven-year tenure, he spent considerable time improving the facilities, building a library and other academic buildings. While Superintendent, he stated that the Academy existed "to obtain, and have some means of preserving and diffusing the improvements in science and the art of war." His leadership efforts were directed towards that goal. Delafield governed the Academy during the time of great academic progress and recognition. His three technical department heads (**Albert Church (USMA 1828), William Bartlett (USMA 1826)**, and **Dennis Mahan (USMA 1824)**) dominated the academic board and kept the technical disciplines as the focus of the Academy. Delafield's next move was just down the Hudson River, as he became the leader of the Army's Board of Engineers for Fortifications, which built and improved fortifications in the New York Harbor. After ten years in New York, the Secretary of War, Jefferson Davis (USMA 1828), sent Delafield, along with two others (**Alfred Mordecai (USMA 1823)** and George McClellan (USMA 1843)), to observe the military operations of the Crimean War and to report on the state of the military system in Europe. Delafield's report, published in 1860, contained numerous illustrations about fortifications and new weapons. This was such a complete and valuable military technical report that the Union Army tried to prevent the Confederates from obtaining copies. From the period 1856 to 1861, Delafield returned to West Point for a second tour as Superintendent. This time the major issue at the Academy was the implementation of a five-year academic program. The additional year was added in 1854 to increase cadet knowledge of the liberal arts. Very few at the Academy supported this change, and West Point returned to a four-year program in 1861. Delafield returned to supervise the defense of New York Harbor during the Civil War and retired from Army service in 1866. He worked as a regent of the Smithsonian Institute after his retirement. In addition to his 12 years as the leader of West Point, his development of rigorous engineering principles in military fortifications and his efficient system for planning civil construction projects were his major contributions. While Delafield staunchly defended the out-of-date fortification system as a military strategy, he did contribute to the Army's increasing scientific approach to military issues and problems, thereby, developing many of the principles of modern military science and technology.

USMA 1919 | **Boyd Wheeler Bartlett** | **Scientist**

20 June 1897 (Castine, ME) – 24 June 1965 (Castine, ME)
Graduate # 6258 (3rd out of 284), (physicist), listed in *AS* (Fall 1965)

Military Service:
1919-1922: Staff duty in Office of Chief of Army Engineers, Washington, DC

Professional Service:
1917: Graduated from Bowdoin College, ME
1919-1920: Engineer duty for Fort Benning railroad
1920-1921: Civil engineering study at Massachusetts Institute of Technology
1922-1927: Physicist at Bell Telephone, NY
1922-1927: Graduate student (M.S. in physics from Columbia University, NY)
1927-1942: Professor of Physics at Bowdoin College, ME
1942-1945: Professor of Physics, USMA
1945-1961: Professor of Electricity, USMA
1961-1965: Trustee for Bowdoin College, ME

B. W. "BRICK" BARTLETT graduated from Bowdoin College before attending USMA. Entering West Point in June 1917, his program was accelerated and his class graduated in November 1918. Since World War I ended just eleven days later, his class was recalled and graduated again in June 1919. He worked on railroad construction at Fort Benning, GA for a few months before entering Massachusetts Institute of Technology. He graduated with a B.S. in Civil Engineering in 1921. After one year of staff work at the Office of the Chief of Engineers, Bartlett resigned from the Army. He worked five years as a researcher on electrical standards and measurements for Bell Laboratory, while he completed an M.S. degree in Physics at Columbia University. In 1927, Bartlett became a professor at Bowdoin College, working his way up through assistant, associate, and full Professor of Physics and teaching all levels and disciplines of college science. He earned his Ph.D. from Columbia University in 1932. From 1934 to 1935, he studied nuclear physics in Germany at the University of Munich. After being so successful at his academic career, Bartlett offered his services back to his country at the outset of the second world war. He was commissioned and sent to West Point to teach physics. A year later, he was made Department Head and Professor of Physics. With a reorganization in 1945, he was made Professor and Head of the Department of Electricity. An active scholar and an effective academic leader, he initiated new courses and lessons in nuclear and modern physics and gave lectures to cadets and faculty on the physics of the atomic bomb. He kept improving the science core courses by adding new, modern laboratory equipment – radiation counters and cloud chambers – and inviting noted physicists to present their latest results to cadets and faculty. He arranged field trips to research labs and the cyclotron at Columbia University. In 1960, Bartlett took a 15,000-mile trip during which he visited engineering schools, military research facilities, and national research laboratories (Oak Ridge and Livermore). From his investigation, Bartlett advocated a full semester of nuclear physics for the Academy's curriculum. This course was approved and implemented during 1961, his last year at USMA. Under his direction, West Point built a nuclear laboratory with a small reactor. Not forgetting the importance of electronics and communications, Bartlett kept these courses up-to-date with the latest advances in technology. Bartlett was an active scholar in every sense of the word – expert researcher, gifted expositor, and dedicated teacher – a man that typified a stalwart *Sentinel* of American science. He was an active member of the American Association for the Advancement of Science, American Physics Society, Association of Physics Teachers, and the American Society for Engineering Education. His research papers appeared in top journals – *Physical Research, American Journal of Physics, Nuclear Science*, and several others. Among his many tributes was an honorary degree from Bowdoin, where he served as a Trustee after his Army retirement. Bartlett's scholarly approach to education kept West Point in the forefront of the national community of science education. His reform initiatives keep the Academy's curriculum up-to-date and effective for the future technological leaders of America's Army.

USMA 1887 | Wirt Robinson | Scientist

16 October 1864 (Buckingham, VA) -- 19 January 1929 (Washington, DC)
Graduate # 3182 (9th out of 64), (zoologist, biologist, geologist, chemist, electrical engineer), listed in
AR (1929)

Military Service:

1887-1891: Garrison duty in RI, GA
1892-1894: Garrison duty in GA and DC
1894-1898: Military science instructor at Harvard University, MA
1898-1899: Garrison duty in DE and NY
1903-1904: Troop duty in Cuba

Professional Service:

1894-1898: Graduate study in mathematics at Harvard University, MA
1904-1906: Instructor of Chemistry and Explosives, School of
            Submarine Defense, Ft. Totten, NY
1906-1911: Assistant Professor of Chemistry, Mineralogy, and
            Geology, USMA
1911-1928: Professor of Chemistry, Mineralogy and Geology, USMA

W. ROBINSON had been a student of nature since his childhood and took every opportunity to travel and explore. He studied at Richmond College, VA for four years before entering West Point. He was fluent in Spanish and taught the subject at the Academy. After five years of garrison duty, Robinson took a trip to Curacao and Columbia in 1892 where he studied the topical animals and vegetation. The result was a popular book entitled *A Flying Trip to the Tropics* in 1895. In 1895, while assigned as a military instructor at Harvard, he took leave and went to Venezuela. He returned there in 1900 with other scientists. Other trips were made to Jamaica, Cuba, and other parts of Central America. His many reports on birds and mammals were published. Three newly found species of birds and one insect were named in his honor. Robinson built a large library for his reference book collection at his home in VA. In addition to his thorough study of birds, mammals, and insects, Robinson collected Indian relics. He thoroughly enjoyed his Army assignment to Cuba in 1903, since he could explore new ecologies and travel easily to other islands. While teaching chemistry to engineers in the graduate program at Fort Totten, NY, Robinson had the opportunity to return to West Point to teach undergraduates. He brought his vast knowledge and intense passion for scientific study to the Department of Chemistry, Mineralogy, and Geology at the Academy. It was an organization of multiple disciplines, which was perfect for Robinson's many interests. Robinson wrote textbooks on heat and electricity that were used by cadets, and he prepared many teaching pamphlets on electricity, chemistry, and mineralogy. Robinson continued to travel and explore while at the Academy. He made five trips to the tropics, discovering over twenty new species. His large collection of species, relics and references was willed to the U.S. National Museum in Washington, DC.

When sent to the museum, his collection included 539 mammals, 163 birds, 20,00 insects, and several reptiles, which were in addition to his previous contributions. His archeology collection included over 20,000 arrowheads, hundreds of axes, pipes, and other relics. Robinson's enthusiasm for science was a tremendous contribution to the Academy as it adjusted to the complex times of the technological advances of the 20th century and World War I. Robinson kept his passion and energy for the sciences as he was burdened with administration and, during the war, chaos at the Academy. He also found time to contribute to the history of the Academy by editing the 1920 edition of the *Graduates' Register*. Having mentored dozens of faculty members and taught hundreds of cadets, Robinson was one of the most versatile, energetic, and successful scholars ever produced by the Academy. He possessed the amazing combination of both an active field scientist and a deep, theoretical thinker. His reputation as a scientist was worldwide, and his contributions to zoology were extensive.

USMA 1824   ## Dennis Hart Mahan   **Engineer**

2 April 1802 (New York, NY) – 16 September 1871 (Hudson River, NY)
Graduate # 361 (1st out of 31), listed in *DAB, ANB, NCAB, AR* (1872)

Military Service:
1824:   Survey duty in Baltimore, MD
1826-1830:   Visitation of military installations in Europe

Professional service:
1824-1826:   Assistant Professor of Mathematics and Engineering, USMA
1829-1830:   Attended Military School of Application for Engineers and Artillerists, Metz, France
1830-1871:   Professor of Engineering, USMA (author of numerous successful engineering textbooks), (one
                   of fifty original corporators of the National Academy of Sciences)

D. H. MAHAN graduated from West Point in 1824 expecting a long career with the field army as an engineer. For three months, he served on a survey team in Baltimore, but that assignment was the only field duty that he would experience. He returned to West Point to teach mathematics for one year and engineering the second year. Mahan was then sent to Europe and spent four years visiting military installations, examining engineering public works projects, and attending the French Military Academy for Engineers and Artillerists in Metz. This experience gave Mahan an exceptional preparation for his long tenure as the Professor of Engineering and Department Head at West Point. For the next 41 years, he taught cadets and developed military faculty in the principles

and skills of engineering. Along with two fellow science-based department heads, **Albert Church (USMA 1828)** in mathematics and **William Bartlett (USMA 1826)** in science, Mahan influenced curriculum, pedagogy, and governance of the Academy. Mahan had the opportunity to teach cadets, including those who became the Army leaders during the Civil War, for nearly half a century. Nearly 2000 cadets graduated during his long tenure. During most years, he personally taught a demanding, senior-level course covering military engineering, field operations, fortifications, and leadership. The course was entitled "Engineering and the Science of War." A strong believer in fundamental principles, Mahan's academic writing consisted of several highly successful textbooks covering engineering, military science, field fortifications, mechanics, and industrial drawing. His books sold many copies, unusual for technical subjects (up to 15,000 for each title) and set the stage for the tremendous rigor, detail, and practicality in engineering courses throughout the country. Some of these books were so military in their perspective, they were valued as field manuals for both the Union and Confederate Armies during the Civil War. Many of the cadets Mahan taught and faculty he developed went on to teach engineering at other technical schools and land-grant universities in America. Mahan's text, *Elementary Course of Civil Engineering* (first published in 1837 with revisions until 1868), incorporated many of the engineering principles that he learned in graduate study in France and as a cadet. However, he had little opportunity over the 40 years as department head to advance his subject or stay attuned to new developments. In many ways, Mahan was the dominating figure at the Academy for four decades. He was a strong advocate of the Thayer Method of education (rigor, detail, feedback, competition) and strict military discipline and protocol. Mahan's tenure ended in tragedy, as the Board of Visitors of the Academy in 1871, having recognized his lack of new ideas and his role in stagnating the curriculum, recommended that he retire. This difficult situation caused him great depression as he pondered his actions. Mahan committed suicide by jumping off a boat as he traveled on the Hudson River on the way to New York City to see a physician. By all measures, Mahan had tremendous impact over the Academy and the Army and considerable influence on the technical foundation of thousands

of American engineers. Some of his publications include: *Complete Treatise on Field Fortifications* (1836*), Course of Permanent Fortification and of the Attack and Defense of Permanent Works* (1850), *Industrial Drawing* (1852), *Descriptive Geometry as Applied to Drawing of Fortifications* (1864), and *An Elementary Course in Military Engineering* (1866-67). However, Mahan's most influential work was his *Elementary Treatise on Advance-Guard, Outpost, and Detachment Services of Troops*. This book followed the military philosophy of Henri Jomini of stressing offensive maneuvering to win battles. Mahan's strategy was embraced by both sides in the Civil War, leading to highly lethal, mobile forces and bloody, devastating battles. He was one of the corporators of the National Academy of Sciences and a member of the Geographical Society of Paris. Among his academic awards were honorary degrees from Brown University, Princeton College, William and Mary College, and Dartmouth College and membership in the American Society of Civil Engineers.

Quotation: By Mahan: "The spirit of the offensive, the doctrine of mobile warfare, has been indelibly written on the pages of American history. From hand-to-hand, the torch would pass down the Long Grey Line to bring victory on battlefields in a global war of such magnitude as was undreamed of by the original exponent of them."

By George Cullum about Mahan: "He had an almost intuitive perception of the exact amount of information possessed by each cadet on the subject matter of the lesson in hand, and by a few dexterous questions would quickly winnow the kernel of knowledge from the chaff of pretension."

References:

Cullum, George, "Professor D. H. Mahan," *Army and Navy Journal*, IX, 7 Oct 1871.

Griess, Thomas, *Dennis Hart Mahan: West Point Professor and Advocate for Military Professionalism, 1830-1871*, Ph.D. Thesis, Duke University, Durham, NC, 1968.

USMA 1826 | William Holms Chambers Bartlett | Scientist

4 September 1804 (Lancaster, PA) – 11 February 1893 (Yonkers, NY)
Graduate # 429 (1st out of 41), (mathematician), listed in *DAB, ANB, BDAS, AR* (1893)

Military Service:

1832-1834: Assistant Chief Engineer, Washington, DC

Professional Service:

1827-1829: Assistant Professor of Engineering, USMA
1829-1832: Construction engineer for Ft Monroe, VA and Ft Adams, RI
1834-1871: Professor of Natural and Experimental Philosophy, USMA
1839-1859: Author of many science books
1840:   Elected to the American Philosophical Society
1840-1841: Visited observatories in Europe
1863:   Corporator of National Academy of Sciences
1871-1889: Actuary for insurance company

W. H. C. BARTLETT is considered by some to be West Point's most brilliant graduate of the 19th century. After graduation from West Point and commissioning in the Corps of Engineers, Bartlett stayed at the Academy to instruct engineering for two years. Over the next five years, he worked as a construction engineer on various coastal fortifications and harbor facilities. He spent 1832 to 1834 in

Washington, DC as the assistant Chief of Army Engineers. In 1834, Bartlett was selected as the Professor of Natural and Experimental Philosophy and Head of the Department at West Point. Serving in that position for 37 years until his retirement from the Army, he and his two other science-based colleagues, **Albert Church (USMA 1828)** in the Mathematics Department and **Dennis Mahan (USMA 1824)** in the Engineering Department, dominated the academic decision making at the Academy. They kept their technical subjects and the engineering-based curriculum entrenched with little changes in the size and content of the program. Bartlett made a trip to Europe to visit observatories and helped build an observatory with a high-quality telescope at West Point when he returned. Bartlett was able to maintain his science research while fulfilling his teaching, administrative, and military duties at the Academy. His work was diverse, ranging from astronomical observations of the comet of 1843 and eclipse of 1854 to theoretical mathematical explanations of movements and properties of comets. A pioneer in the use of new technologies, he was one of the first observers to make use of photographic plates to record accurate measurements. Most of his writings were in the area of science textbooks for college students. His books on optics, mechanics, physics, astronomy, and acoustics were used at West Point and many other colleges in America. Bartlett's most successful textbook, *Elements of Analytical Mechanics,* was based on calculus and thus served as a rigorous foundation course for both scientists and engineers. This

book was published in over nine different editions and was used at West Point and other schools until the end of the 19th century. Bartlett was one of the 50 original corporators of the National Academy of Sciences in 1863 and his paper on rifling of guns appeared in the first volume of the memoirs of the National Academy of Sciences in 1866. He was also a member of the American Philosophical Society. Under Bartlett's leadership, the science curriculum at the Academy serviced the needs of the challenging engineering program at West Point and set the standards for many other technical schools in America. After Bartlett retired from Army service, he became a highly respected actuary for an insurance company and wrote a booklet on finance. Among his academic accolades were honorary degrees from the College of New Jersey (Princeton) and Hobart College.

Reference:

Holden, Edward, "Biographical Memoir of William H. C. Bartlett, 1804-1893," *National Academy of Sciences Biographical Memoirs*, Volume 7, pp. 173-193, 1911.

| USMA 1828 | **Albert Ensign Church** | Mathematician |

16 December 1807 (Salisbury, CT) – 30 March 1878 (West Point, NY)
Graduate # 508 (1st out of 33), listed in *NCAB, AR* (1878)

Military Service:
1831-1833: Artillery duty at Newport, RI and Fort Independence, MA

Professional Service:
1828-1831: Assistant Professor of Mathematics, USMA
1833-1837: Principal Assistant Professor of Mathematics, USMA
1837-1878: Professor of Mathematics, USMA

A. E. CHURCH was groomed at a young age for the legal profession and study at Yale; however, he accepted an appointment to West Point and turned his interest to technical subjects. Even though he was first in his class, there were no vacancies in the Corps of Engineers that year so he accepted his commission as an artillery officer. At the request of Superintendent **Sylvanus Thayer (USMA 1808)**, Church remained at the Academy after graduation as an Assistant Professor of Mathematics from 1828 until 1831. He left the Academy for artillery duty first at Newport, RI and then at Fort Independence in Boston Harbor. A year later, he was recalled to the Academy as the Principal Assistant Professor of Mathematics under **Charles Davies (USMA 1815)**. When Davies resigned from the Army, Church succeeded him as Professor of Mathematics and Department Head in 1838. Church influenced the way the subject was taught at the Academy, although he was often accused of teaching more form than content. Finding the textbooks used at the Academy too abstract and incomplete, Church wrote his own textbooks to replace the ones written earlier by Davies. In 1842 he published his *Elements of the Differential and Integral Calculus,* in 1851 *Elements of Analytical Geometry,* in 1857 *Elements of Analytical Trigonometry*, and in 1865 *Elements of Descriptive Geometry.* All four of these texts were used in the Academy's courses during his tenure as Professor, and some were used into the 20th century. They were also popular in mathematics programs in colleges and universities around the country. As a teacher, Church was viewed with mixed judgments. Some considered him a dry, boring teacher. Others remembered Church as a clear expositor and an ideal mathematics professor. Church, with the support of his colleagues **Dennis Mahan (USMA 1824)** and **William Bartlett (USMA 1826)**, led an effort to keep non-scientific subjects from the curriculum, enabling cadets to devote more hours to the study of mathematics, science, and engineering. These three professors shaped the curriculum at the Academy for nearly forty years never yielding to the demands for fewer mathematics and science courses. Church had the opportunity to educate all the famous Civil War generals who attended West Point. For many of them, he was a mentor and confidant. During his tenure at West Point, Church continued his own development. In 1852 he received his law degree from Yale College and served an additional duty as Staff Judge Advocate at the Academy. He continued to write and publish textbooks during his entire professional career. Constantly revising his books, he produced new editions, supplementing and enhancing versions of his earlier works. Church initiated the use of written examinations in mathematics for admission to the Academy in lieu of oral testing, making the selection of cadets more objective and efficient. Church died while still holding the position of Professor of Mathematics at the Academy.

USMA 1831 | **William Norton** | **Scientist**

25 October 1810 (East Bloomfield, NY) – 21 September 1883 (New Haven, CT)
Graduate # 635 (7th out of 33), (natural philosopher, astronomer, mathematician, engineer), listed in *NCAB, BDAS, AR* (1884)

Military Service:
1831-1833: Army service involved technical duties

Professional Service:
1831-1833: Assistant Professor of Natural and Experimental Philosophy, USMA
1833-1838: Acting Professor of Natural Philosophy and Astronomy, University of the City of New York
1839-1850: Professor of Mathematics and Natural Philosophy, Delaware College
1844:   Elected to the American Philosophical Society
1850:   President, Delaware College
1850-1852: Professor of Natural Philosophy and Civil Engineering, Brown University
1852-1883: Professor of Civil Engineering, Sheffield School of Science, Yale College, CT
1839-1858: Author of technical works
1873:   Member, National Academy of Sciences

W. Norton shared his graduation day from West Point with 32 other distinguished classmates, among them **Roswell Park, A. A. Humphreys**, and **William Emory**. After commissioning, he was part of the expedition in 1832 to capture the Sauk Indian Black Hawk. Following this, he spent the rest of his two years in the Army as a science instructor at the Academy. In 1833, he took the position as Professor of Natural Philosophy and Astronomy at the newly founded University of the City of New York (now called New York University, which was founded in 1831). After building the science program at this new university for six years, Norton moved to Newark College (later Delaware College and University of Delaware) where new President Eliphalet Gilbert was assembling an all-star faculty to grow his school's reputation. However, the college suffered for several years with Norton's science program being the only successful component. During this period, Norton had the opportunity to travel to Europe to bring back scientific instruments that were among the best in the country. In 1850, Norton was elected President of the College, in the hope that he could revive the ailing school. He was the first lay president, and he immediately sought help from other West Point graduates to assist in building a program similar to **Alexander Bache's (USMA 1825)** Central High School in Philadelphia. However, after just one year, Norton was discouraged with the progress and resigned. Norton spent the next two years at Brown University, RI as Professor of Natural Philosophy and Civil Engineering. Norton finally found his academic home at Yale College as the Professor of Civil Engineering in the Sheffield Scientific School, where he taught the college's brightest engineering students for 31 years. Norton became a distinguished scientist with tremendous energy for teaching and scholarship. Some of his writings were *Treatise on Astronomy* (1839), *First Book of Natural Philosophy and Astronomy* (1858), and astronomy and engineering articles in the *American Journal of Science* and *Philosophical Magazine of London*. He built a worldwide reputation for himself and his school. Giving many presentations at the American Association for the Advancement of Sciences and the National Academy of Sciences as a member of these prestigious organizations, Norton was a leader and role model for the American scientific community. He had great influence over the scholarly development of the faculty as well as his students at Yale. At the semicentennial celebration of Sheffield Scientific School in 1897, President Gilman of Yale gave this reflection of Norton: "Norton was an admirable teacher, well trained at West Point, painstaking, accurate, thorough, well acquainted with the progress of his favorite science, and always commanding students of ability."

USMA 1928 | **Roscoe Charles Wilson** | **Engineer**

11 July 1905 (Centralia, PA) – 21 August 1986 (Louisville, KY)
Graduate # 8273 (48th out of 261), (technologist), listed in *AS* (July 1996)

Military Service:
1928-1929: Pilot training, TX
1942-1943: Aviation staff officer, Washington, DC
1951-1954: Commandant Air War College, Maxwell Air Force Base, AL
1954-1956: Command of aircraft in Europe

Professional Service:
1929-1932: Aircraft engineer, Mitchell Field, NY
1932-1937: Student, research, faculty member at Air Corps Engineering School, Wright Field, OH
1937-1940: Assistant Professor of Mechanics, USMA
1940-1942: Aeronautical engineering at Wright Field, OH
1943-1945: Special duty with Manhattan Project
1945-1951: Research and Development leader for Aviation, Science, and Technology
1956-1958: Special duty with Weapon Systems Evaluation Group, Washington, DC
1958-1961: Research and Technology Staff Leader for Air Force, Washington, DC
1960-1961: Director, Scientific Advisory Board

R. C. "BIM" WILSON had an active and successful experience as a cadet before his graduation in 1928. He immediately went to flight school at Brooks Field, TX, becoming a pioneer test pilot and engineer with goals to improve aircraft performance and safety. With the support of Jimmy Doolittle, Wilson studied aeronautical engineering at the Air Corps Engineering School at Wright Field, OH. After graduating, he worked at the school designing and test flying new aircraft. As Chief of Experimental Design (the "Buck Rogers" section), Wilson held patents on dozens of airplanes, including the B-15, B-17, B-19 and P-39. He was called the "Father of the Flying Fortress" for his successful design achievements. In 1937, Wilson returned to West Point to teach mechanics and aeronautics to cadets. He built a wind tunnel for cadet and faculty use and authored a book, *Preliminary Aircraft Design*. In 1940, he was back in his research environment at Wright Field engaged in developing aircraft technologies and experimental aeronautical engineering. After staff work in the Pentagon during the early days of World War II, Wilson was selected for duty with the Manhattan Project. His job was to select and adapt the airplane to drop the bomb and to train the flight crews. He selected the test site at White Sands, NM. After his involvement in the preparations and bombing missions, he was one of the first Americans on site in Japan to assess the effects of the atomic bombs.

From 1945 to 1951, he served in positions related to military science research and development and atomic energy. He was part of the Pentagon team that consolidated research and development programs, established the Rand Corporation, initiated the Scientific Advisory Board, and coordinated the military's use of the technological advances produced during World War II. Later, Wilson commanded the tactical aircraft units with atomic bombs in Europe. Wilson returned to the United States to serve on the Weapons Systems Evaluation Group and to head up U.S. Air Force Research and Development. He retired from the Air Force in 1961. As an expert aviator, he had presided over the beginnings of both the Air Age and the Space Age. He was one of America's aircraft technology leaders and atomic science experts. He received many accolades, and the National Geographic Society honored his contributions by the naming of Wilson Field in Brazil and Wilson Glacier in Antarctica.

| USMA 1854 | **Henry Larcom Abbot** | Engineer |

13 August 1831 (Beverly, MA) -- 1 October 1927 (MA)
Graduate # 1632 (2nd out of 46), listed in *DAB, ANB, NCAB, AR* (1928)

Military Service:
1861-1865: Combat duty in Civil War (Bull Run, New Orleans, Petersburg, Richmond) (Major General)
1854-1895: Army service mainly in technical duties

Professional Service:
1854-1857: Surveyor for Pacific Railroad in CA and OR
1857-1861: Hydraulic engineer duty for improving navigation and flood control on Mississippi River
1862: Elected to the American Philosophical Society
1865-1877: Commander and academic leader of the Engineer School of Application, Willet's Point, NY

1870:	Visit to Sicily to observe the solar eclipse
1872:	Member of the National Academy of Sciences
1875:	Visit to Europe to study torpedoes
1883:	Visit to Europe to study large steel cannon
1895-1915:	Consulting engineer for various projects, including the design of the Panama Canal
1905-1910:	Professor of Hydraulic Engineering, George Washington University

H. L. Abbot attended Boston Latin School in preparation for entrance to the U.S. Military Academy. Upon his graduation from West Point in 1854, Abbot chose to serve in the Corps of Engineers. He was assigned to the survey team for locating the route of the Pacific Railroad through CA and OR. In 1857, Abbot had the opportunity to work with one of the Army's premier engineers, **Andrew Humphreys (USMA 1831)**, on the navigation and flood controls of the lower Mississippi River. The two engineers learned hydraulics, investigated the behavior of the river, and conducted numerous experiments. Their 1861 publication entitled *Report upon the Physics and Hydraulics of the Mississippi River* was not only a valuable contribution to the engineers who worked on the Mississippi but also a superb work of science, read and studied by scientists and engineers around the world. Abbot and Humphreys continued their work and publications on this subject and built a strong reputation in the international science community. During the Civil War, Abbot was a combat leader as both an engineer and artillerist. He was wounded at Bull Run but continued dedicated service throughout the war. After the war, Abbot was given the unique opportunity to become an educator and researcher as an engineer commander at Willet's Point, NY. Abbot changed the training school into an engineering graduate school and research center called the Engineer School of Application. The development of the high scholarship of this school was a major contribution to the professionalism of the Army Corps of Engineers in the last part of the 19th century. Talented Army engineers like **Gustav Fiebeger (USMA 1879)**, **George Goethals (USMA 1880)**, and **Hiram Chittenden (USMA 1884)** studied at the school. Abbot's own research in explosives, submarine mines, and torpedoes was both scholarly and a great benefit to the U.S. military. He was considered the world's foremost expert in underwater mines and their defenses. He was elected a member of the National

Academy of Sciences in 1872. Abbot went on three trips to Europe (1870, 1875, 1883) to confer with European scientists and invited distinguished European scientists and military engineers to come to America. After his retirement from the Army in 1895, Abbot consulted on several engineering projects. Among his most significant contributions was convincing the Panama Canal Commission to build a lock-based canal. In 1905, he became Professor of Hydraulic Engineering at George Washington University. Abbot was a prolific scientific writer. He wrote numerous reports for the Corps of Engineers and several studies for special government commissions. Among his many honors was a degree from Harvard University in 1886. Abbot was a distinguished scholar-leader for American engineering in the last half of the 19th century.

USMA 1802 | Joseph Gardner Swift | Engineer

31 December 1783 (Nantucket, MA) – 21 July 1865 (Geneva, NY)
Graduate # 1, listed in *DAB, ANB, NCAB*

Military Service:
1804-1807: Construction engineer, Ft. Johnston, NC
1808-1809: Construction engineer, defenses of Boston Harbor
1809-1813: Construction engineer, defenses of southern harbors
1812-1815: Combat engineer, War of 1812 (combat at Chrystler Field)
1815-1817: Construction engineer, New York Harbor and Washington, DC

Professional Service:
1812-1817: Superintendent, USMA (absent from Academy in other duties)
1819-1845: Construction engineer on numerous public works projects, New York City
1828-1833: Design engineer of railroads, Lake Pontchartrain
1829-1845: Design engineer, harbor improvements on Great Lakes

President John Adams appointed **J. SWIFT** a cadet in 1801, and in 1802, he became one of the first two graduates of the Military Academy just months after it was founded. He constructed Atlantic Coast fortifications from 1804 to 1812 and was only 28 years old when appointed Chief Engineer of the Army and Superintendent of the Military Academy in 1812. When the War of 1812 began, Swift became Chief Engineer of the Northern Army. He distinguished himself in combat at the Battle of Chrysler's Farm. He also attended to field duties along the Canadian border as the U.S. Army prepared its defenses along the St. Lawrence River and on the shores of Lake Ontario. Working out of Sackett's Harbor, he trained and organized both regular soldiers and militia. After completing defensive works in New York in 1814, he helped to rebuild the burned buildings in Washington. He also reorganized the academic staff and planned new buildings at the Military Academy. Resigning from the Army in 1818, he became Surveyor of the Port of New York, holding that post until 1827. Moving on to become an engineer for various railroads, he made many contributions to both topographic and construction engineering. From 1829 to 1845, Swift worked for the Corps of Engineers as a civilian, improving harbors and navigation channels on Lake Ontario. He was a superb, creative designer of new engineering methods. In addition to being the first graduate of the Academy, its second superintendent, and a major contributor to America's victory in the War of 1812, Swift was a builder of America's infrastructure and a technical leader of the country.

USMA 1805   ┌─────────────────────┐
                       │ **George Bomford** │   **Technologist**
                       └─────────────────────┘

1782 (New York, NY) – 25 March 1848 (Boston, MA)
Graduate # 8, (ordnance, engineer), listed in *DAB, ANB, NCAB*

Military Service:

1805-1808: Construction engineering duty at New York Harbor
1808-1810: Construction engineering duty at Chesapeake Bay
1810-1812: Construction engineer for Governor's Island
1812-1815: Ordnance duty at Watervliet Arsenal during War of 1812
1831-1842: Chief of Ordnance for U.S.Army
1842-1848: Active duty as inspector and advisor on ordnance

Professional Service:

1809-1811: Inventor of the Columbiad-style cannon
1819-1825: Developed mass-production techniques for rifle and cannon production
1825-1848: Foremost expert on ordnance in United States

G. BOMFORD spent just eight months as a cadet, before graduating in 1805. Graduation was achieved by satisfying the faculty's requirements, no matter how long a cadet had attended. Many cadets during this era, spent less than two years at the Academy before being deemed ready for commissioned service and graduation.   For his first seven years in the Army, Bomford served as an engineer, building harbor facilities, fortifications, and buildings in New York Harbor and along Chesapeake Bay. During his engineering duty time, Bomford also researched cannon manufacturing and developed a new design for cannons called the Columbiad. This type of gun bulged out at the breech to accommodate the higher pressures produced in that part of the gun. The first Columbiads were large 50- and 100-pound guns for forts and ships, produced at Columbia Foundry in Washington, DC and used in the War of 1812. Later models were fabricated at many places, including the West Point Foundry. Other popular Columbiads (8- and 10-inch versions) were able to fire as guns, howitzers, or mortars. Many Columbiads, improved from their original design, were used in the Civil War. Bomford, along with fellow West Pointers **Thomas Rodman (USMA 1841)** and **Robert Parrot (USMA 1824)**, with their inventions and innovations, advanced the science of ballistics and the development of artillery. As Chief of Ordnance from 1831 to 1842, Bomford developed mass and uniform production techniques and machine production capabilities for rifle and cannon manufacturing in American arsenals. He was known as the "Father of the Ordnance Department", writing the first set of regulations and policies for the business of making armaments for the Army. Because Bomford's production techniques reduced the need for special craftsmen to produce weapons, many arsenal workers briefly went on strike in 1842.   Bomford was steadfast in utilizing his new, highly effective production methods, but because of this controversy, turned over leadership of the Ordnance Department. He continued on active duty as an arsenal inspector and ordnance consultant until his death in 1848. Much of Bomford's success came from his creativity, technical expertise, and fine organizational abilities. His correspondence and testimony to the Army, Congress, and Presidents were always effective and convincing, making him an influential Army officer. He was considered the foremost expert in ordnance in America and held tremendous influence on decisions involving procurements and policies for the Army. Bomford owned a luxurious Washington estate, "Kalorama", where he often met with influential government people. Among Bomford's many friends was President Andrew Jackson. Bomford's professional life was a vibrant mix of substantial technical and managerial contributions, marking him as one of the foremost technical leaders of America's industrial success.

USMA 1805   ┃ **Joseph Gilbert Totten** ┃   **Engineer**

17 April 1788 (New Haven, CT) – 22 April 1864 (Washington, DC)
Graduate # 10, listed in *DAB, ANB, NCAB*

Military Service:
1812-1815: Combat engineer in the War of 1812 on Niagara Frontier (Plattsburgh, Queenstown Heights, Fort George, Fortymile Creek, Fort Erie)
1838-1857: Command of Corps of Engineers
1847:   Chief of Engineers, Mexican War
1861-1864: Chief of Army Engineers, Civil War

Professional Service:
1805-1808: Surveyor in Northwest Territories
1808-1812: Construction engineer for fortifications in New York Harbor
1815-1816: Construction engineer for fortifications on Lake Champlain
1817-1819: Construction engineer for fortifications at Rouse's Point, NY
1825-1838: Construction engineer for Fort Adams, RI
1825-1836: Engineer for harbors and rivers, East Coast
1836:   Elected to the American Philosophical Society
1838:   Construction engineer for Pensacola Navy Yard and Dry Docks
1851-1858: Member of Lighthouse Board
1846-1864: Regent of Smithsonian Institute
1863:   Corporator of National Academy of Sciences

J. G. TOTTEN graduated from the Military Academy and was commissioned in the Corps of Engineers in 1805. He was an outstanding scholar as a cadet. Totten's uncle, Jared Mansfield, was his mathematics professor at the Academy. Resigning from the Army in 1806, he assisted his uncle, who was then serving as Surveyor General of federal public lands. Totten re-entered the Army and the Corps of Engineers in 1808 and assisted in building Castle Williams and other New York Harbor defenses. During the War of 1812, he was Chief Engineer of the Niagara frontier and of Lake Champlain armies. He fought in the Battle of Plattsburg. As a member of the first permanent Board of Engineers in 1816, he laid down enduring principles of coastal defense construction. Appointed Chief Engineer in 1838, he served in that position for 25 years until his death. During the Mexican War, he served on the war staff and instituted the successful operations plan at Vera Cruz. He was greatly admired by his combat leader, Winfield Scott. After the war, he contributed his expertise in designing Fresnel lenses as a member of the Lighthouse Board and was an active researcher of heavy ordnance effects on structures. Traveling to the Pacific Coast, he helped design coastal defenses and, during the Civil War, returned east to supervise the defenses around Washington, DC. His writings included articles in engineering, ordnance, and conchology (study of seashells). Totten was a regent of the Smithsonian Institution in 1846 and one of the corporators of the National Academy of Sciences. Totten was a versatile scientist and engineer, who was a capable technical leader and administrator.

USMA 1807   **John Anderson**   **Engineer**

1780 (CT) – 14 September 1834 (Detroit, MI)
Graduate # 28, (topographer, surveyor)

Military Service:
1807-1811: Artillery duty in garrisons
1812-1815: Served in Michigan Territory in War of 1812 (prisoner of war)

Professional Service:
1814-1815: Topographic Engineer in War of 1812 and in western expansion
1815-1816: Surveyor of Lake Champlain (NY and VT)
1817-1826: Surveyor for military road in Detroit
1826-1829: Surveyor of fortification sites on New England Coast
1829:   Surveyor of Hudson River
1833:   Surveyor of canals in Massachusetts
1834:   Surveyor of Great Lakes

J. ANDERSON spent only one year at West Point before graduating as an artillerist in 1807. After four years in garrison duty, he resigned from the Army. However, in 1812, with the beginning of hostilities in the War of 1812, he re-entered the Army to serve in defense of the country. Just a month later, Anderson was captured in the surrender of the fortification at Detroit and became a prisoner of war. He managed to resume his service two years later as he was released from prison. His new duties involved using his technical skills as a surveyor and topographic engineer. First he served on the staff in the wartime Army, then he continued his topographic work in the exploration of the Northwestern and Western Territories after the war concluded in 1815. This was just eight years after the Corps of Discovery expedition of Lewis and Clark, and there were still many areas to be explored and mapped. Anderson returned east to survey and chart Lake Champlain in NY. He helped lay out the military road in Detroit. Anderson continued his surveying, mapping, and charting duties as he laid out sites for fortifications on the East Coast and canals for transportation across MA. Returning to the West Point area, Anderson expertly mapped the Hudson River area. His final duties were back on the frontier to map the shorelines and tributaries of the western Great Lakes.

USMA 1811 | John James Abert | Engineer

17 September 1788 (Frederick, MD) – 27 January 1863 (Washington, DC)
Graduate # 71, (topographical engineer), listed in *DAB, NCAB, DBAS*

Military Service:
1814:   Combat duty as soldier in War of 1812 (Bladensburg, MD)
1827-1832:   Staff duty in Topographic Bureau, Washington, DC
1832-1834:   Commissioner for Indian emigration to the West
1838-1861:   Leadership duty as Chief of the Topographic Engineers

Professional Service:
1816-1818:   Surveyor on project mapping the Atlantic Coast
1818-1824:   Surveyor for harbors along the Atlantic Coast
1824-1826:   Surveyor for the route of the Chesapeake and Ohio Canal
1826-1827:   Surveyor for harbors in ME

J. J. ABERT graduated from the Military Academy in 1811. He immediately resigned from the Army and took a position as a lawyer in Washington, DC and later in OH. He joined the District of Columbia militia as a private during the War of 1812 and fought in the Battle of Bladensburg, MD. In 1814, he was commissioned and appointed to the new branch of topographical engineers. He worked on fortifications, border surveys, canals, and river and harbor improvements before being appointed as Chief of the Topographic Bureau in 1829. After special duty involving the relocation of Indians, Abert headed the Corps of Topographical Engineers from its creation in 1838 until he retired in 1861. Under his leadership, the Corps of Topographical Engineers improved the navigability of many rivers and harbors along the Atlantic Coast and inland on the Mississippi River and the Great Lakes. Under his guidance, engineers conducted important scientific surveys of the hydraulics and navigation of the lower Mississippi River. They also constructed lighthouses and canals, explored the West, and conducted border and railroad surveys. As the head of the government's major civil works organization, he made significant contributions to the technical development of the nation, the building of America's infrastructure, and the development of national policy. As a graduate of the Academy, Abert put into the practice Thomas Jefferson's vision of Army engineer officers who could successfully serve both in combat and in peace. Abert carefully directed the geographic explorations conducted by the Corps' officers, making sure that scientific data was collected along with the performance of military reconnaissance. Topographic officers were trained to produce maps with both military and commercial geographic features and to collect specimens of rocks, minerals, plants, and animals. Abert was a close friend of John J. Audubon and helped support his important art and scientific work. Through his influence on the officers in the Topographic

Engineers, Abert played an active role in the emergence of America's scientific community. Abert was one of the founders of the National Institute for the Promotion of Science and Useful Arts, which began to build a significant collection for later inclusion in the museums of the Smithsonian Institute. Abert was one of the visionaries and significant architects who helped lay a solid foundation for the American scientific community.

USMA 1812   **René Edward DeRussy**   **Engineer**

1790 (WI) – 23 November 1865 (San Francisco, CA)
Graduate # 89, listed in *NCAB*

Military Service:
1812-1815: Combat engineer duty in War of 1812 (Chrystler's Field, Plattsburg)
1858-1861: Chief, Army Engineers, Washington, DC
1861-1865: Construction engineer, San Francisco Harbor during Civil War

Professional Service:

1816-1818: Construction engineer for the fortification at Rouse's Pt, NY
1817-1821: Construction engineer for New York Harbor
1821-1825: Construction engineer for coastal defenses on Gulf of Mexico
1825-1833: Construction engineer for New York Harbor
1833-1838: Superintendent, USMA
1838-1854: Construction engineer, Ft. Monroe, VA
1854-1857: Construction engineer, San Francisco Harbor
1845:   Inventor of the Barbette Gun Carriage

R. E. DeRussy graduated from West Point just in time to provide valuable services to the defense of the northern border of the U. S. during the War of 1812. He served in combat action at Sackett's Harbor, NY; Lake Champlain, NY; French Creek, NY; Chrystler's Field, Canada; and Plattsburg, NY. He assisted **Joseph Swift (USMA 1802)**, who was his superior engineering officer. After the war, DeRussy was involved in numerous construction projects– in charge of building coastal defenses in New York Harbor and along the Gulf of Mexico. DeRussy was detailed to West Point to serve as Superintendent of the Academy from 1833 to 1838. This was a big challenge to replace **Sylvanus Thayer (USMA 1808)**, who continued to use his influence in Academy affairs. As an expert engineer, he was assigned to build fortifications at Ft. Monroe and construct harbor defenses along Delaware Bay, Chesapeake Bay, the coast of Virginia, and San Francisco Harbor. In 1858, he moved to Washington, DC as Chief of the Army Engineers. During the Civil War, he was over seventy years old, but still supervised the Union defenses on the West Coast. DeRussy was an active scholar and inventor during his years of military duty. His invention of the Barbette Depressing Gun Carriage was also claimed by British designer Colonel Moncreiff.

USMA 1814   **James Wolfe Ripley**   **Technologist**

10 December 1794 (Windham, CT) – 15 March 1870 (Hartford, CT)
Graduate # 102, (ordnance), listed in *DAB, ANB, NCAB*

Military Service:
1814-1815: Combat duty in War of 1812 (Sacketts Harbor)
1815-1817: Garrison duty
1817-1819: Combat duty in Seminole War
1819-1821: Garrison duty
1824-1832: Garrison duty
1832-1833: Special duty in SC during nullification campaign
1861-1863: Chief of Ordnance of the Army during Civil War
                   (Major General)

Professional Service:
1821-1823: Ordnance duty at Kennebec Arsenal, ME
1823-1824: Surveyor for boundaries of Indian reservations in FL
1833-1841: Ordnance duty at Kennebec Arsenal, ME
1841-1854: Ordnance commander of Springfield Armory, MA
1854-1856: Ordnance commander of Watertown Arsenal, MA
1856-1861: Inspector of arsenals
1863-1869: Inspector of arsenals

J. W. RIPLEY spent just one year at West Point before graduating as an artillery officer in 1814 to enter combat service in the War of 1812. He saw combat action on Lake Ontario, supporting the small American naval operations on the lake. After the war and two years spent in garrison following the war, Ripley transferred to Andrew Jackson's Army in Florida to fight against the Seminole Indians. After his combat time, Ripley served under James Gadsden with duties to survey the boundaries of the Indian reservations in Florida. Ripley's next challenge was in South Carolina in 1832, when there was serious citizen unrest over the federal tariffs. In 1833, Ripley transferred to the Ordnance Corps, and he quickly became an important leader of ordnance design and production. For sixteen years, he commanded armament testing and production facilities at Springfield and Watertown, MA. Through his efforts, these facilities were modernized and new armaments were tested and produced for the Army. Ripley's contributions to the advanced capabilities of the American Army during the Mexican War were recognized and rewarded by Army leaders. In 1857, Ripley was made inspector of all the American Army arsenals. At the outbreak of the Civil War, he was made Chief of Ordnance for the Army. This was a challenging position with duties to arm the huge Union Army with the best weapons possible. He built the ordnance and manufacturing capabilities and standardized weapon specifications and production techniques. Ripley was able to commence the duties of this challenging position of Chief of Ordnance, but was criticized for not embracing new technologies or encouraging new weapons development. In

1863 at age 69, he retired from that position to assist as an inspector of armaments being built under government contracts. As a dedicated technologist, Ripley had the distinction of serving in the Army for 55 years and in four wars.

USMA 1817   **William Gibbs McNeill**   **Engineer**

3 October 1801 (Wilmington, NC) – 16 February 1853 (Brooklyn, NY)
Graduate # 172, (topographic), listed in *DAB, NCAB*

Military Service:
1819-1823: Combat duty in Seminole War as aide-de-camp for Andrew Jackson
1842:   Militia leader in suppressing the Dorr Rebellion in Rhode Island

Professional Service:
1817-1819: Duty with U.S. Coast Survey in the South
1823-1828: Topographic engineering and surveyor for railroads
1828-1830: Visited Europe to study railroad engineering
1830-1837: Topographic engineer for many railroads in the East
1837-1842: Topographic engineer for state of Georgia's railroads
1851-1853: Visited Europe and became the first American elected member of Institute of Civil Engineers of Great Britain

---

W. G. McNeill was a friend of **Joseph Swift (USMA 1802)**, the first graduate of the Academy, and, through Swift's influence, decided to pursue a military career. After McNeill graduated from West Point, he was assigned duties with the United States Coast Survey in the South. He was then ordered to FL and served as General Andrew Jackson's aide-de-camp during the Seminole War. In 1823, he began a new phase of his military service as a topographic engineer and surveyor for the construction of railroad lines. With his military and engineer partner and brother-in-law, **George Whistler (USMA 1819)**, McNeill worked on railways, canals, bridges, and tunnels throughout the eastern United States. He went to Europe, along with Whistler, to investigate railroad technology. Upon return to the United States, he and Whistler resumed their railroad engineering work. In 1837, he resigned from the Army, but continued his railroad work for the state of GA. In 1842, McNeill was appointed a General in the Militia of Rhode Island and took aggressive action against the citizens involved in Dorr's Rebellion. Unfortunately, his actions were judged by many as being too aggressive, which cost him several engineering jobs and military service during the Mexican War. McNeill visited Europe again in 1851 and was elected a member of the Institution of Civil Engineers of Great Britain. He returned to America with the opportunity to work for mining companies, but died before beginning that service. McNeill's reports are very valuable and contain considerable information on the challenges and technical issues of early railroad construction. He was an outstanding surveyor and an effective engineering manager.

USMA 1818  **Mathematician**

21 September 1794 (Hartford, VT) – 12 July 1871 (Geneva, NY)
Graduate # 183 (4ᵗʰ out of 23), listed in *NCAB, AR* (1872)

Military Service:
1818-1825: Army service in technical assignments

Professional Service:
1818-1825: Assistant Professor of Mathematics, USMA
1825-1848: Professor of Mathematics and Natural Philosophy, Geneva College, NY
1848-1869: Principal (President) and Professor of the College of the City of New York

---

H. WEBSTER was a bright, hard-working cadet, who had the opportunity to serve as a mathematics professor at the Academy for all seven years of his military service. This was a critical period at West Point, as **Sylvanus Thayer's (USMA 1808)** new program, which was based on rigorous mathematics, was being initiated. Webster played an important role under department heads Andrew Ellicott, David Douglass, and **Charles Davies (USMA 1815)** in helping to raise the standards and advancing the level of the courses required at the Academy. In 1825, Webster resigned from the Army, leaving West Point to teach mathematics and science at Geneva College, NY (later Hobart College). Webster was one of the founders and first professors at the college; therefore, he established the academic culture and technical standards at this new liberal arts college. He set the college's science on a strong foundation and Hobart produced several noted scientists who studied with Webster during the middle of the 19ᵗʰ century. After 23 years of dedicated service to Geneva College, Webster had the opportunity to help develop another college. He became the Principal of the Free Academy in New York City, which he developed into the College of the City of New York. He was a professor and leader of the school for liberal arts students who were residents of New York City. His 21-year presidency resulted in a strong, successful school that served the educational needs of the diverse, growing city. Amazingly, Webster was instrumental in the successful beginnings of three thriving colleges – West Point, Hobart, and the City College of New York. He proved to be an expert mathematician and a superb educator and administrator. He retired from professional work in 1869 and died in 1871.

USMA 1818   ┌─────────────────────┐   **Engineer**
                       │   **Hartman Bache**   │
                       └─────────────────────┘

3 September 1798 (Philadelphia, PA) – 8 October, 1872 (Philadelphia, PA)
Graduate # 198 (19th out of 23), (topographic), listed in *AR* (1873)

Military Service:
1861-1862: Bureau of Topographic Engineers, Washington, DC
1863-1865: Combat engineer at Ft. Mifflin and Ft. Delaware during the Civil War

Professional Service:
1818-1847: Surveyor and topographic engineer for numerous harbors, roads,
            fortifications in MD, NY, ME, SC, PA, MA, VA, NC, GA, TN, NJ
1831:   Elected to the American Philosophical Society
1835-1855: Engineer for lighthouses along the East Coast
1855-1861: Engineer for numerous lighthouses and military roads along the Pacific Coast
1865-1870: Member of numerous engineer boards for lighthouses and fortifications

---

H. BACHE was the great-grandson of Benjamin Franklin and cousin of **Alexander Bache (USMA 1825)**. He entered the Academy at age sixteen, graduating in 1818 as a talented and dedicated topographic engineer. For thirty years, he conducted numerous surveys for coastal defenses (fortifications, gun emplacements, and harbor obstructions), designed and crafted harbor and river improvements, and built major roads and canals. Eventually, he became America's premier engineer for the location, construction, and operational considerations of lighthouses. Bache was innovative in his methods and built a superb reputation for his lighthouse work, which was challenging to overcome the forces of nature along the coasts. After working on the Atlantic Coast for over 20 years, Bache was called out to the Pacific Coast to perform similar duties in ensuring that the shores and harbors had adequate lighthouses. During the Civil War, Bache performed administrative duties in the Bureau of Topographic Engineers. After the war, he

continued to serve on engineering boards for numerous construction projects. Bache was a talented and dedicated civil engineer who established himself as an expert on harbors, rivers, and lighthouses – three important areas in the development of America. Many of his numerous deeds, in the form of lighthouses and railways, still stand as monuments to his professional technical service to his country.

USMA 1819 | **Henry Brewerton** | **Engineer**

25 September 1801 (New York, NY) – 17 April 1879 (Wilmington, DE)
Graduate # 207 (5th out of 29), listed in *NCAB, AR* (1879)

Military Service:
1819-1867: Army service in technical assignments

Professional Service:
1819-1821: Assistant Professor of Engineering, USMA
1821-1828: Construction engineer for fortifications
1828-1832: Construction engineer for defenses of Charleston harbor, SC
1832-1836: Engineer for Cumberland Road
1836-1842: Engineer for navigation improvements on Hudson River
1842-1845: Construction engineer for fortification at Rouse's Point, NY
1845-1852: Superintendent, USMA
1852-1864: Construction engineer for fortification in MD
1859-1860: Travel in Europe
1861-1865: Construction engineer for harbors during the Civil War
1866-1867: Conducted experiment in using iron in fortifications

H. BREWERTON was just eleven years old when he became a cadet. Six years later Brewerton graduated as an engineer officer. Despite being only eighteen years old and teaching men several years older than himself, he taught engineering at West Point from 1819 to 1821. As **Sylvanus Thayer's (USMA 1808)** new and more rigorous technical program was implemented, Brewerton was an important link in its success. Each generation of graduating cadets had to be more knowledgeable and skilled in engineering and technology than their predecessors. Brewerton was a perfect example of that situation. As a result of Claudius Crozet's (see **Honorable Mentions**) teaching, young Henry Brewerton may have been the most knowledgeable engineer in America upon his graduation from West Point. He began his field career as a construction engineer building numerous fortifications in SC, GA, DE, NY, and LA. In 1832, he took on the important duty of building and improving the Cumberland Road in Ohio. This was the only major overland route directly westward from the East Coast and its completion and upgrade were important for the development of the western territories. Brewerton continued his development and contributions in civil engineering, working on the facilities and navigation on the Hudson River and building fortifications along the East Coast. In 1845, Brewerton assumed the superintendency of West Point and made sure its teaching of science and engineering continued to improve. After seven years at the Academy, he resumed his construction engineering duties in MD and DE. Brewerton was in Europe visiting construction sites in 1859 and 1860 and returned quickly to serve as a construction engineer for fortifications during the Civil War. After the war, he was involved in the experiments to use iron to improve the protection of fortifications as rifled cannon had become too effective to sustain the building of wooden or mortared structures. Brewerton retired from the Army and professional life in 1867.

USMA 1819   ╔═══════════════════════╗   **Engineer**
                          ║   **William Turnbull**   ║
                          ╚═══════════════════════╝

9 October 1800 (Philadelphia, PA) – 9 December 1857 (Wilmington, NC)
Graduate # 211 (9th out of 29), listed in *DAB, ANB, NCAB*

Military Service:

1847-1848: Combat engineering duty in Mexican War (Siege of Vera Cruz, Mexico City, Contreras, Churubusco, Chapultepec)

Profession Service:

1819-1831: Topographic engineering duty
1831-1832: Surveyor for railroad in MS
1832-1843: Construction engineer for aqueduct across Potomac River, Washington, DC
1843-1847: Civil engineer for harbors on the Great Lakes
1848-1849: Construction engineer for buildings in New Orleans
1849-1853: Construction engineer designing lighthouses, bridges, and canals
1853-1856: Construction engineer for harbors and lighthouses on Lake Ontario and Oswego, NY

W. TURNBULL entered West Point when he was 14 years old and graduated five years later in 1819. Commissioned in the artillery, Turnbull served mainly as a topographic engineer and converted to that branch in 1831. He worked on an important survey to locate a railroad in MS. In 1832, he began his most significant engineering assignment, the construction of an aqueduct across the Potomac River. This was one of the most important works of the Corps of Engineers, and Turnbull spent 11 years in this effort. The huge masonry piers for the aqueduct were set 30 feet below the water surface of the river. The successful completion of this project gave Turnbull an outstanding reputation as an innovator and technical problem solver. His reports on the work were published by Congress and because of continued demand were republished in 1873. After working on harbor improvements on the Great Lakes, Turnbull was success as a combat engineer in the Mexican War, decorated and promoted by General Winfield Scott for his leadership in combat. After the war, he returned to construction assignments in New Orleans, LA; NH, MD, and on the Great Lakes. Turnbull was a skillful engineer and his excellent work helped establish America as a world leader in engineering innovation and quality.

USMA 1819   ╔═══════════════════════════════╗   **Engineer**
                    ║ **George Washington Whistler** ║
                    ╚═══════════════════════════════╝

18 May 1800 (Fort Wayne, IN) – 7 April 1849 (St Petersburg, Russia)
Graduate # 214 (12th out of 29), listed in *DAB, NCAB*

Military Service:

1819-1833: In military service

Professional Service:

1819-1821: Duty as topographic engineer

1821-1822: Assistant Professor of Drawing, USMA
1822-1828: Duty as surveyor and topographic engineer, Lake Superior
1828-1830: Visited Europe to study railroad engineering
1830-1833: Topographic engineer for railroads in the East
1833-1837: Mechanical engineer for locative manufacturing
1837-1842: Topographic engineer for railroads in Massachusetts
1842-1847: Topographic engineer and mechanical engineer for a major railroad in Russia

G. W. WHISTLER grew up in a military family and while at West Point distinguished himself in his drafting and drawing courses. His first duties were as a topographic engineer helping to locate several railroads. In 1821, he returned to West Point to teach drawing for one year. Whistler returned to surveying and topographic work along the Canadian border. In 1828, he began using his talents to lay out railroads and construct railway tracks. This was the time when military officers were legally involved in the expansion and development of commercial railroads. He went to Europe to study railroad technologies and returned to America to work with his brother-in-law **William McNeill (USMA 1817)** on constructing America's railroads. In 1833, Whistler resigned from the Army to enter the technological field of locomotive manufacturing, building advanced models and prototypes designed by George Stephenson. In 1837, he returned to topographic work for railroads, ultimately locating and building a railway in the Berkshire Mountains of Massachusetts. This further enhanced his reputation as an expert in railroad construction. In 1842, Czar Nicholas I of Russia hired Whistler to build a railroad between St. Petersburg and Moscow. He supervised the location and laying of the track, the building of the locomotives and cars, the construction of the bridges, the design of the loading docks, and the functions of stations. Decorated for his superb work by receiving the Order of St. Anne in 1847, Whistler died of Asiatic cholera in St. Petersburg shortly before the completion of this railroad. Whistler's son, George William Whistler, continued his father's work in Russia until his own death in 1869. Another son, James Abbott McNeill Whistler (see **Honorable Mentions** and the essay on U.S. Coast Survey), was a famous artist and attended West Point for a short time before pursuing an art career in Europe.

USMA 1819 | **William Henry Swift** | **Engineer**

6 November 1800 (Taunton, MA) – 7 April 1879 (New York, NY)
Graduate # 231 (class rank not applicable*), (railroad & lighthouse construction), listed in *AR* (1879)

Military Service:
1844-1849: Administrator in Topographic Bureau of the Army, Washington, DC

Professional Service:

1819-1830: Topographic engineering duties on fortifications, rivers, harbors, canals, and railroads
1830-1832: Design of United States Postal routes
1833-1843: Engineer and Surveyor for the Coast Survey
1843-1844: Surveyor for railroads, harbors, canals, and rivers
1845-1849: Engineer for various lighthouses
1849-1854: Engineer for various railroads

*Swift was sent on an expedition to the Rocky Mountains and did not return until after his class had graduated. Therefore, he missed classes and his final examinations for graduation. He graduated without a formal class rank and is listed at the bottom of his class for purposes of the Cullum number.

W. H. Swift is the younger brother of **Joseph Swift (USMA 1802)**. He was only 13 years old when he became a cadet. While still a cadet, he was sent on an expedition to the Rocky Mountains. During one of the hunting ventures, he was captured and held for several months by Pawnee Indians, therefore, missing his graduation. He returned to West Point in 1821 and assumed his duties as a topographic engineer and surveyor on several projects on the East Coast. His major efforts were on fortifications, rivers, harbors, and canals. Swift then joined several other West Point-educated engineers (working with **George W. Whistler (USMA 1819)** and **William McNeill (USMA 1817)**) in surveying and constructing railways. He located routes through the rugged Catskill Mountains of New York State and surveyed several routes in New England. From 1830 to 1832, Swift was engaged in a project to map the postal routes throughout the entire United States. His map and plan were tremendous aids in improving postal delivery and the basis of many future plans and natural service maps. In 1833, Ferdinand Hassler (see **Honorable Mentions**) of the United States Coast Survey requested Swift for survey and mapping duties. Swift worked on the coastal area encompassing the state of CT. In 1840-1841, Swift went to Europe to obtain instruments for the survey and to study the hydraulic pumps used in Holland. For the next six years, Swift was in administrative duties in Washington, DC, although he kept active with several field duties on constructing lighthouses as well. In 1848, he resigned from the Army and began to work for railroads, both as chief construction engineer and company president. During these years, he was a successful businessman, always using the latest scientific and engineering technologies to his company's advantage.

USMA 1820 | **Thomas Emery Sudler** | **Mathematician**

1801 (MD) – 31 December 1860 (Wilmington. DE)
Graduate # 234 (3rd out of 30)

Military Service:
1820-1821: Technical service in the Army

Professional Service:

1820-1821: Assistant Professor of Mathematics, USMA
1824-1825: Surveyor for boundary between Virginia and Maryland
1826-1840: Professor of Mathematics, Civil Engineering, St John's College, MD
1840-1851: Professor of Mathematics, Mechanics, and Astronomy, Dickinson College, PA
1851-1852: President, Wesleyan Female College, DE

T. E. SUDLER taught mathematics at West Point both while he was a cadet and for one year immediately following his graduation in 1820. This was during West Point's transition to the rigorous new program instituted by **Sylvanus Thayer (USMA 1808)**. Sudler was able to adjust and excel in this highly demanding and technical environment. He resigned from the Army in 1821. In 1824, he was employed by the Governor of Maryland to survey the boundary between Maryland and Virginia. After a term in the Maryland House of Representatives, Sudler became Professor of Mathematics and Civil Engineering at Saint John's College, MD, which was at that time struggling to survive. Sudler helped the new President of Saint John's, Hector Humphreys, build a quality liberal arts program by adding modern science to the curriculum. He also taught military tactics at the school. In 1840, Sudler moved to a position at Dickinson College, PA as Professor of Mathematics, Mechanics, and Astronomy. This time it was the leadership of Dickinson's new President, John Durbin, that allowed Sudler to modernize and build the program in science at this struggling college. Both colleges, St. John's and Dickinson, two of the oldest in America, received tremendous boosts in their health and vitality through the efforts and expertise of Sudler. In 1851, Sudler used the experience he gained in reviving the two college-level programs by serving as President of Wesleyan Female College in Wilmington, DE.

USMA 1821 | **Edward C. Ross** | **Mathematician**

1801 (PA) – 16 May 1851 (New York, NY)
Graduate # 268 (7th our of 24)

Military Service:

1834-1836: Garrison duty at Ft. Hamilton, NY and Ft. Gratiot, MI
1836-1838: Combat duty in Seminole War
1838-1839: Duty escorting Cherokee Indians west during Trail of Tears

Professional Service:

1820-1821: Acting Assistant Professor of Mathematics as a First Class cadet, USMA
1821-1823: Assistant Professor of Mathematics, USMA
1824:   Instructor of Mathematics at the Artillery School for Practice, Ft. Monroe
1840-1848: Professor of Mathematics, Kenyon College, OH
1848-1851: Professor of Mathematics and Natural Philosophy, Free Academy, NY (later CCNY)

E. C. Ross stayed at West Point to teach mathematics after his graduation. He served under **Charles Davies (USMA 1815)**, eventually becoming the Principal Assistant Professor. Ross also worked at the Academy with David Douglass (see **Honorable Mentions**) and **Horace Webster (USMA 1818)**, whom he would later teach with at Kenyon College and the Free Academy of New York. During his West Point time, he was an important figure in **Sylvanus Thayer's (USMA 1808)** improvements in the Academy's academic program. Since the only mathematics books advanced enough for cadet study were in French, the cadets took French in order to read their textbooks. Ross translated the algebra book of Bourdon so cadets could read the book in English and spend more time on their technical subjects and less on language training. His book was published in 1831 and was titled, *Elements of Algebra Translated from the French of M. Bourdon, for the use of cadets of the U. S. Military Academy*. After 14 years of teaching mathematics at West Point (one of those years was as a cadet), Ross was sent on two years of garrison duty and then to combat in the Seminole War. In 1838, he had the difficult duty of escorting Cherokee Indians from North Carolina west to Oklahoma in the event now called the "Trail of Tears." Ross resigned from the Army after that emotional duty in 1839 to return to academic duties as a civilian professor. His former department head at West Point, David Douglass was President of Kenyon College and invited Ross to join his faculty as Professor of Mathematics. In 1848, Ross was recruited away from Kenyon by another college president, his former colleague in the West Point mathematics department, Horace Webster, to teach at the Free Academy of New York City (later called the College of the City of New York). Ross taught there until his death in 1851, having received honorary degrees from Geneva College and Kenyon College.

USMA 1823 — Alfred Mordecai — Scientist

3 January 1804 (Warrenton, NC) – 23 October 1887 (Philadelphia, PA)
Graduate # 326 (1st out of 35), (mathematician, engineer, ordnance technologist), listed in *DAB, NCAB, AR* (1888)

Military Service:
1828-1832: Assistant to Chief of Army Engineers, Washington, DC
1832-1838: Commander of Ordnance arsenals
1838-1842: Assistant to the Chief of Army Ordnance. Washington, DC
1855-1857: Military commission studying Crimean War (ordnance and weapons)
1857-1861: Commander of Watervliet Arsenal, NY

Professional Service:
1823-1825: Assistant Professor of Natural and Experimental Philosophy, USMA
1825-1828: Construction engineer for Ft. Monroe, VA
1842-1844: Ordnance design duty
1863-1887: Construction engineer for railroad company in Mexico
1833-1850: Author of several technical works

A. Mordecai joined the Corps of Engineers and remained at West Point to teach science for two years after his graduation. He then worked on fortification construction in VA. After four years in Washington, DC as the assistant to the Chief of Engineers, Mordecai joined the newly formed branch of the Ordnance Corps. He took immediate interest in weapons design and learned the latest advances in the branch on a trip to Europe. After commanding the Frankford Arsenal in PA, he returned to Washington, DC as the assistant to the Chief of Ordnance where he produced a report entitled "Artillery for the United States Land Service." He also researched the motion of pendulums, the chemistry of gunpowder, the operations of foundries, and the design of various ordnance and weapons. Conducting tests on gunpowder effects by measuring the muzzle velocity of guns, he was one of the most scientifically minded officers in the Army, and he used his analytic approach to solve problems and improve military operations. In 1841, Mordecai published what has been called the *Ordnance Manual* because it contained the procedures and guidelines on most ordnance activities. In the period 1855 to 1857, he had a special opportunity to affect American science and military development, when he was appointed one of the three members of the Crimean War Commission. During his inspection trip, he investigated the role of ordnance in modern warfare. His detailed report was published by Congress in 1860. He spent four years in command of the largest armament facility, Watervliet Arsenal, NY, but at the onset of the Civil War, he resigned his commission. Mordecai decided that he could not conscientiously fight for either side in the war, although his son **Alfred Mordecai (USMA June 1862)** fought for the Union Army. Spending the first two years of the war teaching mathematics to students in Philadelphia, Mordecai worked as a construction engineer for a railroad out West starting in 1863. Mordecai was known in the Army as a dedicated scholar and skilled technical author. In addition to the valuable *Ordnance Manual,* Mordecai wrote two books on gunpowder and a volume on artillery weapons production. His overall contributions were primarily in the sciences of ballistics and metal manufacturing. Mordecai was a talented engineer, designing new weapons systems and inventing new military equipment. Mordecai's career exemplifies the interest in and growth of science and technology in America and the Army during the middle of the 19th century.

USMA 1823 ┃ **George Sears Greene** ┃ **Engineer**

6 May 1801 (Apponaug, RI) – 28 January 1899 (Morristown, NJ)
Graduate # 327 (2nd out of 35), (mathematician), listed in *DAB, NCAB, AR* (1899)

Military Service:
1827-1836: Artillery and Ordnance duty in various parts of New England
1862-1863: Combat commander in Civil War (Cedar Mountain, Antietam, Chancellorsville, Gettysburg) (wounded at Wauhatchie) (Major General)

Professional Service:
1823-1827:   Assistant Professor of Mathematics, USMA
1836-1847:   Engineer in construction for aqueducts, reservoirs, and canals in MA, NC, TN, KY, and MD
1847-1856:   Construction engineer for railroad companies
1852:   One of the founders of American Society of Civil Engineers
1860-1862:   Engineer for New York City water supply
1866-1880:   Engineer for New York City water supply, elevated rail system, subway system,
                 street planning and construction
1871-1872:   Engineer for Washington, DC sewage and water supplies for several cities
1875-1877:   President, American Society of Civil Engineers.

G. S. GREENE's father intended for his son to attend Brown University, RI, but lack of money made that impossible, so Greene attended the Military Academy. After his graduation, Greene spent four years teaching mathematics for his former professor and department head **Charles Davies (USMA 1808)**. Greene spent the next nine years as an engineer or ordnance

officer at various fortifications in New England. After leaving the Army in 1836, he was engaged in numerous important engineering projects. He laid out and surveyed several railroad lines in the Northeast and designed and constructed reservoirs and aqueducts for New York City's water system. When the Civil War started, Greene volunteered for active military service and soon found himself as a combat commander and general officer. His unit fought in several battles, and then played a keyed role in the Union victory at Gettysburg. Greene's brigade held Culp's Hill against a much stronger Confederate unit thus protecting the Union's flank. Shortly after Gettysburg, Greene's unit was sent west as part of the Chattanooga campaign. Unfortunately, he was severely wounded in his face and saw no further field action from 1863 to 1865. After the war, Greene resumed his engineering profession. Among his first efforts was to return to the challenges of constructing a reliable and robust water supply system for New York City. As the engineer for the city's public works department, Greene faced many challenging construction jobs – elevated trains, the subway system, street and building planning, and the sewer system. Greene's talents were in such demand that he also helped many other cities as a consultant for their public works engineering issues. Greene was well-known as the country's most experienced and talented urban engineer, and he helped establish the American Society of Civil Engineers in 1852 (one of 12 founders), serving as its President from 1875 to 1877.

USMA 1824 | Robert Parker Parrott | Scientist

5 October 1804 (Lee, NH) – 24 December 1877 (Cold Spring, NY)
Graduate # 363 (3rd out of 31), (ordnance, inventor, technologist), listed in *DAB, ANB, NCAB, AR* (1878)

Military Service:
1829-1836: Artillery duty in coastal defense
1836: Staff officer, Indian Wars against Creek Nation
1836: Assistant Chief of Ordnance

Professional Service:
1824-1829: Assistant Professor of Natural and Experimental Philosophy, USMA
1836-1877: Director, West Point Foundry, Cold Spring NY
1858-1861: Inventor of hooped-breech, rifled cannon (patented in 1861)

R. P. PARROTT was a dedicated ordnance officer, creative inventor, and effective technical leader. After graduation from the Academy, he served on the science faculty at USMA for five years building a solid foundation for his later work in ordnance research. Then he spent the next seven years involved in coastal defense duties. His expertise in ordnance was recognized as he was promoted to the Assistant Chief of Ordnance. Despite his success in

the Army, Parrott was recruited by the owner of the West Point Foundry to leave the Army and direct the foundry's operations. Parrott resigned from the Army in 1836 to become Superintendent of the West Point Foundry. Later he leased the foundry and bought an iron furnace to support the foundry's operations. For 40 years, Parrott produced cannons at the foundry and conducted research in ordnance science, production techniques, and artillery ballistics. Parrott's work resulted in the development of a cast-iron, rifled cannon with a reinforced band on the breech and an expanding projectile designed especially for this type of cannon. Parrott's breakthrough in the development of useful cast iron artillery was a significant step in the development of modern artillery. In combination with the related work of **Thomas Rodman (USMA 1841)**, major developments in the advancement of artillery weaponry were achieved in America. These new, state-of-the-art guns were available for use in the Civil War, and more than 1500 Parrott Guns were purchased by the Union Army. His patent for reinforced cast iron cannon was granted in 1861. Parrott was a patriot and desired to serve in combat duty in the war in spite of his advanced age, but the Army denied him a combat assignment. Therefore, he became a government contractor, supplying cannons and other equipment to the Army. Parrott made special arrangements to insure the government would be protected from unsuitable or ill-timed contracts. He sold his cannons strictly at cost to the government. He had such a fine reputation that he was allowed to inspect the cannons produced at his own foundry, and he sent the government only the best weapons that he produced. At the beginning of the war, the Confederate Army had 12 Parrott guns, previously obtained by the Virginia Military Institute. Confederate foundries went on to manufacture another 133 copies. The 8-inch Parrott gun was the most formidable gun in the Civil War. There were also 10-, 20-, and 30-pounders and a 15-inch gun with a range of over 3 miles. Parrott's invention played a role in introducing rifled artillery to the military arsenal, along with enhancing the role of artillery in the Civil War. Parrott was one of the innovative West Point graduates who applied his technical education in mathematics, sciences, and engineering to contribute to the advancement of military technology and industrialization.

USMA 1824 || **William George Williams** || **Engineer**

1801 (SC) – 21 September 1846 (Monterey, Mexico)
Graduate # 375 (15th out of 31), (topographer)

Military Service:
1824-1846: Army service in technical duties

Professional Service:
1824-1826: Survey of canal from Chesapeake to Ohio River
1826-1830: Topographic engineering duty in various frontier locations
1830-1831: Travel to Europe to study art and engineering
1831-1834: Topographic engineering duty in various frontier locations
1834-1836: Construction duty for canal around Niagara Falls
1836-1837: Topographic duty for location railroad in SC and OH
1837-1838: Military and scientific reconnaissance of Cherokee Lands
1838-1843: Survey of Lake Erie
1841-1846: Survey of Great Lakes
1846:   Combat duty in Mexican War (Monterey- killed in action)

W. G. WILLIAMS was an Assistant Professor of Drawing and traveled in Europe several times – all while he was still a cadet. The Army commissioned Williams in the infantry since there were no vacancies in the topographic engineers at the time of his graduation in 1824. However, he was immediately placed on special duty with the Topographical Corps. Working for **William NcNeill (USMA 1817)**, Williams established a reputation as an expert topographer while surveying for canals and roadways. A talented artist, Williams took a one-year trip to Europe to study both art and engineering. He returned to more topographic duties, mostly on the frontier. After ten years of proving himself as an expert surveyor, mapmaker, and engineer, Williams won an appointment and promotion as a Captain in the Topographical Engineers in 1834. The Corps was limited to ten officers, so there was intense competition for such vacancies. Williams became involved in the project to survey the Great

Lakes. The development of commerce on the Great Lakes during the 1830s, as a result of the completion of the Erie Canal, required the government to provide the necessary charts and information for safe navigation. Although some earlier surveys had been performed, Williams designed and began a systematic survey from his headquarters in Buffalo, NY in 1841. During the time that Williams was in charge, surveys were made of all the Great Lakes harbors except those on Lake Superior. He had several assistants, J. H. Simpson (USMA 1832), W. H. Warner (USMA 1836), J. N. Macomb (USMA 1832), **J. W. Abert (USMA 1842)** and **W. B. Franklin (USMA 1843),** engaged on these surveys. Williams was sent into combat engineering duty at the outbreak of the Mexican War. While conducting an assault on Monterey, Mexico in 1846, he was killed in action. The citizens of Buffalo, whom he had served and supported through his important surveys, recovered his remains and buried him with military honors back in their city. Williams was married to George Washington's great-granddaughter and had many famous friends in the world of art, including Samuel Morse, the inventor of the telegraph and the President of the National Academy of Design.

Reference: Kail, Wendy, "George Washington's Great-Granddaughter and the Topographical Engineer: The Life and Times of William G. Williams, Class of 1824," *Assembly*, July 2000, pp. 35- 39.

USMA 1825 | **Alexander Hamilton Bowman** | **Engineer**

1803 (PA) – 11 November 1865 (Wilkes Barre, PA)
Graduate # 394 (3ʳᵈ out of 37), listed in *NCAB*

Military Service:
1825-1864: Army service in technical duties

Professional Service:
1825-1826: Assistant Professor of Geography, USMA
1826-1834: Construction engineer, coastal defense and harbor improvements on Gulf Coast
1834-1839: Construction engineer, military road from Tennessee to Arkansas
1839-1851: Construction engineer, Ft. Sumter, SC and Charleston Harbor, SC
1851-1852: Assistant Professor of Practical Military Engineering, USMA
1852-1853: Construction engineer, Savannah, GA
1853-1861: Construction engineer, Treasury Building, Washington, DC
1861-1864: Superintendent, USMA

A. H. Bowman began teaching geography at West Point immediately after his graduation in 1825. The valedictorian of his class was the famous scientist **Alexander Bache**. Most of Bowman's military and professional career was spent in construction engineering of fortifications, harbors, roadways, lighthouses, and buildings. Considered a highly successful engineer, he worked intermittently for 12 years on the protection and defenses of Ft. Sumter, SC. However, it was quickly evident at the outbreak of the Civil War with the shelling of

Sumter that fortification construction had not been able to keep pace with artillery improvements. Just 36 hours after Confederate General **Pierre Beauregard (USMA 1838)** began his highly effective artillery barrage on the fort, Bowman's West Point classmate, Robert Anderson, had to surrender the ruined fort. Bowman spent two more tours at West Point, one as an Assistant Professor of Practical Military Engineering and the other as Superintendent during the Civil War years. His challenge as Superintendent was to keep the Academy running with just a few cadets and faculty and expend minimal resources in the accomplishing his educational mission. Bowman's efficiency enabled him to successfully complete his leader-development goals as Superintendent. Bowman's son Charles Bowman graduated from USMA in 1860.

USMA 1825	William Fenn Hopkins	Scientist

1802 (CT) – 13 July 1859 (Jamaica)
Graduate # 402 (11th out of 37)

Military Service:
1825-1835: Army service spent in technical and education-related assignments

Professional Service:
1825-1835: Acting Professor of Chemistry, Mineralogy, and Geology, USMA
1843-1846: Principal of Norfolk Academy, VA
1846-1849: Professor of Natural Sciences, Western Military Institute, KY
1849-1850: Professor of Chemistry and Natural Philosophy, William and Mary College, VA
1850-1859: Professor of Natural and Experimental Philosophy, U.S. Naval Academy, MD

W. F. HOPKINS spent his entire 10-year military career at West Point teaching science in the Department of Chemistry, Mineralogy, and Geology. Hopkins replaced the surgeon, John Torrey, as the department head in 1827. He was then replaced as professor by the eminent scientist **Jacob Bailey (USMA 1832)**. After leaving the Army in 1835, Hopkins declined teaching jobs in mathematics to work in business. However, in 1843, he returned to education, first as a school principal in VA, then as a science professor at a military school in KY. Finding his true calling as a college science professor, Hopkins taught at Western Military Institute; William and Mary College, VA; and the U.S. Naval Academy, Annapolis,

MD. Distinguishing himself as a fine teacher, he was considered a faculty leader at the three schools. In 1859, Hopkins decided to try his hand in another service capacity and went to Jamaica as the U.S. Consul. He died just five months later while still in Jamaica. Among his many tributes were honorary degrees from Yale College and Hobart College.

USMA 1826   **Thomas Jefferson Cram**   **Engineer**

1803 (NH) – 20 December 1883 (Philadelphia, PA)
Graduate # 432 (4th out of 41), (surveyor, topographer), listed in *AR* (1884)

Military Service:
1861-1863: Aide-de-Camp for General Wool during Civil War (Norfolk) (Major General)
1862: Inspector General during Capture of Norfolk, VA

Professional Service:
1826-1829: Assistant Professor of Mathematics, USMA
1829-1836: Assistant Professor of Natural and Experimental Philosophy, USMA
1836-1838: Railroad construction engineer in MD and VA
1838-1844: Topographic engineer supporting roads, harbors, and river improvements in West
1844: Survey of the Mississippi River and the Ohio River
1845-1846: Military and scientific reconnaissance of Texas
1847-1855: Geodetic Survey of coast of New England
1855-1858: Topographic engineering on Pacific Coast
1858-1861: Geodetic Survey of coast of CA
1863-1869: Construction engineer for Ft. Wayne, MI
1868-1871: Construction engineer for harbor improvements, Lake Michigan, Lake Erie, Buffalo Harbor

T. J. CRAM was a gifted student while at the Academy and upon his graduation was asked to remain at West Point to teach. He spent his first ten years in the Army teaching mathematics and science. He was a dedicated teacher and so successful that he was allowed to stay in these positions much longer than usually allowed. After completing that long assignment in 1836, Cram resigned from the Army to try his hand at railroad construction. After two years, he took advantage of an opportunity to return to the Army in the topographical engineers. His new Army duties included building roads, constructing harbor facilities, and improving river navigation. He was also engaged in the survey of the boundary between Michigan and Wisconsin. In 1845, he made a reconnaissance of Texas during the military occupation. Just a year later, he was back to survey work along the coast of New England, then the Pacific Coast, and finally in CA. During the Civil War, Cram was aide-de-camp for General Wool. After the war, he supervised the harbor works on the Great Lakes. He retired from the Army in 1869, but continued his topographic service until 1871. Cram is remembered for his brilliant achievements as an educator and as an expert topographic engineer and surveyor.

USMA 1827   **John Childe**   **Engineer**

30 August 1802 (West Boylston, MA) – 2 February 1858 (Springfield, MA)
Graduate #471 (2nd out of 38), (topographer, ordnance), listed in *DAB, NCAB*

Military Service:
1827-1828: Artillery duty at Ft. Monroe, VA
1828-1834: Ordnance duty
1834-1835: Engineer duty, Ft. Wolcott, RI

Professional Service:
1835-1848: Topographic engineer for railroad company
1849-1850: Engineer to improve St. Lawrence River navigation
1848-1856: Topographic and construction engineer for Mobile and Ohio Railroad
1857-1858: Engineer for enlarging and improving Montreal Harbor, Canada

J. CHILDE spent a year at Georgetown College before attending West Point. He began his career as an artillery officer after graduating from the Academy in 1827. He then moved to ordnance duties for six years and one year more as an engineer for his last year in the Army. After resigning from the Army in 1835, Childe worked as a surveyor, topographic engineer, and construction engineer for many railroad companies. Building his reputation as an effective engineer by building a rail line across the rugged Green Mountains in MA, he then built the 500-mile railway between Mobile, AL and the Ohio River. Childe showed his versatility as an engineer in working on improvements to the Montreal Harbor; however, this work was not completed as he became ill and died. Childe was considered a genius for his creative railroad construction across some of the most challenging terrain in eastern United States.

USMA 1827   **Gabriel James Rains**   **Scientist**

4 June 1803 (Craven, NC) – 6 August 1881 (Aiken, SC)
Graduate # 482 (13th out of 38), (chemist, military technologist), listed in *DAB, ANB, NCAB, AR* (1882)

Military Service:
1828-1839: Frontier duty in Indian Territories

1839-1842: Combat duty in Seminole War in FL (wounded in action)
1842-1845: Garrison duty in FL and LA
1845-1846: Combat duty in military occupation of Texas
1846-1847: Combat duty in Mexican War
1848-1850: Combat duty in Seminole War
1850-1860: Frontier duty and combat duty against Indians in CA and WA
1861-1862: Combat duty in Civil War for Confederate Army

Professional Service:
1862-1865: Research and development of explosives, mines, and torpedoes
            for the Confederate military
1866-1881: Research and development of explosives and munitions for the
            U.S. military

G. J. Rains was commissioned in the infantry after his graduation from West Point. He spent most of his service time either on the frontier or in combat. His duties took him out West to the Indian Territories. He was promoted for gallantry for his actions in the Seminole War, serving in FL from 1839 to 1842. Rains was wounded during the war. He also fought in the Mexican War. Further action against the Seminoles in FL and in the Indian Wars out West brought Rains promotion to Brigadier General. In 1861, Rains left the United States Army to become a Brigadier General in the Confederate Army. Serving under **D. H. Hill (USMA 1842)**, Rains commanded at the Battle of Yorktown. He had become an expert in explosives by studying this military technology during his spare time. Using his technical skills to build mines, he placed them in the harbor at Yorktown. He also began to mine the roads as his unit retreated from Yorktown and Williamsburg. These actions were the first use of this kind of mine warfare and were reported in the northern newspapers. This type of warfare so upset the citizens of the country that Rains was forbidden to use land mines for a period of time. Later Rains convinced Confederate President Jefferson Davis (USMA 1828) of the ethical legitimacy and military value of such mining techniques. Others on both sides of the conflict began using land mines, so Rains was allowed by Davis to resume his mining development and operations. He used mines to protect his fortifications at Richmond, Mobile, and Charleston. Rains was severely wounded in battle in 1862 and was given duty as head of conscription for the Confederate Army. However, Rains spent most of his time working on the chemistry of explosives and the technologies of mines and torpedoes. In 1863, he took over command of the Torpedo Bureau of the Confederacy. He designed, built and deployed sea mines and torpedoes. His invention of an effective contact fuse helped advance the Confederate efforts in this technical aspect of warfare. Rains worked with his brother **George W. Rains (USMA 1842)** who manufactured fuses for both torpedoes and mines. Rains' mines had considerable success in restricting Union use of southern harbors and in blowing up enemy ships and barges. After the Civil War, Rains continued his pioneering research in explosives working for the U.S. military. As the inventor of the technology for explosive weaponry, he raised a debate that continues today about the moral and ethical limits of the military's use of this technology.

USMA 1828 | **William Williams Mather** | **Scientist**

24 May 1804 (Brooklyn, CT) – 25 February 1859 (Columbus, OH)
Graduate # 522 (15th out of 33), (geologist), listed in *DAB, ANB, DSB, NCAB, BDAS, AR* (1884)

Military Service:
1828-1829: Field duties at Fort Jessup, LA
1836:   Frontier duty at Fort Gibson, OK, Indian Territory

Professional Service:
1829-1835: Assistant Professor of Chemistry, Mineralogy, and Geology, USMA
1835-1836: Topographic engineer, Wisconsin Territory
1836-1841: Geologist, New York Geological Survey
1837-1840: Geologist, Ohio Geological Survey
1838-1839: Geologist, geological survey of Kentucky
1842-1850: Professor of Natural Sciences, Ohio University (acting Vice President and President
                 at various times)
1846:   Professor of Chemistry, Mineralogy, and Geology, Marietta College, OH
1850-1854: Agricultural Chemist, OH
1854-1859: Geological engineer for railroad companies

W. W. MATHER studied medicine in Providence, RI for a short period of time and came to West Point as a student with an intense interest in chemistry. He was a top student in his chemistry, mineralogy, and geology courses. He spent most of his eight-year army career teaching these courses at West Point and performing geological field work in the western territories. Mather's first position in civilian life was to lead a geological survey of New York State, and later he led similar efforts in Ohio and Kentucky. Mather then used his knowledge and experience to teach others about geological surveying at Ohio University in Athens, OH, from 1842 to 1846. He served as Vice President and Acting President of the university for three years as well. In 1846, he taught briefly at Marietta College, OH. Serving as Ohio's agricultural chemist on the State Board of Agriculture, he performed numerous surveys and mineral analyses for railroad companies. As one of America's early professional geologists, conducting several important geological surveys, he published his survey results in several reports. His massive book, *Geology of New York* (Part I), is still used today and set the standard for geological reports. These works contained many details of the structure of the strata in New York State and the other states he surveyed. While Mather did not support the theory of glacial formation for the geological structures in the northeast, he was the first to establish several consequential theories in rock formation. He also wrote several important journal articles and a popular geology textbook in 1833. He was a first-quality scientist who made a strong impact on geology, its teaching, and the businesses, which used his geological information. Mather was a pioneer in geological surveys, which were important components of American science during the first half of the 19th century.

USMA 1829 | Robert Edward Lee | Engineer

19 January 1807 (Westmoreland City, VA) – 12 October 1870 (Lexington, VA)
Graduate # 542 (2nd out of 46), listed in *DAB, ANB, ACAB, NCAB, AR* (1871)

Military Service:

1834-1837: Duty with Office of Chief of Army Engineers, Washington, DC
1840-1841: Duty with Office of Chief of Army Engineers, Washington, DC
1846-1847: Combat engineer duty in Mexican War
1847-1849: Duty with Office of the Chief of Army Engineers, Washington, DC
1855-1861: Frontier duty in Cavalry, Kansas Territory and TX
1861-1865: Combat duty in command of Army of Northern Virginia for the Confederacy

Professional Service:

1827-1829: Instructor of Mathematics, USMA
1829-1834: Construction engineer at Fort Pulaski, GA and Fort Monroe, VA
1837-1840: Construction engineer in St. Louis working on navigation improvements of Mississippi River
1841-1845: Construction engineer for New York Harbor
1849-1852: Construction engineer for defenses of Baltimore
1852-1855: Superintendent, USMA
1865-1870: President, Washington College, VA

R. E. Lee enjoyed mathematics at West Point and during his 3rd and 4th years as a cadet taught mathematics to underclassmen. This was the only period (1818-1827) in the Academy's history when cadets taught other cadets. Lee attended mathematics class all morning for six days a week for his first two years. Then he took a heavy load of science and engineering his last two years while spending time teaching as well. The new mathematics program put in place by Department Head **Charles Davies (USMA 1815)** included Legendre's *Geometry*, Lacroix's *Algebra*, Biot's *Analytic Geometry*, Crozet's *Descriptive Geometry*, Crozet's *Treatise on Perspectives,*

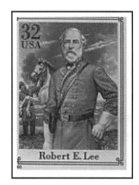

Robert E. Lee

Shades and Shadows, and Lacroix's *Fluxions* (calculus). Graduating in 1829, Lee entered the Corps of Engineers and began his career as a construction engineer at Fort Pulaski, GA. He soon worked on other engineering projects, building Fort Monroe, VA and improving navigation on the Mississippi River. In 1841, Lee moved to New York City to work on its defenses and fortifications. He also had opportunity to serve on the examination board of the Academy. During his service as a combat engineer in the Mexican War, Lee distinguished himself as both a technically competent officer and a strong combat leader. After the war, he worked on defenses in Baltimore and then was assigned as the Superintendent of the Military Academy in 1852. During Lee's tenure, the Academy leadership debated adding more courses in liberal arts and humanities. However, the powerful science-based Department Heads, **Dennis Mahan (USMA 1824)** in engineering, **William Bartlett (USMA 1826)** in science, and **Albert Church (USMA 1828)** in mathematics, resisted any reductions in their programs. An ill-fated compromise was reached. The Academy went to a five-year program, adding more humanities, and the science-based programs were unaffected. In 1855, Lee had the opportunity to test his field leadership on the frontier. He became a cavalry commander in KS and TX. In 1859, he was back in New York, when he and James Stuart (USMA 1854) were sent after John Brown in Harper's Ferry, VA. At the outbreak of the Civil War, Lee was offered generous commands by both sides, but ultimately decided to fight with his native state of Virginia as chief advisor to Confederate President Jefferson Davis (USMA 1828) and as commander of the Army of Northern Virginia. He proved to be a brilliant commander, but eventually lost to a larger, better equipped Union Army. After the war, Lee accepted the reunion of the country and filled the position of President of Washington College in Lexington, VA. By 1870, through Lee's powerful leadership, the college had grown to 400 students and prospered in terms of new facilities and quality faculty. Lee died in 1870 while actively filling the duties of President of his college. Lee was a brilliant man, both technically and as a military strategist. While somewhat aloof, he was respected as a leader and a tremendous contributor to the advancement of American science.

References:

Preston, Walter, *Lee, West Point and Lexington*, Antioch Press, Yellow Springs, 1934.

Thomas, Emory, *Robert E. Lee: A Biography*, W. W. Norton, New York, 1995.

USMA 1829   **Catharinus Putnam Buckingham**   **Mathematician**

14 March 1808 (Zanesville, OH) – 30 August 1888 (Chicago IL)
Graduate #546 (6th out of 46), listed in *NCAB, AR* (1889)

Military Service:
1861-1863:   Various administrative and staff duties in the War Department (Civil War) (Brigadier General)

Professional Service:
1829-1830:   Duty as topographic engineer
1830-1831:   Assistant Professor of Natural and Experimental Philosophy, USMA
1833-1836:   Professor of Mathematics and Natural Philosophy, Kenyon College, OH
1849-1861:   Superintendent of Iron Works, Ohio
1868-1873:   Construction engineer for grain elevators, IL
1869-1875:   Author of two mathematics books and teacher

Upon graduation from West Point, **C. P. BUCKINGHAM** was commissioned in the artillery but served as a topographic engineer for the first year. His second year was spent back at the Academy teaching Natural and Experimental Philosophy for the Department Head and famous scientist, **Edward Courtenay (USMA 1821)**. In 1831, Buckingham left the Army and moved West to Kenyon College, OH, where he became the full Professor of Mathematics and Natural Philosophy in 1833. Buckingham was the first of several West

Pointers to teach technical subjects and serve as President of Kenyon College. After just three years, he changed his career field, becoming a merchant and businessman. Eventually, he entered the iron business and used his technical background and problem solving expertise to improve iron manufacturing. At the outbreak of the Civil War, Buckingham re-entered Army service and took on administrative and staff duties in OH and Washington, DC. He was promoted to Brigadier General. After the war, he continued as a merchant and engineer, spending time constructing grain elevators and writing two mathematics textbooks. His two books, one on arithmetic and the other on calculus, were published in 1869 and 1875, respectively. Periodically teaching at colleges and schools, Buckingham spent the bulk of the time during the last years of his life as president of a steel company and a successful businessman.

USMA 1829　　　　**Charles William Hackley**　　　　**Mathematician**

1809 (NY) – 10 January 1861 (New York, NY)
Graduate # 549　(9th out of 46), (author)

Military Service:
1829-1833:　Military service in technical duties

Professional Service:
1829-1833:　Assistant Professor of Mathematics, USMA
1833-1839:　Professor of Mathematics, University of New York
1839:　　　　President, Jefferson College, MS
1843-1857:　Professor of Mathematics, Columbia College, NY
1857-1861:　Professor of Astronomy, Columbia College, NY
1846-1850:　Author of books in mathematics and engineering

C. W. HACKLEY was commissioned in the artillery, but spent his four years of military service teaching mathematics at West Point. He resigned from the Army in 1833 and was an Episcopal clergyman throughout his civilian life. Among Hackley's classmates were Civil War generals, railroad executives, scientists, farmers, merchants, and fellow clergyman and mathematician **James Clark**. In 1833, Hackley began a six-year period as Professor of Mathematics at the University of the City of New York working with several other West Point graduates on the staff. Then for just one year, he moved to Washington, MS to serve as President of Jefferson College. He returned to New York City to fill the Professor of Mathematics position at Columbia College for fourteen years. In 1857, Hackley converted to the position of Professor of Astronomy, when his former professor and department head **Charles Davies (USMA 1815)** arrived at Columbia to fill the Mathematics chair. Hackley authored several technical books, both textbooks in undergraduate subjects and research-level treatises. His works included: *Elements of Trigonometry* (1838), *An Elementary Course of Geometry* (1847), *A Treatise on Trigonometry, Plane and Spherical, with its*

Application to Navigation and Surveying, Nautical and Practical Astronomy and Geodesy (1851), and *A Treatise on Algebra* (1856). Hackley's major contributions were in teaching and text authoring.

USMA 1829 | James Clark | Mathematician

1813 (PA) – 9 September 1885 (Georgetown, DC)
Graduate # 574 (34th out of 46), listed in *AR* (1886)

Military Service:
1829-1830: Garrison duty at Fort St. Philip, LA

Professional Service:
1837-1839: Professor of Mathematics, Mt. St. Mary's College, MD
1839-1844: Professor of Mathematics, Natural Philosophy, and Chemistry, Mt. St. Mary's College, MD
1845-1849: Professor of Mathematics and Chemistry, Georgetown College, DC
1849-1850: Professor of Mathematics and Chemistry, College of Holy Cross, MA
1850-1861: Professor of Mathematics, Georgetown College, DC
1859-1861: Vice President, Georgetown College, DC
1861-1867: President, College of Holy Cross, MA
1868-1874: President, Gonzaga College, Washington, DC
1874-1878: Professor of Mathematics, Georgetown College, DC

J. CLARK spent one year in military service after his graduation from West Point. The remainder of his 39-year professional career was as an educator and clergyman. He became a Jesuit priest in the Roman Catholic Church in 1847 and spent his teaching and academic assignments at Catholic colleges. At various times from 1837 to 1859, Clark taught mathematics, chemistry, and natural philosophy at three schools – Mt. St. Mary's College, Georgetown College, and Holy Cross College. Starting in 1861, he became more of an administrator and educational leader at Holy Cross, Georgetown, and another school in Washington, DC – Gonzaga College. During his professional career, he also served as President of Holy Cross and Gonzaga. In 1874, at age, 63, Clark returned to teaching his favorite subject of mathematics. He was a beloved teacher and a successful academic leader.

USMA 1830 | Thomas Jefferson Lee | **Engineer**

1808 (France) – 30 December 1891 (Baltimore, MD)
Graduate # 593 (7th out of 42), (topographer), listed in *AR* (1892)

Military Service:
1830-1831: Garrison duty in MD
1833-1835: Garrison duty in MD
1836: Aide-de-camp for General Scott and special duty in removal of Indians of Creek Nation to OK
1838-1839: Staff duty with Topographic Bureau, Washington, DC
1848-1855: Staff duty with Topographic Bureau, Washington, DC

Professional Service:
1831-1833: Topographic engineering duty on frontier
1836-1838: Civilian engineer on harbor improvements in MD and NC
1839-1840: Survey duty on boundary between U.S. and Texas
1840-1844: Survey duty on boundary between U.S. and Canada
1844-1848: Surveyor and astronomer for Coast Survey
1858-1860: Survey duty for border of MD and VA
1861-1862: Civilian engineer for Coast Survey
1862-1889: Civilian engineer for Topographical Bureau and Corps of Engineers on river and harbor improvements

---

T. J. LEE was commissioned in the artillery upon his graduation from West Point in 1830. After six years of Army service (three in artillery, two in topographic engineering, and one year on difficult special duty transferring Indians to the West), Lee resigned from the Army. He immediately sought employment as a civilian engineer and began survey and construction work on harbors and canals in MD and NC. Lee re-entered the Army when he was able to secure a commission in the highly-competitive Topographical Engineer Corps. After a year of staff work, Lee spent the next nine years in field survey work on the southern and northern boundary of the U.S. and as an astronomer in the Coast Survey. He found this work both challenging and rewarding. He was considered one of America's best surveyors and astronomers. Lee spent seven years back with the Topographic Bureau in Washington, DC, and he used that time to write three major technical works. The books are: *On the use of the zenith and equal altitude telescope in the determination of the latitude*, (1848); *A collection of tables and formulae useful in geodesy and practical astronomy, including elements for the projection of maps. Prepared by order of the Topographical Bureau for the use of the Corps of Topographical Engineers*, (1849); *A collection of tables and formulae useful in surveying, geodesy, and practical astronomy, including elements for the projection of maps. Prepared for the use of the Corps of Topographical Engineers*, (1853). Lee resigned from the Army for a second time in 1855. Back to civilian work in engineering and surveying, Lee set the border between Maryland and Virginia and worked again as an astronomer for the Coast Survey. For the last seventeen years of his professional career, Lee focused on improvements of river navigation and harbor facilities. His contributions in these areas were substantial. Lee was primarily an astronomer, who used his talents in surveying and engineering. The Superintendent of the Coast Survey, **Alexander Bache (USMA 1825)**

used Lee to perform his most challenging surveys and make his most important astronomical observations.

USMA 1830 | **Albert Taylor Bledsoe** | Mathematician

9 November 1809 (Frankfort, KY) – 8 December 1877 (Alexandria, VA)
Graduate # 602 (16th out of 42), listed *in DAB, ANB, NCAB, AR* (1878)

Military Service:
1830-1832: Frontier duty in infantry at Ft. Gibson, Indian Territories
1861-1862: Chief of the Bureau of War, Confederate Army
1861:   Assistant Secretary of War, Confederate Army

Professional Service:
1832-1833: Tutor at Kenyon College, OH
1833-1834: Adjunct Professor of Mathematics, Kenyon College, OH
1835-1836: Professor of Mathematics, Miami University, OH
1848-1854: Professor of Mathematics, University of Mississippi
1854-1861: Professor of Mathematics, University of Virginia

A. T. BLEDSOE grew up in Kentucky and came north to attend West Point. After graduation and two years of field duty on the frontier, he left the Army to teach mathematics at the college level. He held short-term positions at Kenyon College and Miami University in Ohio. After just three years, Bledsoe left mathematics education to pursue other interests in religion and law. After disagreeing with the doctrine of the Episcopal Church, he concentrated on the legal profession. He practiced law in Springfield, IL, along with famous colleagues Abraham Lincoln and Stephen Douglas. He then returned to his southern roots and education career, teaching mathematics at the University of Mississippi for over 6 years. Moving to the University of Virginia in 1854, he succeeded the distinguished Professor **Edward Courtenay (USMA 1821)**, who had passed away, and began his tenure as leader of the university's mathematics program. At Virginia, he had the opportunity to teach outstanding students some of the most advanced undergraduate mathematics courses in America. Maintaining the program established by Courtenay with the addition of a course on the philosophy of mathematics, Bledsoe was known for his superb memory and deep concentration. As secession and the Civil War loomed on the horizon, Bledsoe lobbied vigorously for Virginia to secede and organized his students and the local citizens to support this movement. Once the Confederacy was established, Bledsoe played an active role as first Chief of the Bureau of War and then as Assistant Secretary of War. He traveled to Europe to research a book in support of his mentor Jefferson Davis (USMA 1828) and to influence British public opinion. His technical book, *The Philosophy of Mathematics,* published in

1865, attacked the traditional teaching methods of geometry and algebra. At the close of the war, Bledsoe became a staunch defender of the legalities of secession and the Southern lifestyle. His public and private writings and the numerous articles that he wrote as editor of the *Southern Review* supported the aggressive views of a non-reconstructed Southerner. Bledsoe never returned to his technical pursuits after the war, but he did continue his religious activities and political writings until his death in 1877.

Reference:

Despeaux, Sloan; Martini, Laura; Parshall, Karen Hunger; and Rice, Adrian; "The University of Virginia, 1825-1900: A Case Study in the Institutionalization of Mathematics in the United States," *Proceedings of the History of Undergraduate Mathematics in America*, 2001.

USMA 1831　　　 **Roswell Park**　　　**Scientist**

1 October 1807 (Lebanon, CT) – 16 July 1869 (Chicago, IL)
Graduate #629 (1st out of 33), (natural philosopher, chemist, engineer, educator), listed in *DAB, NCAB*

Military Service:
1831-1836:　Army service involving technical duties

Professional Service:
1831-1836:　Construction engineer for Ft. Adams, RI; Ft. Warren, MA; and Delaware Breakwater
1836-1842:　Professor of Natural Philosophy and Chemistry, University of Pennsylvania
1848:　　　Original member of American Association for the Advancement of Science
1850-1863:　President and Chancellor and Professor of Natural Sciences of Racine College, WI
1863-1869:　President and Founder, Immanuel Hall, IL

R. PARK was a schoolteacher and student at Hamilton College, NY before attending West Point. He graduated first in his class and entered the Corps of Engineers. Park served five years as a construction engineer before resigning from the Army in 1836. He took the position of Professor of Natural Philosophy and Chemistry at the University of Pennsylvania, serving in that position in between the two terms of **Alexander Bache (USMA 1825)**. In 1848, at the Academy of Natural Sciences in Philadelphia, Park was one of the 87 distinguished scientists, including Bache, who established the new science-support organization, the American Association for the Advancement of Science (AAAS). (See the essay on the AAAS.) The aims of the Association were "to promote intercourse between those who are cultivating science in different parts of the United States, to give a stronger and more general impulse, and a more systematic direction to scientific research in our country; and to procure for the labours (sic) of scientific men, increased facilities and a wider usefulness." These were things Park had accomplished or advocated throughout his career. While in Philadelphia, he decided to enter the clergy of the Episcopal Church. He fulfilled his pastoral duties by heading a church-run preparatory school in CT for seven years. Building a fine reputation as an educator and scientist, he was offered the presidency of Norwich University in 1850. However, he declined the offer and took a six-month trip to Europe instead. Returning to the U.S., Park then accepted the position as the first President of Racine College in Wisconsin, attempting to fill the need for church-related colleges in the Northwest Territory. For 11 years, he served the college as its leader and as its Professor of Natural Sciences. In 1863, Park left Wisconsin and set up another new school, Immanuel Hall Seminary, near Chicago, IL where he worked until his death. Park was a successful author of several articles and books. Park's books were varied in their subject, but two were relevant to his technical career -- *A Sketch of the History and Topography of West Point and of the United States Military Academy* (1840) and the ambitious *Pantology: or a Systematic Survey of Human Knowledge* (published in 1841 and partially written when Park was a cadet).

| USMA 1831 | | Jacob Ammen | | Mathematician |

7 January 1807 (Fincastle, VA) – 6 February 1894 (Lockland, OH)
Graduate # 640 (12th out of 33), listed in *DAB, NCAB, AR* (1894)

Military Service:
1832-1834: Artillery duty at Charleston, SC
1861-1863: Combat commander in Civil War (Shiloh, Corinth)
            (Brigadier General)
1863-1865: Administrative duties during Civil War

Professional Service:
1831-1832: Assistant Professor of Mathematics, USMA
1837-1839: Professor of Mathematics, Bacon College, Georgetown, KY
1839-1840: Professor of Mathematics, Jefferson College, Washington, MS
1840-1843: Professor of Mathematics, University of Indiana
1843-1848: Professor of Mathematics. Jefferson College, Washington, MS
1848-1855: Professor of Mathematics and Astronomy, Georgetown
            College, KY
1865-1872: Civil engineer, OH
1874:   Member of Isthmus Canal Commission

J. AMMEN was commissioned in the artillery upon his graduation from West Point in 1831. His first duty was to stay at West Point to teach mathematics. There, in addition to teaching, he helped Department Head **Charles Davies (USMA 1815)** with the details of writing textbooks. After six years of service, three of which were at West Point, Ammen resigned to teach in civilian colleges. He filled the Professor of Mathematics positions at Bacon College, Jefferson College, Indiana University, and Georgetown College.

Ammen found it difficult to earn a good salary in teaching at these small colleges. When the Civil War started, Ammen joined the Union Army despite his southern roots and connections. Having witnessed the nullification proceedings in South Carolina during his early Army service, Ammen staunchly supported the Union. He raised a company of volunteers in OH and commanded a brigade at Shiloh and Corinth. Illness prevented him from further field duty, so Ammen was placed in administrative command of the District of East Tennessee. After the Civil War, Ammen worked as a surveyor and civil engineer in OH. In 1874, he was part of the first commission to investigate possible routes for a canal across the isthmus of Panama. He surveyed and designed routes for the commission, which was important work for later decisions on the route of the canal. Ammen was a superb educator and an innovative problem solver.

USMA 1831 | **William Hemsley Emory** | **Scientist**

7 September 1811 (Queen Anne's County, MD) – 1 December 1887 (Washington, DC)
Graduate # 642 (14th out of 33), listed in *DAB, ANB, NCAB, BDAS, AR* (1888)

Military Service:
1831-1832: Garrison duty in MD
1832-1833: Security duty in SC during the threatened nullification
1833-1836: Garrison duty in NY
1836: Special duty in transporting Indians of the Creek Nation
1843-1844: Assistant in the Topographic Bureau, Washington, DC
1846-1848: Combat engineer and Adjutant General in Mexican War
 (Kearney's Expedition, San Pasqual, San Bernardino)
1857-1858: Frontier duty, Ft. Riley, KS
1858: Utah Expedition against the Mormons
1859-1861: Frontier duty in Indian Territory
1861-1865: Combat duty in Civil War (Yorktown, Williamsburg, Port
 Hudson, New Orleans, Red River, Shenandoah,
 Cedar Creek) (Major General)
1866-1871: Command and staff duty in Washington, DC
1871-1876: Command of Department of the Gulf

Professional Service:
1836-1838: Civil engineering duties
1838-1843: Engineer duty improving harbors in DE
1844-1846: Survey duty on boundary between U.S. and Canada
1848-1853: Survey duty on boundary between U.S. and Mexico
1854-1857: Survey duty on boundary set by Gadsen Treaty between U.S. and Mexico

W. H. EMORY was born on his family's "Poplar Grove" estate in MD and graduated from West Point in 1831. After five years of garrison and security duty, he resigned from the Army in 1836 to work as a civil engineer but then returned to military service in 1838. As a topographic engineer, Emory specialized in exploring and conducting boundary surveys along the Texas-Mexican border (1844), the United States-Canadian border (1844-1846), the United States-Mexican border (1848-1853), and the Gadsden Purchase line (1854-1857). In 1844, Emory produced a new map of Texas. He came to public attention as the author of *Notes of a Military Reconnaissance from Fort Leavenworth in Missouri to San Diego in California*, published by Congress in 1848. This report described the terrain, rivers, forts, pueblos, prehistoric ruins, animals, plants, and Indian culture in NM, AZ, and CA. It was very scientific in its content and was considered an important description of the Southwest, especially for its detailed and accurate maps. Emory was a skilled cartographer and produced dozens of important maps over his career. He acquired his greatest fame while on duty with the United States-Mexican boundary survey between 1848 and 1853. In his report to Congress, he confronted the positions of other explorers who portrayed the West as a paradise. He used scientific data to argue that his analysis was accurate. By his geological facts, Emory built a description of Texas as an imposing land of canyons and deserts with considerable mineral deposits. Because of this unique geology and geography, Emory argued for government and military control of the development of Texas, not the usual approach of civilian business control. When Emory became the supervisor of the boundary survey, four others had already failed. Under his technical leadership, Emory's survey team finished setting and mapping the boundary within a year. Emory's report completely contradicted that of his predecessor John Bartlett. At the heart of Emory's criticism was that Bartlett was unsuited for the task because he lacked military discipline and was a "hypothetical geographer" searching for publicity rather than truth. This quest for authenticity became a motivating factor in Emory's scientific work. During the Mexican War, Emory served in the Southwest as a topographical engineer and later as an Adjutant General. After a brief stay in Washington, DC, where he produced maps and reports, he returned to Mexico. At the outbreak of the Civil War, he was stationed in the Indian Territory. Anticipating combat action on the frontier, he withdrew his unit safely to Fort Leavenworth. During this withdrawal, he captured the first Confederate soldiers held as prisoners by the Union Army. He served as a brigade commander in the East in 1862. Then he went out West to command a division in Louisiana in 1863. He concluded his combat service in the Shenandoah Valley. After the war, Emory was commander of the Department of Washington and then the Department of the Gulf. While a successful military leader, Emory was first and foremost an accomplished scientist.

References:

"Emory, William Hemsley." The Handbook of Texas Online. http://www.tsha.utexas.edu/handbook/online/articles/view/EE/fem3.html

Dawson, Joseph, *Army Generals and Reconstruction: Louisiana, 1862-1877*, Louisiana State University Press, Baton Rouge, 1982.

Goetzmann, W. H., *Army Exploration in the American West, 1803-1863*, Yale University Press, New Haven, 1959.

Norris, L. David, Milligan, James and Faulk, Odie, *William H. Emory: Soldier–Scientist*, University of Arizona Press, Tucson, 1998.

Traas, Adrian, *From the Golden Gate to Mexico City - The U. S. Army Topographical Engineers in the Mexican War, 1846 - 1848,* Government Printing Office, Washington, DC, 1992.

USMA 1831   ┌─────────────────────────┐   **Scientist**
                 │ **Charles Whittlesey** │
                 └─────────────────────────┘

4 October 1808 (Southington, CT) – 18 October 1886 (Cleveland, OH)
Graduate # 660 (32nd out of 33), listed in *BDAS, AR* (1887)

Military Service:
1831-1832: Frontier duty at Ft. Howard, WI
1861-1862: Staff officer and combat commander
            in Civil War (Ft. Danelson, Shiloh)

Professional Service:
1837-1838: Geological survey of Ohio
1848-1850: Mineral survey in MI, WI, MN
1853-1856: Mining engineer, Lake Superior
1858-1860: Geological survey of WI
1862-1886: Author of various technical and non-technical works

C. WHITTLESEY spent one year in military service and several years practicing law before finding his calling as a geologist. He began this work as an assistant to **William Mather (USMA 1828)** on a geological survey of the state of Ohio. He then continued his geological work in studying mineral deposits in several states. His publications were very scientific and appeared in the finest journals in America. Whittlesey worked for the U.S. Government on a survey of the area around Lake Superior. He worked on the Wisconsin's survey until the outbreak of the Civil War. During the war, Whittlesey helped with defensive preparations of Ohio and then fought in the battle of Ft. Donelson, TN. Whittlesey was given a brigade command and faced **Pierre Beauregard's (USMA 1838)** charge at Shiloh. Whittlesey survived the battle, but never returned to combat duty and eventually resigned from the Army. Returning to his geological work in the western Great Lakes and upper Mississippi River, he became President of the Western Reserve and Northern Ohio Historical Society and spent considerable energy making lasting contributions to the heritage of the West. As a productive member of the American Association for the Advancement of Science, Whittlesey was a prolific author, writing over 200 works on geology, archaeology, and history.

Quotation: In Cullum's *Register* from a Western Reserve Historical Society meeting: "For the duties of his position he [Whittlesey] was eminently fitted. The scientific training at West Point, the active duties of the Indian campaign, the years spent in the wilds of the Northwest in land survey and in the mineralogical and geological investigations, developed and strengthened his natural love for the useful sciences, for historical research, and for archaeological investigation, and gave him such an extended and practical knowledge of men and things as is seldom granted to scientific men."

USMA 1832   **Benjamin Stoddert Ewell**   **Mathematician**

15 June 1810 (Washington, DC) – 19 June 1894 (Williamsburg, VA)
Graduate # 664 (3rd out of 45), listed in *DAB, ANB, NCAB, AR* (1895)

Military Service:
1862-1865: Adjutant in Confederate Army during Civil War

Professional Service:
1832-1835: Assistant Professor of Mathematics, USMA
1835-1836: Assistant Professor of Natural Philosophy, USMA
1836-1839: Construction engineer for railroad company
1839-1846: Professor of Mathematics, Hampden-Sidney College, VA
1846-1848: Professor of Mathematics, Washington College, VA
1848-1854: Acting President and Professor of Mathematics, William and Mary College, VA
1854-1888: President, William and Mary College, VA

B. S. EWELL attended the preparatory department of Georgetown College before arriving at West Point. He was commissioned in the artillery after graduation but spent his time in the Army as a mathematics and natural philosophy professor at the Academy. After four years of military service, Ewell resigned and spent his next three years as a construction engineer for a railroad company. In 1839, he returned to education, teaching mathematics for seven years at Hampden-Sidney College, VA. Then he moved to Washington College as the Cincinnati Professor of Mathematics. In 1848, he became the Acting President of William and Mary College, which would become his academic home for the rest of his life. In 1854, he was made President and the college began to prosper. However, the college was forced to suspend classes during the Civil War and Ewell served as an adjutant and chief-of-staff for the Confederate Army in Joseph E. Johnston's (USMA 1829) Army. Ewell's brother, Richard Stoddert Ewell (USMA 1840) was a famous Confederate General during the Civil War. Benjamin Ewell was a strong Unionist, but supported his fellow college colleagues in VA in secession. After the war, Ewell returned to service as President of William and Mary, which was struggling to survive. Its buildings had been burned, and it took until 1869 to rebuild the facilities and reopen the college. Having successfully lobbied Congress for help in this effort, Ewell worked hard to keep the school operating, using much of his own money, but eventually he had to close the school again in 1881. Finally in 1888, the State of Virginia agreed to establish a teachers college at William and Mary. In this same year, Ewell retired from his life's work as an educator and college administrator. Ewell was a both a skilled teacher of technical subjects and a strong academic leader. The students and faculty at William and Mary during his tenure loved Ewell for his dedication and perseverance on their behalf. Today, William and Mary College owes its very existence to Ewell's selfless sacrifices for the school and his strong commitment to education.

USMA 1832   **George Washington Cass**   **Engineer**

12 March 1810 (Dresden, OH) – 21 March 1888 (New York, NY)
Graduate # 665 (4th out of 32), listed in *DAB, ANB, AR* (1888)

Military Service:
1832-1836: Military service in technical duties

Professional Service:
1832-1836: Construction engineer for Cumberland Road (east of Ohio River) while in the Army
1836-1841: Construction engineer of Cumberland Road (PA, VA, OH) as civilian
1844-1857: Engineer for improvements on Monongahela River and in steamship, stagecoach, and express business
1856-1881: Engineer and president for various railroad companies

G. W. Cass lived in Detroit with his uncle, Michigan Governor Lewis Cass, who was a former Secretary of State and Secretary of War. After attending Detroit Academy, he obtained an appointment to West Point. Upon graduation in 1832, Cass was assigned to the construction engineering staff of **Richard Delafield (USMA 1818)** working on the Cumberland Road. Cass enjoyed this work so much that he resigned his commission in 1836 when the Army ordered a transfer. Cass signed on to Delafield's staff as a civilian performing similar engineering work. One of his projects was the supervision of the iron tubular-arch bridge across Dunlap's Creek. This bridge was designed by Delafield and was the first of its type in the world. It still stands today and was recently designated a National Landmark. In 1844, Cass began work on the locks and improvement of navigation on the Monongahela River. After a few years, his interest changed from engineering the means of transportation to providing transportation services. He coordinated steamship lines on the Monongahela and also designed and established stagecoach and express service throughout the Northeast. In 1856, Cass moved to Pittsburgh, PA to use his engineering skills in the railroad industry. He was successful and soon became President of several railroad companies. His adventure into politics was not as successful, as he lost two gubernatorial campaigns in PA. He did not return to military service during in Civil War, but he did continue to operate his railroad in support of the Union Army needs. After the Civil War, he expanded his railroad business westward. Cass built a large estate in Sewickley, PA called

"Casella". His legacy was in the numerous transportation improvements that he initiated. He was a national expert in designing, building, and operating roadways, waterways, and railways.

USMA 1833   **George Washington Cullum**   **Engineer**

25 February 1809 (New York, NY) – 28 February 1892 (New York, NY)
Graduate # 709 (3rd out of 43), listed in *DAB, ANB, NCAB, AR* (1892)

Military Service:
1833-1846: Construction engineer for coastal fortifications in New England (Ft. Adams) and in the Washington, DC area
1846-1848: Recruiter and Engineer trainer for Mexican War
1855-1861: Construction engineer for coastal fortifications in New England, NY, Carolinas (Ft. Sumter)
1861-1864: Aide-de-camp for Winfield Scott and Chief of Staff for Henry Halleck during Civil War
1866-1874: Construction engineer for coastal fortifications in New England, NY, Carolinas

Professional Service:
1848-1850: Instructor, Practical Military Engineering, USMA
1852-1855: Assistant Professor, Practical Military Engineering, USMA
1864-1866: Superintendent, USMA
1877-1892: Vice President, American Geographic Society

G. W. Cullum developed into a skilled construction engineer after his graduation from West Point. His primary focus during three periods of his life (1833-1838, 1855-1861, 1864-1874) was the construction and maintenance of seacoast fortifications. Cullum was America's expert on this subject. He also served as a combat engineer in the Mexican War, having recruited and trained a company of sappers. During his two tours of duty as a Professor of Practical Military Engineering at West Point, Cullum brought his combat and garrison experience into the classroom. Cullum had the opportunity to contribute to the operations of the Union Army while serving as Chief of Staff for the Army commander, **Henry Halleck (USMA 1839)**. Cullum's duties involved the communication between Halleck and his field commanders and the government leadership. After the war, Cullum returned to West Point as Superintendent for two years. His primary effort was to resurrect the standards of the Academy after the war and bring stability to the school. For his last eight years of Army service, Cullum returned to construction engineering. Throughout his career, Cullum maintained an extremely scholarly approach to engineering. He authored several books and papers on various engineering topics. He was considered a military scholar and staunch defender of West Point and its role in the Army. In addition to his technical work, Cullum compiled a biographic register of West Point graduates and published volumes in 1850,

1868, and 1891. He also actively served in the American Geographic Society and left part of his large estate to build a building for the Society, which was established in 1851. His

Memorials inside Cullum Hall (Howitzer)

legacy supported many explorations and science projects around the world and endowed the Cullum Geographic Medal for outstanding geographical contributions. Among the winners of the award are Robert Peary in 1896 and **George Goethals (USMA 1880)** in 1917. The rest of Cullum's estate went to construction (of Memorial Hall or Cullum Hall), the procurement of art, and the publication needs at the Academy. The professional scientist Cullum left a legacy in both deeds and results.

USMA 1833 | **Francis Henney Smith** | **Mathematician**

18 October 1812 (Norfolk, VA) – 21 March 1890 (Lexington, VA)
Graduate # 711 (5th out of 43), (educator, geographer), listed in *DAB, ANB, NCAB, AR* (1890)

Military Service:
1833-1834: Garrison duty in CT and MD
1861-1865: Advisory and organizer for VA and Southern activities during Civil War (Major General)

Professional Service:
1834-1835: Assistant Professor of Geography, History and Ethics, USMA
1836-1839: Professor of Mathematics, Hampden Sidney College, VA
1839-1861: Superintendent and Professor of Mathematics, Virginia Military Institute
1865-1890: Superintendent, Virginia Military Institute

F. H. SMITH was commissioned in artillery upon his graduation from West Point. After a year in garrison duty, he taught at the Academy for a year before resigning from the Army. In 1836, he became Professor of Mathematics at Hampden-Sidney College, VA. Three years later, with the support of famous engineer and former professor at West Point, Claudius Crozet (see **Honorable Mentions**), Smith was appointed the first Superintendent and the Professor of Mathematics at Virginia Military Institute (VMI). The Institute had a meager beginning – only one other professor and 28 cadets. However, under Smith's capable and effective leadership for the next 40 years, VMI was destined to grow and prosper. Smith imported the science- and mathematics-based curriculum and the strict military discipline of West Point. During the 1850's, VMI expanded greatly. In 1858, Smith went to Europe to study scientific and military schools. He published his findings and science was emphasized even more in the succeeding years. Smith was a popular leader and successful professor. However, the Civil War caused tremendous interruption in the school's progress. All the VMI cadets went into service, and Smith was forced to close the Institute. Smith tried to reopen in 1862, but found it impossible to attract students. In 1864, VMI's buildings were burned by Union forces. By 1865, VMI reopened and Smith began to rebuild his belovedIinstitute. By 1870, the school was restored and back in full operation. In 1879, Smith returned to West Point for the annual reunion along with other Confederate graduates, their first time included in the reunion after the war. Smith stepped down as Superintendent in 1881, some 42 years after he started VMI, having produced a successful school of mathematics, science, engineering in a military setting. As a capable mathematics educator, Smith translated and published a treatise by French mathematician Biot on analytic geometry in 1840. He also wrote other books and papers on technical, educational, and historical subjects.

USMA 1833   **Benjamin Alvord**   **Mathematician**

18 August 1813 (Rutland, VT) – 16 October 1884 (Washington, DC)
Graduate # 728 (22nd out of 43), (author), listed in *DAB, NCAB*

Military Service:
1833-1835: Garrison duty in LA
1835-1837: Combat duty in Seminole War, FL
1839-1841: Frontier duty in Indian Territory
1841-1842: Combat duty in Seminole War, FL
1842-1845: Frontier duty in MO
1845-1847: Combat duty in Mexican War
1848-1862: Frontier duty in MI, CA, and OR
1862-1865: Command of Department of Oregon during Civil War (Brigadier General)

Professional Service:
1837-1839: Assistant Professor of Mathematics and Assistant Professor of Natural and Experimental Philosophy, USMA
1833-1867: Author of numerous technical works, papers, and memoirs

B. ALVORD was commissioned in the infantry upon his graduation from West Point, and he served for over 40 years in field duty assignments. At the Academy, he was considered a brilliant mathematician. Four years after his graduation, he had the opportunity to teach mathematics and science at the Academy for two years. Alvord spent two tours of intense combat duty in the Seminole War in FL. After frontier duty in the Indian Territories, he served in the Mexican War. Alvord was sent back to the frontier, where, with his vast experience, he was considered an expert Indian fighter. During the Civil War, he was given

the mission of keeping peace in Oregon between the Indians and whites. After the war, he continued his military service, finally taking on more administrative duties in the northeastern cities. Despite his many frontier and combat assignments, Alvord was highly studious and scholarly. He somehow found time and opportunity to continue his interest and work in mathematics and science, writing several highly technical manuscripts while living on the frontier – his geometry book was published by the Smithsonian in 1856. He had a paper accepted for publication by the Smithsonian Institute, but the paper was lost in a fire in the Institute's building. He was able to recreate the paper, and it was later published in the *American Journal of Mathematics*. His technical results were published in distinguished scientific journals: *Smithsonian Contributions to Knowledge, Bulletin of the American Geographic Society, The Mathematical Monthly,* and *Proceedings of the American Association for the Advancement of Science.* He was also a historical and social scholar and wrote important studies on American Indians. Alvord's work was notable both in quality of the results and the conditions under which they were written. Alvord's career was amazing in its diversity – 40 years of rugged military field duty while producing many brilliant, highly technical, mathematical and scientific publications.

USMA 1834 — Richard Somers Smith — Scientist

30 October 1813 (Philadelphia, PA) – 23 January 1877 (Annapolis, MD)
Graduate # 779 (30th out of 36), (mathematician, draftsman, engineer, topographer), listed in *DAB, NCAB, AR* (1877)

Military Service:
1834-1836: Tour of military service
1840-1856: Tour of military service
1861-1863: Administrative and combat duties in Civil War (Chancellorsville)

Professional Service:
1834-1836: Topographic engineering duty
1836-1840: Topographic engineer for railroads and canal construction
1840-1855: Assistant Professor of Drawing, USMA
1856-1859: Professor of Mathematics, Engineering, and Drawing, Brooklyn Collegiate
and Polytechnic Institute, NY
1859-1861: Director, Cooper Union, NY
1863-1867: President, Girard College, PA

1868-1870:   Professor of Engineering, Polytechnic College of Pennsylvania
1870-1873:   Professor of Mathematics, U.S. Naval Academy, MD
1873-1877:   Professor of Drawing, U.S. Naval Academy, MD

R. S. Smith had three separate tours of duty in the Army. Serving his first two years of Army duty as a topographic engineer after his graduation from West Point, he resigned from the Army to take up engineering projects in civilian life. He worked on railroad and canal construction projects in PA, SC, KY, and OH. Smith then returned to active Army service as a drawing teacher at West Point while performing additional duties as quartermaster and treasurer of the Academy. He resigned for a second time in 1856 to become the Professor of Mathematics, Engineering, and Drawing at Brooklyn Collegiate and Polytechnic Institute (now Polytechnic University). He spent two years as a drawing teacher and director of Cooper Union, NY. At the outbreak of the Civil War, Smith re-joined the Army of the Potomac and engaged in the battle of Chancellorsville. Shortly thereafter, Smith resigned and accepted the presidency of Girard College, PA. His tenure was stormy, as his strict discipline caused considerable faculty and student resistance. He was removed from his position in 1867. Smith became the Professor of Engineering at Polytechnic College of Pennsylvania for two years, before moving to Annapolis, MD, to teach at the U.S. Naval Academy. At Annapolis, he was Professor of Mathematics for three years and four years as Professor of Drawing. Smith was a dedicated scholar, with a special talent in art that provided him the opportunity to teach drawing for both engineering and artistic applications. He authored two practical textbooks, *Manual of Topographic Drawing* in 1853 and *Manual of Linear Perspective* in 1857.

USMA 1835   **Henry Lane Kendrick**   **Scientist**

20 January 1811 (Lebanon, NH) – 24 May 1891 (New York, NY)
Graduate # 801 (16th out of 56), (chemist), listed in *AR* (1891)

Military Service:
1847-1848:   Combat duty in Mexican War (Vera Cruz, Cerro Gordo)
1848-1852:   Frontier duty and combat duty against Navajo and Mojave Indians
1852-1857:   Commander of Ft. Defiance, NM

Professional Service:
1835-1847:   Assistant Professor of Chemistry, Mineralogy, and Geology, USMA
1848:   Ordnance and engineering duty in New York Harbor
1857-1880:   Professor of Chemistry, Mineralogy, and Geology, USMA

H. L. Kendrick graduated from West Point and stayed there for twelve years to teach chemistry, mineralogy, and geology. Serving under department head and famous geologist **Jacob Bailey (USMA 1832),** Kendrick was a faculty colleague of **William Mather (USMA**

1825) and **George Rains (USMA 1842)**. Kendrick spent his next ten years in frontier and combat duty. He fought in the Mexican War and Indian Wars and had the opportunity to command Ft. Defiance, NM, after the war. When his former department head Bailey died, Kendrick was called back to West Point to replace him. For 23 years, he chaired the Department and served as Professor of Chemistry, Mineralogy, and Geology. During his long tenure after the Civil War, Kendrick served on the Academic Board as it maintained its science emphasis with civil engineering applications. His department's program consisted of chemistry and electricity for the second class (juniors) and geology and mineralogy for the first class (seniors). Among his many accolades were honorary degrees awarded by Dartmouth College, University of Missouri, and University of Rochester.

USMA 1835 | Herman Haupt | Engineer

26 March 1817 (Philadelphia, PA) – 14 December 1905 (Jersey City, NJ)
Graduate # 816 (31st out of 56), (mathematician), listed in *DAB, NCAB, AR* (1906)

Military Service:
1862-1863: Chief of construction, U.S. military railroads during Civil War

Professional Service:
1835-1840: Construction engineer and surveyor for railroad companies
1840-1845: Civil engineer for bridge construction
1845-1847: Professor of Mathematics, Pennsylvania College at Gettysburg
1847-1855: Construction engineer for railroad companies
1855-1862 and 1864-1867: Construction engineer for railroad tunnels
1867: Visit to Europe to investigate mining and tunneling technologies
1871: Elected to the American Philosophical Society
1876-1877: Design engineer for oil pipeline

H. HAUPT was just 18 years old when he graduated from USMA in 1835. He spent only three months in the Army before he resigned his commission to become a surveyor and engineer for a railroad company. After a few years of railroad construction, he concentrated his efforts on bridge construction. In 1842, he published the controversial pamphlet, "Hints on Bridge Construction," where he advocated using completely new techniques. He taught engineering classes part-time at Pennsylvania College in Gettysburg before becoming the Professor of Mathematics for two years. During that time, he wrote his most important book entitled *General Theory of Bridge Construction*. In 1847, he returned to railroad construction. He started an investigation of tunnel construction, and in 1855, began work on a tunnel in MA that resulted in many financial and legal problems. However, it was a tremendous success in the area of technological development. While working on the tunnel, Haupt invented an advanced pneumatic drill and other tunneling and mining equipment. Eventually his case against the state of MA for payment for his tunneling work went to the Supreme Court, where a settlement was finally made. During the Civil War, Haupt, as the country's premier railroad construction engineer, was appointed chief of construction and transportation on military railroads. He served less than two years in this position because he could not accept the restrictions of his commission. Haupt returned to railroad construction after his war service. In 1867, he designed a pipeline to carry crude oil and oversaw its construction. Starting in 1880, Haupt managed a railroad business, along with other businesses in compressed air equipment and food production. Haupt had a superb reputation as a creative, successful engineer. Writing extensively about his work on bridge construction and tunneling, Haupt was a member of the American Philosophical Society and a major contributor to American's technical innovations.

| USMA 1836 | **Joseph Reid Anderson** | Technologist |

6 February 1813 (Walnut Hill, VA) – 7 September 1892 (Isle of Shoals, NH)
Graduate # 845 (4th out of 49), (ordnance, engineer), listed in *DAB, ANB, NCAB, AR* (1893)

Military Service:
1836-1837:   Engineering duty at Ft. Pulaski, GA
1861-1865:   Support duty for Confederate Army during the Civil War

Professional Service:
1837-1841:   Engineer building highway between Staunton and Winchester, VA
1841-1861:   Technologist for the production of iron and the manufacturer of locomotives and cannon, Tredegar Iron Works, VA

J. R. ANDERSON spent one year in the Army after his graduation from USMA in 1836. He turned his engineering talents to service of his native state of VA by supervising the construction of a highway across the state. In 1841, he found interests in other fields – the production of iron and the manufacture of heavy equipment. Taking over Tredegar Iron Works, he developed this facility into the leading iron manufacturing plant in America. He built over 40 locomotives and 1200 cannons for the United States government. His plant also built navy boats, iron-clad hulls, general machinery, boilers, cables, artillery shells, and small arms. At the outbreak of the Civil War, his iron works was considered such a critical resource for the Confederate States that the decision to locate the capitol at Richmond was influenced by the need to protect the Tredegar Iron Works. Anderson made agreements with the Armies of the southern states and the Confederacy to supply cannons and ammunition. He briefly entered the Confederate Army with the understanding that he would still supervise the operation of the Iron Works. The Tredegar Iron Works was also known as J. R. Anderson and Company. Anderson used many slaves as workers, and he became so anti-Union that he refused to accept the technologies developed in the North, such as the Rodman method of casting cannons. It was not until 1864 that he allowed his Iron Works to use this cannon production technique, but it was too late to help the Confederacy. Between 1861 and 1865, the Tredegar plant produced over 1000 cannons, all the armor plating for Confederate ships, and many thousands of miles of rail for Southern railroads. After the war, Anderson was able to put Tredegar back in business with contracts to repair damaged military ordnance and civilian work. Tredegar eventually slipped in its business capacity and technological development as steel overtook iron as the primary building material. Anderson was no longer the technological leader and successful businessman that he once was; but during his peak, he was America's premier industrial technologist.

Reference: Dew, Charles, *Ironmaker to the Confederacy: Joseph R. Anderson and the Tredegar Iron Works*, Yale University Press, New Haven, CT, 1966.

USMA 1836 | **Montgomery Cunningham Meigs** | **Engineer**

3 May 1816 (Augusta, GA) – 2 January 1892 (Washington, DC)
Graduate # 846 (5th out of 49), listed in *DAB, ANB, NCAB, AR* (1892)

Military Service:
1861-1865: Duties as Quartermaster General of the Union Army during Civil War
1865-1882: Duties as Quartermaster General of Army

Professional Service:
1838-1841: Construction engineer on Fort Delaware, Fort Wayne in Detroit, and Fort Montgomery in NY
1853-1861: Construction engineer on Washington Aqueduct
1853-1859: Construction engineer on Capitol Building in Washington, DC
1854: Elected to the American Philosophical Society
1860-1861: Construction engineer, Fort Jefferson, FL
1863: Elected to the National Academy of Sciences

M. C. MEIGS attended the University of Pennsylvania in Philadelphia for one year before entering USMA. He was commissioned in the artillery, but subsequently entered the Corps of Engineers. Meigs worked as a construction engineer for sixteen years building fortifications, coastal defenses, various buildings in Washington, DC, and the Washington Aqueduct. Distinguishing himself in these duties, he earned *Celebrity* status as an engineer. His design and construction of the aqueduct across the Cabin John Branch created the world's largest masonry arch. Following that service, he took on special duties to build new wings and domes for the United States Capitol Building in 1853 to 1859. At the outbreak of the Civil War, military engineer Meigs became Army logistician Meigs, as he was made the

Quartermaster General of the Union Army. Meigs used his engineering skills to transform the logistics operations of the Army from limited capabilities using old technology into a smoothly functioning system using the most advanced modern transportation technologies. Meigs' position gave him responsibilities for overhauling railroads, ships, and wagon transportation systems. Seeing only limited combat duty in the field, most of his contributions were from staff offices in Washington, DC. Through his dedication and intellect, he persevered and contributed in one of the most difficult and challenging duties in the Army. After the war, Meigs continued as the Quartermaster for the Army. As an ardent engineer, he was given additional duties to supervise the construction of the new War Department building and the new museum building of the Smithsonian Institute. Meigs retired in 1882 but continued with his construction duties. As an original corporator of the National Academy of Sciences in 1863 and a member of the American Philosophical Society and Smithsonian Institute, Meigs was a brilliant man with immense skills as a scientist and engineer.

Reference: Weigley, Russell, *Quartermaster General of the Union Army, a Biography of M. C. Meigs*, Columbia University Press, New York, 1959.

| USMA 1836 | **Henry Hayes Lockwood** | **Mathematician** |

17 August 1814 (Kent City, DE) – 7 December 1899 (Washington, DC)
Graduate # 863 (22nd out of 49), (educator), listed in *NCAB, AR* (1900)

Military Service:
1836-1837: Combat duty in Seminole War, FL
1841-1876: Active service in the U.S. Navy
1861-1865: Army officer and Commander of expedition in VA, defenses in MD, and engagements in Civil War (Gettysburg, Cold Harbor, Richmond, Baltimore)

Professional Service:
1845-1861: Professor of Mathematics, U.S. Naval Academy, MD
1867-1870: Professor of Natural and Experimental Philosophy, USNA, MD
1870-1876: Professor at the Naval Observatory, Washington, DC

H. H. LOCKWOOD served in the Seminole War after his graduation in 1836. After a year of combat duty, he resigned from the Army to become a

farmer in Delaware. In 1841, he joined the Navy to serve as a Professor of Mathematics. However, his first duty was a naval engagement in Monterey, CA. In 1845, Lockwood was one of the first seven faculty at the new Navy School (later the U.S. Naval Academy). They taught mathematics and science to 50 midshipmen who entered the school. Serving as the new academy's Professor of Mathematics and Mechanics, Lockwood's West Point heritage was always suspect at the Navy School. He suggested that the Navy School adopt military drill; however, the midshipmen were aroused to new heights of anger at the recommendation. As sailors-in-training, they believed in the maxim: "A messmate before a shipmate, a shipmate before a stranger, a stranger before a dog, but a dog before a soldier." Lockwood was not too popular after this suggestion and was hanged in effigy from the school's flagstaff. Remaining at Annapolis despite his problems with the midshipmen, he served as the Professor of Mathematics and Gunnery for the next nine years. His next position was titled Professor of Mathematics and Artillery and Infantry Tactics. Lockwood authored a textbook in 1852 for his courses entitled *Exercises in Small Arms and Field Artillery Arranged for the Naval School*. During the Civil War, Lockwood joined the Delaware Volunteers and served as a Brigadier General. He led an expedition into VA, then commanded a war prison at Point Lookout. He commanded a brigade at Gettysburg and a division at Cold Harbor. Later, he led his troops against Early's Confederate attack on Washington. After the war, he returned to the Naval Academy as the Professor of Natural and Experimental Philosophy and ultimately finished his professional career working at the Naval Observatory. Lockwood's contributions to the establishment of a strong, mathematical- and science-based academic program at the Naval Academy were substantial. In many ways, he did for the Naval Academy what people like **Charles Davies (USMA 1815)** and **Edward Courtenay (USMA 1821)** did for West Point.

USMA 1837 │ **Henry Washington Benham** │ **Engineer**

8 April 1813 (Quebec, Canada) – 1 June 1884 (New York, NY)
Graduate # 891 (1st out of 50), listed in *DAB, NCAB, AR* (1884)

Military Service:
1847-1848: Combat duty in Mexican War (Buena Vista, wounded)
1861-1865: Combat and engineer duty in Civil War (Carrick's Ford, New Creek, Boston, Ft. Pulaski, Chancellorsville, Petersburg) (Major General)

Professional Service:
1837-1847: Engineer for fortifications in FL, MD, and PA and harbors in GA, FL, MD
1848-1853: Construction engineer for harbors in NY, MA, DC
1853-1856: Assistant in charge of U.S. Coast Survey, Washington, DC
1856-1861: Construction engineer for fortifications in MA, RI, NJ, NY
1865-1882: Construction duty in Boston, MA and New York Harbors

H. W. Benham studied at Yale College for one year before attending West Point. After his graduation in 1837, Benham joined the Corps of Engineers. He spent ten years engaged in engineering duties building fortifications and improving harbors in several locations along the East Coast. His work was of such high quality that he built a reputation as a fine engineer. After serving in combat and being wounded in the Battle of Buena Vista in the Mexican War, Benham spent five years in construction engineering, building harbor facilities and lighthouses. From 1853 to 1856, he had the opportunity for special duty with the U.S. Coast Survey as **Alexander Bache's (USMA 1825)** assistant. During his tour in the Washington, DC office of the Survey, Benham went on a successful mission to Europe to hire engravers for the Survey. (See the essay on the Coast Survey.) From 1856 to 1861, he

supervised important projects in Boston, MA and Sandy Hook, NJ. He also supervised the construction of the Potomac Aqueduct in Washington, DC. During the Civil War, Benham quickly adjusted to the duties of a troop combat commander. He was bold and aggressive, but controversial in his combat leadership – accused by his superiors of disregarding orders and attacking without authorization. Because of this controversy, he was relieved of his combat duties and sent back to engineering defenses in New England. After an investigation, he was exonerated and sent back into combat leadership. Commanding an engineer brigade, he built several important pontoon bridges for movement of the Army of the Potomac. After the war, Benham returned to Boston and New York harbors, where he supervised construction projects until retiring in 1882. Benham was a brilliant, innovative, and versatile engineer, who as a project supervisor was able to meet or exceed the project's design specifications.

USMA 1837   **Alexander Brydie Dyer**   **Technologist**

10 January 1815 (Richmond, VA) – 20 May 1874 (Washington, DC)
Graduate # 896 (6th out of 50), (ordnance), listed in *NCAB, AR* (1874)

Military Service:
1837:   Garrison duty at Ft Monroe, VA
1837-1838: Combat duty in Seminole War, FL
1846-1848: Combat duty in Mexican War (Santa Cruz, Taos)
1861-1863: Commander of Springfield Armory, MA during Civil War (Major General)
1863-1874: Chief of Ordnance, U.S. Army, Washington, DC

Professional Service:
1838-1841: Ordnance duty in TN and at Liberty Depot, MO
1841-1846: Ordnance duty at Watervliet Arsenal, NY; St. Louis Arsenal, MO; and Baton Rouge
            Arsenal, LA

1848-1861: Ordnance duty at St Louis Arsenal, MO; North Carolina Arsenal, Little Rock Arsenal, AR; and Ft. Monroe Arsenal, VA

A. B. Dyer entered the artillery branch upon his graduation from West Point in 1837. After assignments at Ft. Monroe, VA and combat duty in the Seminole War, he transferred to the Ordnance Corps as it expanded in 1838. He served at several small arsenals and then at the Army's largest ordnance facility at Watervliet, NY until the outbreak of the Mexican War. Once again in combat, he fought in several battles and was wounded in action. Dyer spent the next 13 years performing various ordnance design and production duties. He was a fine technologist and invented an effective projectile for the new models of cannon being produced. He was offered a considerable sum of money for its royalties, but refused the offers, preferring to give his new invention to his country. At the outbreak of the Civil War, he did not hesitate to show his loyalty to his country despite his southern upbringing. Dyer transferred to the important duty of commanding the Springfield Armory in MA. This facility built the rifles and small arms for the Union Army. He was a master of retooling his factory for large-scale production. His armory began to produce the amazing result of over 1,000 rifles per day. In 1863, he was promoted to Chief of Ordnance for the Army, replacing **James Ripley (USMA 1814)**, who was 69 years old. Dyer had been offered this position two years earlier, but had declined in respect of Ripley's stature as the leader of Ordnance. His administration of the Ordnance Corps was superb, and his contributions had tremendous impact on the success of the Union combat forces. Both a capable scientist and effective administrator, Dyer was a faithful and dedicated soldier. His invention of the "Dye-Artillery" shell was a major advance in munitions technology. Continuing duty as the Chief of Ordnance until his death, Dyer, along with other leaders of the branch, gave the Ordnance Corps a strong foundation in science to develop the new technologies of modern weapons and transportation systems.

USMA 1837   **Eliakim Parker Scammon**   **Mathematician**

27 December 1816 (Whitefield, ME) – 7 December 1894 (New York, NY)
Graduate # 899 (9th out of 50), (topographic engineer, geographer), listed in *NCAB, AR* (1895)

Military Service:
1838-1840: Combat and topographic engineer in Seminole War, FL
1847:   Combat duty in Mexican War (Vera Cruz)
1861-1865: Combat duty in Civil War (Bull Run, Antietam) (Prisoner of War – 1864)

Professional Service:
1837-1838: Assistant Professor of Mathematics, USMA
1840-1841: Topographic mapping duties (area west of Mississippi River)
1841-1846: Professor of Geography, USMA
1846:   Topographic engineer of harbor in Maine
1847-1855: Topographic engineer, surveying the Great Lakes area
1858-1859: Professor of Mathematics, Mt. St. Mary's College, OH
1860-1861: President and Professor of Mathematics, Polytechnic College of the Catholic Institute, OH
1872-1875: Civil engineer
1875-1885: Professor of Mathematics, Seton Hall College, NJ

Having graduated from West Point in 1837, **E. P. SCAMMON** remained at the Academy for one year as an Assistant Professor of Mathematics. Among his students were many future Civil War Generals, such as Grant, Rosecrans, and Newton. His first experiences as a topographic engineer were mapping and charting duties on the frontier. He then returned to West Point to teach geography for six years. Seeing active combat service in the Seminole War in FL, in 1847 he became one of General Winfield Scott's aides during the Mexican War. From 1847 to 1854, he was attached to the Topographical Corps, surveying harbors and shorelines along the Great Lakes. In 1856 he resigned from the Army to teach mathematics at Mount Saint Mary's College, OH and at the Polytechnic College of the Catholic Institute, Cincinnati, OH. Scammon also served as President of the Polytechnic College for one year. Volunteering for service in the Civil War, he received the rank of Brigadier General in the volunteers. He was a prisoner of war for part of the war, but survived the ordeal. The President appointed him U.S. Consul to Prince Edward Island from 1866 to 1871, and, for a brief period, he returned to civil engineering construction work. From 1875 until 1885, Scammon performed teaching duties as Professor of Mathematics at Seton Hall College, NJ. This was the perfect position for Scammon, who was both a versatile scientist and a dedicated educator.

USMA 1838   **Pierre Gustave Toutant Beauregard**   **Engineer**

28 May 1818 (St. Bernard, LA) – 20 February 1893 (New Orleans, LA)
Graduate # 942 (2nd out of 45), listed in *DAB, ANB, NCAB*

Military Service:
1846-1848: Combat engineer in Mexican War

1861-1865: Combat commander for Confederate Army in Civil War (Fort Sumter, Manassas, Cornith, Shiloh, Charleston, Bermuda Hundred) (General)

Professional Service:
1838-1846: Construction engineer on fortifications in FL and LA
1848-1861: Construction engineer in Louisiana
1888-1890: Commissioner of public works in New Orleans

P. G. T. BEAUREGARD had private schooling in New Orleans and New York City before entering West Point. He was a gifted and successful student and was commissioned as an engineer. His first engineering duties were to construct fortifications in FL and LA. During

the Mexican War, Beauregard was distinguished as a combat engineer and leader in several battles and received promotion and accolades. After his combat duties, Beauregard returned to LA to resume his construction engineering duties. He so impressed the Army leaders that he was made Superintendent at West Point in 1861. However, just two days later with the outbreak of the Civil War, he was replaced. Beauregard resigned his commission and was soon appointed a General in the Confederate Army. Beauregard did not waste any time in his new position as he started the hostilities of the Civil War by ordering the bombardment of Fort Sumter. He was gracious in accepting the Union forces surrender. Beauregard continued his combat leadership as a superb tactician, directing troop positions and leading combat forces in many engagements. At Manasses, he had a horse shot out from under him, but kept leading his forces to a tactical victory. Beauregard was an aggressive commander, who came under political fire in his disagreements with Jefferson Davis (USMA 1828). He was also a scholar and somehow found time to write a book on the art of war while performing his combayt duties. After the war, Beauregard returned to New Orleans as a railroad company president, manager of the state lottery company, and commissioner of public works for the city. Beauregard was a controversial figure who displayed tremendous potential in several technical areas. Despite his political or personal difficulties, he made significant contributions over course of his professional life.

Reference:
Williams, Thomas, *P. G. T. Beauregard: Napoleon in Gray*, Louisiana State University Press, Baton Rouge, 1995.

USMA 1839 | Isaac Ingalls Stevens | Engineer

25 March 1818 (North Andover, MA) – 1 September 1862 (Chantilly, VA)
Graduate # 986 (1ˢᵗ out of 31), listed in *NCAB*

Military Service:
1847-1848:   Combat duty in Mexican War (wounded)
1861-1862:   Combat duty in Civil War (Department of the South, Newport News, Manassas, Chantilly)
                   (killed in action)

Professional Service:
1839-1846:   Construction engineering at Ft. Adams, MA and various harbors in New England
1848:   Construction engineering at harbors in GA
1849-1853:   Assistant Superintendent of Coast Survey, Washington, DC

I. I. STEVENS attended Phillips Academy in MA before attending West Point. Upon graduation and commissioning in 1839, he helped with the construction of Ft. Adams, RI; the defenses in New Bedford Harbor, MA; facilities in Portsmouth Harbor, NH; and navigation improvements on Penobscot River, ME. In 1847, he was called to combat duty in the Mexican War, where he was wounded in action. After the war, Stevens was selected to be **Alexander Bache's (USMA 1825)** assistant in the Coast Survey. For four years, he managed significant research projects and the production of numerous maps and charts. Stevens wrote a technical analysis of the Mexican War and participated in several important topographic projects. Interested in political activities and government leadership, Stevens was appointed governor of the Washington Territory in 1853. He remained active as a scientist by personally working on surveys and railroad designs to develop the western frontier. His report on the territory was filled with excellent engineering assessments and scientific information. Stevens lobbied the federal government for support for roads, mail service, and lighthouses in his vast frontier territory. Having negotiated numerous Indian treaties, he always added provisions to the treaties for Indians to keep hunting and fishing rights on public lands. Stevens fought with the Union Army in the Civil War and was deployed in combat service in VA and SC. He was killed in action in a battle in VA. Stevens was a fine engineer, who had many other interests. His leadership and technical work at the Coast Survey was important for the development of that organization. He was also a leader of the expansionist movement for the U. S., both to take control of the continent and to develop the modern technologies for the construction of infrastructure for the western territories.

Reference:
Richards, Kent, *Isaac I. Stevens, Young Man in a Hurry*. Brigham Young University Press, Provo, UT, 1979.

USMA 1839   ║ **Henry Wager Halleck** ║   **Engineer**

16 January 1815 (Westerville, NY) – 9 January 1872 (Louisville, KY)
Graduate # 988 (3rd out of 31), listed in *DAB, ANB, NCAB, AR* (1872)

Military Service:

1846-1854: Various duties in combat and garrison in CA
1861-1862: Combat commander in Civil War
           (Department of Missouri, Battle of Corinth)
1862-1864: General-in-Chief, Union Forces, Washington, DC
1864-1865: Chief-of-Staff, Union Army
1865-1869: Commander, Division of the Pacific
1869-1872: Commander, Division of the South

Professional Service:

1838-1839: Assistant Professor of Chemistry, USMA, as a senior-year
           cadet
1839-1844: Construction engineer for fortifications in New York Harbor
1844-1845: Visit to Europe to investigate fortifications
1846:   Delivered lecture series at Lowell Institute, Boston, on military
           science

H. HALLECK attended Union College before entering West Point in 1835. Halleck took his final examination at Union while a cadet at the Academy and was awarded an A.B. degree from Union in 1837. Halleck taught chemistry to underclass cadets while still a cadet and was a favorite student of the Professor of Engineering, **Dennis Mahan (USMA 1824)**. After graduation from West Point, he worked as a construction engineer on fortifications in New York Harbor. Halleck's next assignment, an investigative trip to Europe to visit fortifications, led to a publication by Congress of his work entitled "Report on the Means of National Defense." Halleck was also invited to give lectures on military science by the Lowell Institute of Boston. These twelve highly-technical presentations were captured in Halleck's book *Elements of Military Art and Science* (1846). This volume was popular in the military and was used to help civilian volunteers understand the military profession during the Civil War. In 1843, Halleck turned down the professorship at the Lawrence Scientific School at Harvard, desiring to stay in military service and building on his reputation as an authority on military science. From the beginning of the Mexican War in 1846 until Halleck's resignation from the Army in 1854, he was stationed in CA. Halleck was involved in numerous combat, public works, and political affairs in the West. As an engineer, he designed and built fortifications and lighthouses. Once out of the Army, Halleck turned to various business pursuits as a lawyer and railroad executive. Writing several publications on mining law and international law, he also helped to write the State's constitution. At the outbreak of the Civil War, Halleck was returned to the Regular Army and was made a Major General in charge of the Department of Missouri. With bold leadership from subordinate Ulysses S. Grant (USMA 1843), Halleck managed several successful battles and took to the field himself in the Battle of Corinth. In 1862, President Lincoln appointed Halleck General-in-Chief of all the Union Armies. Halleck had mixed success as the Union's top general. He was primarily a scholar, who preached doctrine and theory, but never was able to motivate his generals into decisive action. His nicknames "Old Brains" and "Cold Calculating Owl" made him seem aloof and too mathematical in his dealings with politicians and generals. No matter what his shortcomings were, Halleck brought professionalism and organization to the Union Army. He showed tremendous stamina and dedication in his service. In 1864 when he was replaced by Grant and made the Chief of Staff, the Union Army had found the proper assignment for this brilliant administrator. After the war, he stayed in the Army serving in the West and the South. Unfortunately, Halleck was more of a technical leader and scientist, who was placed in difficult positions of military and political leadership. Halleck had great potential as an academic and scientist, but never was able to take full advantage of the opportunities afforded him in those areas.

References:

Ambrose, Stephen E., *Halleck: Lincoln's Chief of Staff*, Louisiana State University Press, Baton Rouge 1962.

Anders, Curt. *Henry Halleck's War: A Fresh Look at Lincoln's Controversial General-in-Chief*, Guild Press of Indiana, Inc., Carmel, 1999.

USMA 1841   ## Zealous Bates Tower   **Engineer**

12 January 1819 (Cohasset, MA) – 20 March 1900 (Cohasset, MA)
Graduate # 1059 (1st out of 52), listed in *DAB, NCAB, AR* (1900)

Military Service:

1841-1842:	Assistant to the Army Board of Engineers
1846-1848:	Combat duty in Mexican War (Vera Cruz, Cerro Gordo, Contreras, Mexico City, Chapultepec -- wounded)
1861-1865:	Combat duty in Civil War (Santa Rosa, Cedar Mountain, Manassas -- wounded, Nashville) (Major General)

Professional Service:

1842-1843:	Assistant Professor of Engineering, USMA
1843-1846:	Construction engineer for fortifications in VA
1848-1853:	Construction engineer for harbors in New England
1853-1858:	Construction engineer for fortifications in CA
1860-1861:	Special duty designing iron platforms for seacoast guns
1864:	Superintendent, USMA
1866-1867:	Construction engineer in New England
1867-1883:	Construction engineer for river and harbor improvements in LA, NC, AL, MI, TX, NJ, NY

Z. B. TOWER was commissioned in the Corps of Engineers after finishing at the top of his West Point class of 1841. He taught engineering at the Academy for a year and then began fortification construction duties at Hampton Roads, VA. During the Mexican War, Tower led combat assaults on enemy fortifications and was wounded in the assault at Chapultepec. After the war, he spent five years on engineering projects in New England. Tower moved out West to continue his engineering service on the Pacific Coast for the next five years. At the outbreak of the Civil War, Tower found himself in FL where he led Union troops in the defense of Fort Pickens. After his success in FL, he transferred to the Virginia campaign as a brigade commander at the battles of Cedar Mountain and Manassas. Severely wounded at Manassas, he was no longer able to pursue combat field duty for the rest of the war. After two years of recuperation, he became the Superintendent at West Point for a few months in 1864. Tower was needed in the field by the Union Army to design the defenses of Nashville. His combat engineering expertise and dedicated service was timely and significant in that conflict. After the war, Tower returned to important construction engineering projects, especially for harbor facilities. As a senior officer in the Corps of Engineers, he was on many commissions and boards providing designs and guidance to projects involving river navigation, harbor facilities, canals, aqueducts, and fortifications. Tower was an accomplished engineer with excellent leadership and problem solving skills.

USMA 1841 | **Horatio Gouverneur Wright** | **Engineer**

6 March 1820 (Clinton, CT) – 2 July 1899 (Washington, DC)
Graduate # 1060 (2nd out of 52), listed in *DAB, NCAB, AR* (1900)

Military Service:
1841-1842: Assistant to the Army Board of Engineers
1844-1846: Assistant to the Army Board of Engineers
1856-1861: Assistant to the Chief Army Engineer, Washington, DC
1861-1865: Combat duty in Civil War (Manassas, Hilton Head, Gettysburg, Rappahannock Station, Wilderness, Spottsylvania, Cold Harbor, Petersburg, defense of the Capitol, Cedar Creek -- wounded, Sailor's Creek) (Major General)
1866-1867: Commander of Department of Texas
1879-1884: Chief of Army Engineers, Washington, DC

Professional Service:
1842-1844: Assistant Professor of Engineering, USMA
1846-1856: Construction engineer in FL on various projects
1856-1867: Special duty conducting experiments on the use of iron in defenses
1867-1879: Construction engineer for harbors, rivers, fortifications along East Coast, Gulf of Mexico, and Mississippi River

---

H. G. WRIGHT graduated in the Military Academy class of 1841 and was commissioned in the Corps of Engineers. As a young engineer, he superintended the construction of Fort

Jefferson, FL for nearly ten years. He also worked on canals and lighthouses in FL. While assistant to the Chief Engineer of the Army, he was a member of ordnance boards to study iron carriages for seacoast guns and the adaptability of the 15-inch gun for heavy ordnance. He wrote a "Report on Fabrication of Iron for Defenses," with John Barnard (USMA 1833) and Peter Michie (USMA 1863). As a successful division engineer at the first Battle of Bull Run in the Civil War, Wright advanced to command an important combat corps, which was deployed to save Washington, DC, from capture in 1864. Through his bold actions, his unit also spearheaded the assault on Petersburg and the pursuit of Lee to Appomattox in 1865. After the war, Wright commanded the Department of Texas and served as a member of the Board of Engineers for Fortifications. Wright chaired many river and harbor planning boards until he was appointed Chief of Army Engineers in 1879. During the five years that Wright was Chief of Engineers, Corps of Engineer officers began to build a reservoir system at the headwaters of the Mississippi River and initiated the first substantial controls on the lower Mississippi. Wright retired from the Army in 1884. Among his many accolades is an honorary degree from Norwich University, VT.

| **USMA 1841** | **Josiah Gorgas** | **Technologist** |

1 July 1818 (Running Pumps, PA) – 15 May 1883 (Tuscaloosa, AL)
Graduate # 1064 (6th out of 56), (ordnance, engineer), listed in *DAB, ANB, NCAB, AR* (1883)

Military Service:
1846-1848: Combat duty in Mexican War (Veracruz)
1860-1861: Commander of Franklin Arsenal, Philadelphia, PA
1861-1865: Chief of Ordnance, Confederate Army (Brigadier General)

Professional Service:
1841-1845: Ordnance duty at Watervliet Arsenal, NY
1845-1846: Visited Europe to study ordnance factories and new armaments
1848-1860: Ordnance duty at various arsenals in the South
1869-1872: Professor of Engineering at University of the South, TN
1872-1878: President of University of the South, TN
1878-1879: President, University of Alabama
1879-1883: Librarian, University of Alabama

J. GORGAS began his working career as a newspaper apprentice, but made the most of his opportunities by seeking an appointment to West Point. His first duties after graduation were in his branch of ordnance, where he quickly became an expert at the design and manufacture of arms and ammunition. After four years at Watervliet Arsenal, he went to Europe to study military ordnance facilities. Gorgas returned to the United States just in time to serve in the Mexican War, where he furthered his knowledge of weapons and saw first hand the importance of effective armaments. For the next twelve years, Gorgas was in charge of various arsenals and ordnance depots, mostly in the South. When the Civil War began, Gorgas reluctantly decided to resign from the Army and join the Confederacy. He was appointed the Confederacy's Chief of Ordnance by Jefferson Davis (USMA 1828) and became one of the most successful Confederate staff officers. Despite the tremendous needs for more armaments and ammunition and the scarce resources to produce these items, Gorgas met the challenges and accomplished his mission for the Confederate forces. His system of manufacturing, importing, and maintaining the small arms, cannons, bullets, projectiles, and other ordnance needs worked to perfection. Unlike, his Union counterparts **James Ripley (USMA 1814)** and **Alexander Dyer (USMA 1837)**, Gorgas began with little established infrastructure. He displayed a genius for improvising and became one of the Confederacy's most important military assets. After the war, Gorgas worked as an engineering professor at the University of the South and later served as President of this school. In 1878, he accepted the position as President of University of Alabama, but stepped down after one year because of his failing health. He was the university librarian for the last five years of his life.

Reference: Vandiver, Frank, *Ploughshares into Swords: Josiah Gorgas and the Confederate Ordnance*, University of Texas Press, Austin, 1952.

USMA 1841 ┌──────────────────────────────┐ **Scientist**
              │ **Thomas Jackson Rodman**   │
              └──────────────────────────────┘

30 July 1815 (Salem, IN) – 7 June 1871 (Rock Island, IL)
Graduate # 1065 (7th out of 52), (ordnance), listed in *DAB, NCAB, AR* (1871)

Military Service:
1848-1849: Ordnance duty in Mexican War (Camargo, Point Isabel)
1861-1865: Ordnance duty at Watertown Arsenal, MA during Civil War
          (Brigadier General)

Professional Service:
1841-1848: Ordnance duty at Allegheny Arsenal, PA
1849-1859: Ordnance duty at Allegheny Arsenal, PA
1859-1861: Ordnance duty at Watertown Arsenal, MA
1865-1871: Ordnance duty at Rock Island Arsenal, IL

T. J. Rodman was 22 years old when he became a cadet. After intense study, he graduated from West Point and was commissioned in the Ordnance Corps. His assignment to the Allegheny Arsenal in western PA was the perfect situation for supporting his experiments in casting cannon and improving gunpowder and projectiles. Rodman was a highly successful inventor and a talented scientist. He constantly sought a better understanding of metallurgy, iron casting, materials science, and gunpowder production. He used precise experimentation to inform his scholarly work and develop improved production methods. In the 1840s, he sought an understanding of internal strains, imperfections, and variations in densities and tensile strengths so he could design better casting procedures. As a result of this work, he was able to cast better and larger artillery weapons. Rodman had an opportunity to test cannons in the field during the Mexican War through his special duty to experiment with **George Bomford's (USMA 1805)** huge 12-inch Columbiad gun. After the war, Rodman perfected his manufacturing techniques to produce a denser, more reliable cannon; however, the Army did not immediately accept his design. Luckily, private manufacturers did and soon it was obvious that Rodman's guns were superior to all others. At the same time, he used careful chemical experiments to develop better gunpowder. Rodman discovered that the rate of combustion could be controlled by compressing gunpowder into larger grains of higher density. By 1859, the Army used his methods to forge new guns and produce better gunpowder. During the Civil War, he was in charge of Watertown Arsenal, producing hundreds of sophisticated and effective 12-inch, 15-inch, and 20-inch smooth bore cannons and 12-inch rifled guns. In 1861, he designed new instruments to measure internal weapon pressures, thereby, further advancing the science of weapon construction. After the war, he went to Rock Island Arsenal, IL where he build up the infrastructure of the plant in order to mass produce his Rodman guns. Rodman was a brilliant and successful scientist-soldier. His book, *Reports of Experiments on the Properties of Metals for Cannon, and Qualities of Cannon Powder*, was published in 1861. It contained details of his ground-breaking work and was a valuable reference for both ordnance officers and scientists.

USMA 1841 | Claudius Wistar Sears | Mathematician

8 November 1817 (Peru, MA) – 15 February 1891 (Oxford, MS)
Graduate # 1089 (31st out of 52), listed in *AR* (1891)

Military Service:
1841:   Garrison duty in NY
1841-1842: Combat duty in Seminole War
1861-1865: Combat duty in Civil War for Confederate Army (Vicksburg, Atlanta, Murfreesboro, Nashville - wounded and captured) (Brigadier General)

Professional Service:
1844-1845: Teacher of Mathematics, St. Thomas' Hall, MS
1847-1861: Professor of Mathematics and Civil Engineering, University of Louisiana
1865-1884: Professor of Mathematics and Civil Engineering, University of Mississippi

C. W. Sears was a cadet classmate of accomplished engineers and ordnance scientists, **Zealous Tower, Horatio Wright, Josiah Gorgas,** and **Thomas Rodman**. While Sears' overall ranking was in the bottom half of his class, he obtained a quality technical education at the Academy. After a year of combat service fighting in the Seminole War, Sears resigned

from the Army. He spent the next 17 years teaching mathematics mostly at the University of Louisiana. At the outbreak of the Civil War, Sears joined the Confederate Army. As a combatant in many of the important battles of the war, he was severely wounded and lost his leg at the Battle of Nashville. After the war, Sears became the Department Chair and Professor of Mathematics and Civil Engineering at the University of Mississippi. While the development of technical programs in the southern colleges was challenging, Sears continued to slowly build quality courses in mathematics and engineering. Beloved by his students, Sears became a respected and successful professor at the university. His contributions to his students and the university were significant and lasting.

USMA 1842   **Henry Lawrence Eustis**   **Engineer**

1 February 1819 (Boston, MA) – 11 January 1885 (Cambridge, MA)
Graduate # 1111 (1st out of 56), listed in *DAB, NCAB, BDAS, AR* (1885)

Military Service:
1842-1843:   Staff officer in Office of Chief of Army Engineers, Washington, DC
1862-1864:   Combat duty in Civil War (Williamsport, Fredericksburg, Gettysburg, the Wilderness, Spotsylvania, Cold Harbor) (Brigadier General)

Professional Service:
1843-1845:   Construction engineer for Ft. Warren, MA
1845-1847:   Construction engineer at Newport, RI
1847-1849:   Assistant Professor of Engineering, USMA
1849-1862:   Professor of Engineering, Lawrence Scientific School, Harvard College, MA
1871-1885:   Dean and Professor of Engineering, Lawrence Scientific School, Harvard College, MA
1880:   Fellow of the American Academy of Arts and Sciences

H. L. Eustis graduated from Harvard College before attending West Point. He finished first in his USMA class and entered the Corps of Engineers. Eustis followed his family's military service tradition as he served his first assignment as an assistant to the Chief of Army Engineers in Washington, DC. He returned to New England to supervise construction of Ft.

Warren, the seawall in Boston Harbor, and various fortifications in RI. From 1847 to 1849, he taught engineering at West Point serving under the preeminent engineering educator in America, **Dennis Mahan (USMA 1824)**. In 1849, Eustis had the opportunity to head his own engineering department at the Lawrence Scientific School of Harvard College. For twelve years, he built the program and advanced both engineering research and engineering education. Despite his failing health, Eustis volunteered for combat duty in the Civil War. As a brigade commander, he led troops in numerous battles. In 1864, he had to leave field service because of his failing health. Returning to Harvard as both the Dean and Professor of Engineering, Eustis became a fine researcher and a capable administrator. Leading Harvard to new heights as a research institution in science and engineering, Eustis personally published many technical papers and built a high-quality reputation for himself and his college. Eustis was both a man of deep thoughts and a man of action. A first-

class scholar and leader, Eustis was a pioneer for technical engineering scholarship at Harvard and built an educational model for other quality colleges in America. His scholarly achievements made the European academic community take notice of American engineers.

USMA 1842 | John Newton | Engineer

24 August 1823 (Norfolk, VA) – 1 May 1895 (New York, NY)
Graduate # 1112 (2nd out of 56), listed in *DAB, ANB, NCAB, AR* (1895)

Military Service:

1842-1843: Assistant to the Board of Engineers
1861-1866: Combat engineer in Civil War (defenses of Washington, Gaines' Mill, Antietam, Fredericksburg, Marye's Heights, Gettysburg, Pine Mountain, Atlanta) (Major General)
1884-1886: Chief of Army Engineers, Washington, DC

Professional Service:

1843-1846: Assistant Professor of Engineering, USMA
1846-1849: Construction engineer for fortifications in New England
1849-1852: Construction engineer for fortifications on Great Lakes
1852-1856: Civil engineer for navigation improvements on rivers and canals in ME, FL, and GA
1856: Special duty with Board to establish defenses on Gulf Coast
1858: Chief engineer for Utah expedition
1858-1861: Construction engineer for Sandy Hook, NJ
1866-1884: Construction engineer for fortifications in New York Harbor
1868-1885: Civil engineer removing obstruction from New York Harbor

1870-1875:   Civil engineer for canals and waterways in TX, SC, and along the Mississippi River

---

J. Newton was commissioned in the Corps of Engineers. His first assignment from 1842 to 1843 was as an assistant to the Army Board of Engineers. Newton returned to teach his specialty of engineering at the Military Academy for three years. He followed his academic work with field duty to construct fortifications along the Atlantic Coast and Great Lakes from 1846 to 1852. He was a member of a special Gulf Coast Defense Board in 1856 and Chief Engineer for the Utah Expedition in 1858. Though born in Virginia, he did not support the Confederate cause and fought for the Union during the Civil War. Newton helped construct Washington's defenses and then led a brigade at the Battle of Antietam. As a division commander, he stormed Marye's Heights at Fredericksburg and led his unit at the Battle of Gettysburg and the siege of Atlanta. He commanded the Florida engineering district from 1864 until 1866. After the war, Newton oversaw improvements to the waterways around New York City and to the Hudson River above Albany. In particular, Newton removed several large obstructions in the form of rocks and reefs in the East River and Hell Gate in New York Harbor. In a remarkable engineering feat, he used 50,000 pounds of explosives to blast away Pot Rock in 1876. In 1885, he used 200,000 pounds of dynamite to clear away Flood Rock. Earth tremors were recorded 180 miles from the blast site. He continued his duties of maintaining and improving New York Harbor defenses until he was appointed Chief of Army Engineers in 1884. Retiring from the Army in 1886, he served as Commissioner of Public Works for New York City from 1886 to 1888 and as President of the Panama Railroad Company from 1888 to 1895. Among his honors was a degree awarded by Francis Xavier College. While Newton is primarily remembered for directing the two large explosions in New York Harbor, he was a productive and talented construction engineer throughout his entire career.

USMA 1842   **George Washington Rains**   **Scientist**

1817 (Craven, NC) – 21 March 1898 (Newburgh, NY)
Graduate # 1113 (3rd out of 56), listed in *DAB, ANB, AR* (1898)

Military Service:
1847-1848:   Artillery officer during Mexican War
1849-1850:   Combat duty in Indian War in Florida
1850-1856:   Military duty in the Northeast of U.S.
1861-1865:   Ordnance duty with Confederate Army during Civil War

Professional Service:
1842-1844:   Construction engineer for Ft. Warren, RI and Ft. Monroe, VA

1844-1847: Assistant Professor of Chemistry, Geology, and Mineralogy, USMA
1856-1861: Director of iron works, Newburgh, NY (inventor of devices for steam engines)
1865-1877 and 1883-1894: Professor of Chemistry, Medical College of Georgia
1877-1883: Dean, Medical College of Georgia

G. W. RAINS was commissioned as an engineer and worked on fortifications for two years before teaching science at USMA in the Department of Chemistry, Geology, and Mineralogy for three years. In 1847, he was sent into combat duty in the Mexican War, where he earned promotions and accolades for his bravery and leadership. After several years of military duties, Rains resigned from the Army in 1856 to manage two iron works in the Newburgh, NY area. His research in steam engines and boilers earned him several important patents on his inventions. Rains joined the Confederate Army at the start of the Civil War and served in ordnance duties, assisting the Chief of Ordnance, **Josiah Gorgas (USMA 1841)** and leading the Confederate efforts in gunpowder production. Given a free hand by Gorgas, Rains developed new manufacturing processes and built several facilities to successfully produce enough gunpowder to fulfill the tremendous needs of the Confederate Army and Navy. In addition to his expertise in gunpowder, Rains became an advisor to Gorgas on other ordnance issues. During the war years, Rains also worked with his brother, **Gabriel Rains (USMA 1827)**, in the manufacture of fuses for torpedoes that his brother had designed. After the Civil War, Rains accepted a professorship in Chemistry at the Medical College of Georgia. Six years later, he became the Dean of the College for six more years of academic service. Rains successfully combined his tremendous technical knowledge with his leadership abilities to accomplish his missions in science, technology, and education.

USMA 1842   **Alexander Peter Stewart**   **Mathematician**

2 October 1821 (Rogersville, TN) – 30 August 1908 (Biloxi, MS)
Graduate # 1122 (12th out of 56), listed in *DAB, ANB, NCAB, AR* (1909)

Military Service:
1842-1843: Garrison duty at Ft. Macon, NC
1861-1865: Combat duty in Confederate Army in Civil War (Belmont, Shiloh, Corinth, Chattanooga, Chickamauga, Missionary Ridge, Atlanta) (wounded at Ezra Church) (Lieutenant General)

Professional Service:
1843-1845: Assistant Professor of Mathematics, USMA
1845-1849; 1850-1854; 1956-1861; 1866-1870: Professor of Mathematics and of Natural and Experimental Philosophy, Cumberland University, TN
1849-1850; 1854-1855: Professor of Mathematics and of Natural and Experimental Philosophy, Nashville University, TN
1874-1887: Chancellor of the University of Mississippi

At West Point, **A. P. Stewart** roomed with future Union General John Pope and future Confederate leader James Longstreet. After graduation and commissioning in the artillery,

he spent a year in garrison duties at Fort Macon, NC, before returning to the Academy to teach mathematics for two years. Resigning from the Army in 1845, he took teaching positions in mathematics and science at Cumberland University and the University of Nashville (both in TN). Stewart was opposed to secession, but reluctantly volunteered for duty with the Confederate Army in 1861. He began his war service in artillery units along the Mississippi River, but soon was in field command. A lackluster performance at Shiloh was followed by brilliant combat leadership in later battles. Given the nickname "Old Straight," Stewart was wounded at the Ezra Church Battle, but showed tremendous stamina by coming back to his command very soon and serving until the end of the war. After the war, Stewart returned to his life's work as an academic and technical leader, teaching at Cumberland University for five years. He worked in business for a life insurance company for a short period, but turned down his business salary of $6000 per year to return to academics with a salary of $2500 as the Chancellor of the University of Mississippi. He was a successful leader for the university, bringing his experience as a teacher and leader to the important position. During his years there, he was still called, "Old Straight" by the students. During this tenure, Stewart made several bold initiatives, establishing Ph.D. programs in 1875, making the school coeducational in 1882, and appointing a woman faculty member in 1885. In 1890, Stewart began work as a commissioner of the nation's first military park on the site of the Battle of Chattanooga. He worked there until 1906, when he moved to Biloxi, MS.

USMA 1842 | **Daniel Harvey Hill** | **Mathematician**

12 July 1821 (York, SC) – 24 September 1889 (Charlotte, NC)
Graduate # 1138 (28th out of 56), listed in *DAB, ANB, NCAB, AR* (1890)

Military Service:
1842-1845: Garrison duty in ME, SC, GA
1845: Combat duty in Occupation of Texas
1846-1847: Combat duty in Mexican War (Monterey, Vera Cruz, Cerro Gordo, Contreras, Churubusco, Chapultepec)
1861-1865: Combat duty in Confederate Army (Yorktown, Williamsburg, Seven Pines, South Mountain, Richmond, Chickamauga, Bentonville)

Professional Service:
1849-1854: Professor of Mathematics, Washington College, VA
1854-1859: Professor of Civil Engineering, Davidson College, NC
1859-1861: Superintendent, North Carolina Military Institute
1877-1884: President, Arkansas Industrial University
1885-1889: President, Middle Georgia College

D. H. Hill was motivated for his military duties when he graduated from West Point in 1842. Among his classmates were **John Newton** and **Alexander Stewart**. After serving three years in various garrison duties in the artillery, Hill had his first combat experiences in the occupation of Texas and in the Mexican War. He proved to be bold and brave in action and led his troops well in several important battles. However, after the Mexican War, he resigned from the Army to pursue an academic career, becoming the Professor of Mathematics at Washington College, VA for five years, then the Professor of Civil Engineering at Davidson College, NC for five more years. During this time, he was a tough disciplinarian, who emphasized rigid standards and strict behavior as much as technical learning for his students. He published the textbook *Elements of Algebra* in 1854. After serving from 1859 to 1861 as the Superintendent of the North Carolina Military Institute, Hill volunteered for service in the Army of the Confederacy. Hill was given successive commands and promotions for outstanding leadership in combat. As a controversial and maverick general, he was often at odds with his fellow generals. Jefferson Davis (USMA 1828) held up his promotion to Lieutenant General over Hill's controversial disagreement with Braxton Bragg (USMA 1837). After the war, Hill edited magazines and wrote papers with the expressed purpose of vindicating the South. In 1877, he accepted the Presidency of University of Arkansas and then in 1884 became President of Middle Georgia College (later Georgia Military College). Hill was an accomplished instructor of mathematics and strong leader both in academics and military settings.

USMA 1843   **William Buel Franklin**   **Engineer**

27 February 1823 (York, PA) – 8 March 1903 (Hartford, CT)
Graduate #1167 (1st out of 39), (topographer, scientist), listed in *DAB, NCAB, AR* (1903)

Military Service:
1845-1846: Assistant in Topographic Bureau, Washington, DC
1846-1848: Combat duty in Mexican War (Buena Vista)
1861-1865: Combat duty in Civil War (Bull Run, Peninsular Campaign, Yorktown, Malvern Hill, Antietam, Fredericksburg, Red River Expedition, Sabine Cross Roads)
            (wounded, Prisoner of war – escaped) (Major General)

Professional Service:

1843-1845: Topographic engineering duty in Northwest and for Kearny's expedition in Rocky Mountains
1848-1851: Assistant Professor of Natural and Experimental Philosophy, USMA
1851-1852: Professor of Natural and Experimental Philosophy and Civil Engineering, Free Academy (later City College of NY)
1852-1859: Construction engineer for harbors, lighthouses, and buildings in NY, NC, ME, and IL
1859-1861: Construction engineer on Capitol in Washington, DC
1865-1888: Ordnance expert as President of Colt Firearms
1868-1889: Consulting engineer for various projects including the Capitol at Hartford, CT

W. B. Franklin was the top cadet in his West Point class of 1843. Among his classmates was Ulysses S. Grant. Franklin entered the Corps of Topographical Engineers, which was a separate branch at that time. He spent two years surveying the Great Lakes and performing scientific investigations on General Kearny's expedition in the Rocky Mountains. During the Mexican War, Franklin was engaged in combat engineering operations. After the war, he spent four years teaching science and mechanics at West Point and the Free Academy in New York City (on a leave of absence from the Army). In 1852, his engineering duties involved construction projects. In 1859, he took on the task of supervising engineer for the dome on the U.S. Capitol in Washington, DC. During the Civil War, Franklin became a combat commander. His service was so outstanding that he soon had command of a Corps as a Major General. However, he was blamed for failures of his unit in the Fredericksburg Battle and was sent out West. Soon Franklin was in Corps command in his new Army. Captured by Confederate soldiers while riding on a train, he escaped after only one day in captivity. After the war, Franklin resigned from the Army to take an ordnance management position with Colt Firearms. While in that position, he continued to consult on numerous engineering projects for the government. He was considered one of the leading engineers in America, and represented the nation's engineers at the Paris Exposition. While Franklin's reputation as a military commander was hurt by the controversy over his performance and leadership at Fredericksburg, Ulysses S. Grant (USMA 1843) always supported him as a reliable commander. Franklin's skills as an engineer were never questioned. He was a brilliant man, who, through his rich experiences and valuable insights, built an enviable record of leading many important engineering projects to successful and efficient completion.

Reference:

Snell, Mark, *Major General William Buel Franklin: A Biography*, 2 vols. University of Missouri Ph.D. Thesis, Kansas City, MO, 1998.

USMA 1843   ║ **Isaac Ferdinand Quinby** ║   **Mathematician**

29 January 1821 (Morristown, NJ) – 18 September 1891 (Rochester, NY)
Graduate # 1172 (6th out of 39), listed *DAB, AR* (1892)

Military Service:
1843-1844: Garrison duty at Ft Mifflin, PA
1847-1848: Combat duty in Mexican War (Vera Cruz)
1848-1851: Garrison duty in VA and RI
1861-1863: Combat duty in Civil War (Bull Run, Yazoo Pass Expedition, Champion Hill, Vicksburg)
            (Brigadier General)

Professional Service:
1844-1847: Assistant Professor of Mathematics, USMA
1845-1847: Assistant Professor of Natural and Experimental
            Philosophy, USMA
1851-1861: Professor of Mathematics and of Natural and
            Experimental Philosophy, University of Rochester, NY
1863-1884: Professor of Mathematics and of Natural and
            Experimental Philosophy, University of Rochester, NY
1885-1890: City Surveyor of Rochester, NY

I. F. QUINBY graduated from West Point in 1843 having made friends with his classmate, Ulysses S. Grant. After garrison duty in PA, Quinby returned to West Point to teach his favorite subjects, mathematics, physics, and mechanics. During the Mexican War, Quinby fought in several skirmishes. After the war, Quinby resigned from the Army to take a professorship at the newly established University of Rochester, NY. Teaching mathematics, physics, and mechanics, Quinby was the technical expert and an academic leader at the University. At the outbreak of the Civil War, he volunteered to serve in combat. Raising a regiment of New York State soldiers, he led his troops well at Bull Run. After a brief return to the University, Quinby came back to military duty, working as a commander under his close friend General Grant. Quinby suffered a serious illness and in 1863 had to relinquish his command. Back again at the University of Rochester, Quinby began a 21-year run as an experienced professor and university academic leader. Grant appointed Quinby a United States Marshall in New York during the eight years of Grant's presidency. Quinby also served as city surveyor and a consulting construction engineer from 1885 to 1889. Quinby edited an important series of books entitled Robinson's *Course of Mathematics* and wrote his own calculus textbook in 1868. He was both a talented scholar and a dedicated teacher.

USMA 1844   ┌─────────────────────┐   **Mathematician**
                        │ **William Guy Peck** │
                        └─────────────────────┘

16 October 1820 (Litchfield, CT) – 7 February 1892 (Greenwich, CT)
Graduate # 1206 (1st out of 25), listed in *NCAB, BDAS, AR* (1892)

Military Service:
1845:   Member of Fremont's Expedition in Rocky Mountains
1846-1847:   Combat in Mexican War

Professional Service:
1844-1845:   Topographic engineer, Portsmouth, NH
1845-1846:   Assistant Professor of Natural and Experimental Philosophy, USMA
1847-1855:   Assistant Professor of Mathematics, USMA
1855-1857:   Professor of Physics and Civil Engineering, University of Michigan
1857-1865:   Professor of Mathematics and Astronomy, Columbia College, NY
1865-1892:   Professor of Mathematics, Mechanics, and Astronomy, Columbia College
1855-1892:   Author of several mathematics books

W. G. PECK was commissioned in the Corps of Topographical Engineers and served as a topographic engineer for the survey of Portsmouth Harbor in NH. He then traveled as a surveyor/scientist with Fremont's third expedition of the Rocky Mountains which was connected to actions in the Mexican War. Returning to West Point in 1846, Peck taught in the Natural and Experimental Philosophy Department. Peck entered combat duty during the Mexican War for two years service under General Kearney. He then returned to West Point, where he became an Assistant Professor of Mathematics as a principal assistant for Department Head **Albert Church (USMA 1828)**. After teaching for eight years, he resigned from the Army in 1855 to teach physics and engineering for the University of Michigan. Two years later, Peck moved to Columbia College in NY, where he taught for thirty years. Peck was a highly successful and respected mathematics professor, writing several popular textbooks and co-authoring a mathematical dictionary with his father-in-law **Charles Davies (USMA 1815),** who also taught at Columbia. Peck also wrote books and articles on geometry, trigonometry, calculus, determinants, mechanics, physics, and astronomy. Peck taught the fundamentals of engineering to some students in Columbia's growing program as well. When the highly successful School of Mines opened at Columbia in 1864, he chaired the new Department of Mechanics. Among Peck's numerous accolades were honorary degrees from Trinity College, CT and Columbia College, NY.

USMA 1845   ┌─────────────────────┐   **Engineer**
                        │ **Edward Bissell Hunt** │
                        └─────────────────────┘

1822 (NY) – 2 October 1863 (Brooklyn, NY)
Graduate # 1232 (2nd out of 41), listed in *NCAB, BDAS*

Military Service:
1862-1863: Combat duty in Civil War (Shenandoah)

Professional Service:
1845-1846: Duty as construction engineer in New York City
1846-1849: Assistant Professor of Engineering, USMA
1849-1851: Duty as construction engineer, Ft. Warren, MA
1851-1855: Coast Survey duty
1855-1857: Duty as construction engineer for lighthouses in RI
1857-1861: Duty as construction engineer, Ft Taylor, FL

E. B. HUNT, who was one of the most scientifically inclined of the ante-bellum West Pointers, graduated second in his class of 1845. Hunt served as a construction engineer at various harbors, forts, and lighthouses. He made the most of his opportunity to teach engineering at the Academy by also developing his own skills as an engineer. Serving with the Coast Survey through most of the 1850s, he conducted many special studies for Coast Survey Superintendent **Alexander Bache (USMA 1825)**. Hunt published a number of articles in the *Proceedings of the American Association for the Advancement of Science* and in the annual reports of the Coast Survey. Strongly allied with Bache on most issues, he served as a spokesman for the Coast Survey on many occasions. Hunt delivered one of the more interesting papers at the annual meeting of the American Association for the Advancement of Science on the technologies of warfare – predicting the use of shells containing gas, reconnaissance balloons using telegraphic communications, illuminated night battlefields, the use of rifled guns, and much more. Many of Hunt's predictions came true sooner than anyone expected. During the Civil War, he performed combat engineering duties in the Shenandoah campaign and transferred to special duty with the Navy, researching the science of firing guns and launching projectiles from underwater. During a firing experiment, he was affected by escaping gas, fell down into the hold of a ship, and died from his injuries.

USMA 1845   **William Farrar Smith**   **Engineer**

17 February 1824 (St. Albans, VT) – 28 February 1903 (Philadelphia, PA)
Graduate # 1234 (4th out of 41), (mathematician, topographer), listed in *DAB, ANB, NCAB, AR* (1903)

Military Service:
1861-1865: Combat duty in Civil War (Bull Run, Peninsular Campaign, Yorktown, Williamsburg, White Oak, South Mountain, Antietam, Fredericksburg, Gettysburg, Chattanooga, Missionary Ridge, Cold Harbor, Petersburg) (Major General)

Professional Service:

1845-1846: Topographic engineer on survey of Great Lakes
1846-1848: Assistant Professor of Mathematics, USMA
1848-1850: Topographic engineer on surveys in Texas
1850-1852: Surveyor for boundary between United States and Texas
1852-1853: Survey for canal across Florida
1853-1855: Topographic engineer for exploration of Texas
1855-1856: Assistant Professor of Mathematics, USMA
1856-1861: Secretary for Lighthouse Board
1881-1895: Civil engineer for rivers and harbors

W. F. SMITH was called "Baldy" by his West Point classmates. Following graduation, Smith performed surveys along the shores of Lake Erie. He then returned to West Point to teach mathematics for two years. Back in the field and working as a topographic engineer, Smith conducted surveys in Texas and along the Mexican border for four years. From 1852 to 1855, he continued field survey work and laid out plans for a canal across FL. He returned to teach mathematics at the Academy but had to relinquish his duties after just one year due to malaria that he had contracted in Texas in 1855. Smith served as secretary of the Lighthouse Board in Detroit from 1856 to 1861. At the start of the Civil War, Smith took command of combat units. Although he was a brave, bold, innovative combat leader, he often fell into disputes with his superiors and moved from one command to another. While successful in battle, Smith continually fell out of favor because of his criticism of others. He was eventually denied a promotion and relieved of Corps command by Ulysses S. Grant (USMA 1843). Grant called him obstinate, but never thought of Smith as incompetent. After the war, Smith became wealthy as President of a successful telegraph  company and took his family to Europe for two years, living in luxury, and touring the continent. However, by 1875, Smith was forced to return to work because of financial needs and became the police commissioner of New York City. In 1881, Smith returned to technical service for the government, supervising river and harbor construction on Chesapeake and Delaware Bays. The versatile, but stubborn Smith was often his own worst enemy, alternately achieving success in science, military, and business affairs, only to lose headway through unnecessary conflict and argument.

References:

Siciliano, Stephen. *Major General William Farrar Smith: Critic of Defeat and Engineer of Victory*, Ph.D. Dissertation, College of William and Mary, Williamsburg, VA, 1984.

Smith, W. F., *Autobiography of Major General William F. Smith, 1861-1864*, edited by Herbert M. Schiller, Morningside House, Dayton, OH, 1990.

Wilson, James, *Life and Service of William Farrar Smith*, John M. Rogers Press, Wilmington, DE, 1904.

USMA 1845   ┌─────────────────────────┐   **Mathematician**
                       │   **Edmund Kirby-Smith**   │
                       └─────────────────────────┘

16 May 1824 (St. Augustine, FL) – 28 March 1893 (Sewanee, TN)
Graduate # 1255 (25th out of 41), listed in *DAB, ANB, NCAB, AR* (1893)

Military Service:

1845-1846: Combat duty in occupation of Texas
1846-1848: Combat duty in Mexican War (Palto Alto, Vera Cruz, Gerro Gordo, Contreras, Churubusco, Chapultepec, Mexico City)
1848-1849: Garrison duty Ft. Jefferson, MD
1853-1859: Combat duty in Indian Wars (severely wounded)
1861-1865: Combat duty in Confederate Army in Civil War (Manassas, Cumberland Gap, Lexington, Red River) (General, Commander of the Trans-Mississippi Department)

Professional Service:

1849-1852: Assistant Professor of Mathematics, USMA
1865-1868: President, telegraph company
1868-1870: President, Western Military Academy, KY
1870-1875: Chancellor, University of Nashville, TN
1875-1893: Professor of Mathematics, University of the South, TN

E. KIRBY-SMITH had soldiering in his blood and was prepared by his family to attend West Point. Entering the Academy in 1841, Smith (his given family name) was nicknamed "Seminole" by fellow cadets.   Despite being severely nearsighted, he was commissioned in the infantry and sent into combat duty in Texas and Mexico. He distinguished himself in combat service under General Zachary Taylor.   From 1849 to 1852, Smith taught mathematics at West Point. Then for most of the next nine years, Smith lived on the western frontier. In 1852, he commanded an escort unit for the Mexican Boundary Commission and served as the botanist of the expedition under **William Emory (USMA 1831)**.   The Smithsonian published his valuable report of botanical observations. In 1858, he resumed the Army's pursuit of Commanche Indians and was wounded in the Battle of Nescatunga. In 1861, he resigned from the U.S. Army to join the Confederacy. Attempting to hold Camp Colorado, with all its equipment and troops, for the Confederacy, he eventually relinquished his position and returned to FL. He changed his name to Kirby-Smith, since his mother's maiden name was Kirby and he wanted to avoid confusion with several other Confederate generals named Smith.   Having served successfully under J. E. Johnston (USMA 1829) at Manassas, Jefferson Davis (USMA 1828) sent him out west to command a division and, eventually, he took command of a corps. In 1863, he was made a full General and commanded all Confederate forces west of the Mississippi River. This was a difficult command because his unit was virtually cut off from his superiors in Richmond. He persevered and maintained the integrity of his command. The "Kirby-Smithdom," as his command was called, suffered morale problems, sometimes because of his controversial policies. After the war, Kirby-Smith went to Mexico and Cuba, but eventually returned to KY.   After failed business endeavors, he headed a military academy and the academic program at the University of Nashville. In 1875, Kirby-Smith found his calling as a Professor of Mathematics at the University of the South, Sewanee, TN. He was an excellent teacher there for eighteen years, well liked by his students for his highly effective teaching style. The last surviving full general of the civil war, Kirby-Smith was an intelligent, resourceful leader and professor.

Reference:

Kerby, Robert, *Kirby Smith's Confederacy: The Trans-Mississippi South, 1863-1865,* Columbia University Press, New York, 1972.

Parks, Joseph Howard. *General Edmund Kirby-Smith C.S.A,,* Louisiana State University Press, Baton Rouge, 1954.

"Smith, Edmund Kirby," The Handbook of Texas Online. www.tsha.utexas.edu/handbook/online/articles.

USMA 1846   **Edward Carlisle Boynton**   **Scientist**

1 February 1824 (Windsor, VT) – 13 May 1893 (Newburgh, NY)
Graduate # 1283 (12th out of 59), (chemist), listed in *DAB, AR* (1893)

Military Service:
1846-1847:   Combat duty in Mexican War (Saltillo, Vera Cruz, Cerro Gorgo, Ocalaca,
                 Contreras, Churubusco)
1855-1856:   Combat duty in Seminole War, FL
1861-1871:   Adjutant, USMA

Professional Service:
1848-1855:   Assistant Professor of Chemistry, Mineralogy, and Geology, USMA
1856:   Professor of Chemistry, Albany Normal School, NY
1856-1861:   Professor of Chemistry, Mineralogy, and Geology, University of Mississippi

Upon graduation from West Point, **E. C. BOYNTON** joined an artillery battery engaged in the Mexican War. After several fierce battles, he was severely wounded at Churubusco. He then returned to West Point to serve on the faculty for the next seven years. Teaching his favorite subject of chemistry, he served as principal assistant to the famous scientist and Department Head **Jacob Bailey (USMA 1832)**. Boynton was a fine researcher in his own right, publishing his technical work in professional journals. Having built a strong reputation as a scientist, Boynton received offers for faculty positions from several schools. After serving in the Seminole War, he resigned from the Army to become Professor of Chemistry, Mineralogy, and Geology at the University of Mississippi. Boynton enjoyed this position until the outbreak of the Civil War. Opposing secession and finding himself deep in the Confederacy at the outbreak of hostilities, Boynton had to pledge not to serve in combat against the Confederacy for his freedom to move back north. A man of his word, Boynton returned to West Point and spent the duration of the war and five more years after its completion as the Adjutant of the Academy. In 1872, he resigned from the Army for the second time and moved to Newburgh, NY. Supplementing his technical works, Boynton authored the *History of West Point* and the *Army and Navy Dictionary*, both published by Websters. In addition to a successful military life, Boynton found time to become a fine chemist thanks to the mentorship of Bailey and his own dedication and talent.

USMA 1848   ┌──────────────────────────┐   **Engineer**
                       │ **James Chatham Duane** │
                       └──────────────────────────┘

30 June 1824 (Schenectady, NY) – 8 November 1897 (New York, NY)
Graduate # 1371 (3rd out of 38), listed in *DAB, NCAB, AR* (1898)

Military Service:
1848-1852 and 1854-1858: Engineer duty with sappers, miners, and pontooniers
1861-1865: Combat engineer duty in Civil War (Yorktown, Antietam) (Brigadier General)
1866-1868: Command engineer duty at Willet's Point, NY
1886-1888: Chief of Army Engineers, USMA

Professional Service:
1852-1854 and 1858-1861: Assistant Professor of Military Engineering, USMA
1868-1878: Construction engineering for fortifications along the coasts of ME and NH
1888-1897: Engineer and commissioner for the Croton Aqueduct, NY

J. C. DUANE had graduated from Union College, NY before attending West Point. He entered the engineer branch and served for five years as an assistant professor in the Department of Practical Military Engineering while **Robert E. Lee (USMA 1829)** was Superintendent. Serving with the Army's company of sappers, miners, and pontooniers for eight years before the Civil War, he along with General Albert Johnston, led its celebrated 1,100-mile march to Utah in 1858. During the Civil War, Duane designed new pontoon and fixed bridges, which proved to be successful combat support equipment during the war. Filling the important position of General McClellan's chief of engineers for the Army of the Potomac, he built the first military pontoon bridge over the Potomac at Harper's Ferry in 1862, and, in seven hours in 1864, built the longest pontoon bridge of the Civil War (2,170 feet) across the James River. He taught engineering at the Engineer School of Application, Willet's Point, NY from 1866 to 1868, and for ten years constructed fortifications and lighthouses along the coasts of ME and NH and worked on river and harbor improvements in New England. He was President of the Board of Engineers from 1884 to 1886. Appointed as the Chief of Army Engineers in 1886, he served in that capacity until his Army retirement in 1888, when he became Commissioner of the new Croton Aqueduct, the major water source for New York City. Duane was in charge of constructing the 31-mile long aqueduct and a huge dam to supplement the old Croton Aqueduct system that had been in place for 45 years. This aqueduct and dam were intricate and challenging engineering projects. Iron pipe encased in brick masonry was laid along the route, and several large bridges were built to carry water to the City. To build the dam, Duane imported thousands of stonemasons from Europe. The dam for this project was the second-largest masonry structure in the world. The old system, dating from 1842, had provided New York City with its first dependable source of drinking water. Without the aqueducts, New York City could never have grown as it did, since the only water available came from wells and springs, which had eventually become polluted and unsanitary. Later, two other water-supply systems were added for the city: the Catskill Aqueduct, 92 miles long, completed in 1917; and the Delaware System, 105 miles long, completed in 1965. Duane was an accomplished and talented engineer, publishing an important technical paper on the "History of the Bridge Equipage in the United States Army."

Quotation: Cyrus Comstock (USMA 1855) said of Duane: "Duane possessed that sound good sense which can look at all sides of a question without prepossessions, and which can see the great features of it, without giving the details too much importance, gifts that are rare."

USMA 1849   **Quincy Adams Gillmore**   **Engineer**

28 February 1825 (Black River, OH) – 7 April 1888 (Brooklyn, NY)
Graduate # 1407 (1st out of 43), listed in *DAB, NCAB, AR* (1888)

Military Service:
1856-1861: Commander of Engineer Agency, shipping supplies to fortifications
1861-1865: Combat duty in Civil War (Siege of Ft. Pulaski, Somerset, Charleston, Ft. Sumter, Ft. Wagner, Swift Creek, Drury's Bluff, Bermuda Hundred) (Major General)
1865-1866: Assistant to Chief of Army Engineers, Washington, DC

Professional Service:
1849-1852: Construction engineer, Ft Monroe, VA
1852-1856: Assistant Professor of Practical Military Engineering, USMA
1856-1861: Construction engineer for New York Harbor
1866-1867: Conducting experiments in using iron in fortifications
1866-1869: Construction engineer for fortifications in NY
1869-1888: Civil engineer on improving rivers and harbors in SC, GA, FL
1871: Conducting tests on depressing gun carriage
1876-1878: Construction engineer for buildings and monuments, Washington, DC
1879-1888: President of Mississippi River Commission

1862-1875: Author of numerous papers and reports on combat engineering, use of cement, building stones, bricks, roads, and pavement

---

Q. A. GILLMORE taught school for three years before arriving at West Point as a cadet in 1845. He was an outstanding student, finishing at the top of his graduating class of 1849 and entering the Corps of Engineers. For three years, he was engaged in construction projects on fortifications; then for four years, he taught practical military engineering to cadets at West Point. Gillmore then worked on various construction projects in the New York City area until the outbreak of the Civil War. During the Civil War, he served both as a combat engineer and as a field commander. His combat service was brilliant. Innovative in his tactics and brave under fire, he gained a superb reputation as an expert in both artillery and engineering. When he was injured by a fall from his horse, he took on rear-area technical duties for the testing of munitions for new cannons while he recovered from his injury. After the war, Gillmore served on several important engineering commissions and boards. He became an expert on rivers and harbors and was President of the Mississippi River Commission. A prolific author, Gillmore wrote many technical reports for the Corps of Engineers. Among his honors were degrees from Oberlin College, OH and Rutgers College, NJ.

Quotation: About Gillmore by General Stewart Woodward: "I believe that he ranked in ability, learning, and reputation among the really great engineers… His record makes him a worthy type of the American scholar and soldier."

USMA 1849 | **Stephen Vincent Benét** | **Technologist**

22 January 1827 (FL) – 22 January 1895 (Washington, DC)
Graduate # 1409 (3rd out of 43), (ordnance), listed in *NCAB, AR* (1895)

Military Service:
1850-1852: Duty at Ordnance Bureau, Washington, DC
1869-1874: Duty at Ordnance Bureau, Washington, DC
1874-1891: Chief of Ordnance, Washington, DC

Professional Service:
1849-1850: Ordnance duty at Watervliet Arsenal, NY
1852-1854: Ordnance duty at Frankfort Arsenal, PA
and Pikeville Arsenal, MA
1854: Special duty with Coast Survey
1854-1859: Ordnance duty at St. Louis Arsenal, MO
1859-1861: Assistant Professor of Geography, USMA
1861-1864: Assistant Professor of Ordnance and the Science of Gunnery, USMA
1864-1869: Ordnance duty at Frankford Arsenal, PA

S. V. BENÉT entered the Ordnance Corps upon graduation from West Point in 1849. He immediately reported to Watervliet Arsenal, NY for his first assignment in his branch. After one year, he moved to the Ordnance Bureau in Washington, DC. Benét then had a series of assignments at various arsenals in PA, MD, and MO. In 1859, he returned to his alma mater

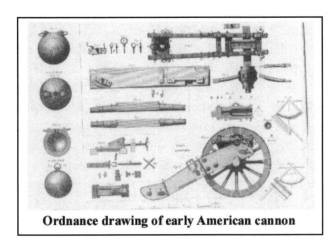

Ordnance drawing of early American cannon

to teach geography for two years before the outbreak of the Civil War. During the war, he remained at the Academy to teach ordnance and gunnery science. During that time, he conducted experiments with the Parrott Guns being built at the West Point Foundry by **Robert Parrott (USMA 1824)**. Benét also inspected cannons and projectiles being produced in the New York area. After the war, he commanded the Frankford Arsenal and continued his service as a munitions inspector. Benét served on various boards and commissions for the manufacture and design of cannon, rifles, carriages, and projectiles. In 1869, he assisted the Chief of Ordnance, and in 1874, he assumed the position of Chief of Ordnance becoming known for developing cartridge cases and specialized primers, which helped with the design and operation of the Gatling gun. Benét retired from the Army and his position of Chief of Ordnance in 1891. Benét wrote several works on ordnance issues, including a futuristic report on electro-ballistic machines. Among his honors was a degree from Georgetown University, DC.

USMA 1849      **Mathematician**

20 August 1824 (Washington, PA) – 14 June 1905 (Relay, MD)
Graduate # 1415 (9th out of 43), listed in *DAB, ANB, NCAB, AR* (1905)

Military Service:
1850-1852: Combat duty in Seminole War
1859-1860: Indian Wars in Texas
1861-1865: Combat duty in Civil War (artillery, infantry) (Bull Run, Chickamauga, Chattanooga, Atlanta,
            Sherman's March to the Sea) (Major General) (Medal of Honor)
1865-1888: Inspector General (Brigadier General)

Professional Service:
1852-1859: Assistant Professor of Mathematics, USMA

A. Baird studied law for three years before entering the Academy at age 21. After graduation from USMA, he learned the technical aspects of the artillery branch. Thereafter, he transferred to Florida, but suffered from fever and disease that he contracted in his service in the Seminole War. He was sent to Europe to recover. When he returned to America, he relocated to the Department of Mathematics at West Point, where he taught cadets for seven years. His department head was **Albert Church (USMA 1828)**, who used Baird to help teach the weaker students and edit his various editions of textbooks. One of Baird's favorite students was the artist James McNeill Whistler (see **Honorable Mentions**), who was found deficient in mathematics despite Baird's help and was dismissed from the Academy. During the Civil War, Baird held several staff positions before assuming field leadership duties. After service as an adjutant general and inspector general, Baird was assigned a brigade command position and later assumed division command. At Chickamauga, Baird was instrumental in holding the defensive line, helping his corps commander, George Thomas (USMA 1840), gain the title "Rock of Chickamauga." Baird was also a leader of the legendary charge up Missionary Ridge. Later, during a charge at Jonesboro, Baird had two horses shot from under him as he led his command to a route of the Confederate defenders. For his actions at Jonesboro, Baird received the Medal of Honor. After the war, Baird, who had always been known for his efficiency, precision, and excellent staff work, served as an Inspector General (IG). By 1881, he was the IG for the entire Army. Baird did not return to technical work after the Civil War, but as an excellent teacher, he influenced many West Point graduates to pursue careers in technical branches and civilian scientific study.

Reference: Baird, John, *Profile of a Hero: The Story of Absalom Baird, his Family, and the American Military Tradition*, Dorrance, Philadelphia, 1977.

USMA 1850 | **Gouverneur Kemble Warren** | **Engineer**

8 January 1830 (Cold Spring, NY) – 8 August 1882 (Newport, RI)
Graduate # 1451 (2nd out of 44), (topographical), listed in *ANB, NCAB, BDAS, AR* (1883)

Military Service:
1861-1865: Combat duty in Civil War (Gaines Mills and Gettysburg -- wounded) (Major General)

Professional Service:
1850-1854: Engineering duties on Mississippi River
1854-1855: Mapping and charting for Pacific railroads
1855-1859: Topographic engineering in Indian Territories

1859-1861: Assistant Professor of Mathematics, USMA
1865-1870: Engineer for navigational improvement on Mississippi River
1869-1870: Engineer for Rock Island Bridge across the Mississippi River
1876: Elected as member of the National Academy of Sciences
1870-1882: Engineer for harbor improvements on Atlantic Coast

---

G. K. Warren entered the Corps of Topographical Engineers upon graduation from USMA in 1850. He immediately went to work on projects along the Mississippi River. His contributions to the navigation systems in the delta, around the Ohio Falls, and through the rapids at Rock Island were substantial. Warren's next duties took him west, first along the Pacific Coast and then to the Indian Territories. Working for the famous Army engineer, **Andrew Humphreys (USMA 1831)**, Warren prepared a report and map for the proposed route of the Pacific Railroad in 1859. Warren spent two years before the Civil War (1859-1861) teaching mathematics at West Point. During the Civil War, he saw action in several battles as both a combat leader and an engineering staff officer. He was wounded in battle twice. His bronze statue stands on top of Little Round Top on the Gettysburg Battlefield. After the war and back in his profession of engineering, Warren spent five more years improving navigation on the Mississippi River and other rivers in the Midwest. He published several reports on his earlier findings of engineering issues in the Indian Territories and the bridging opportunities for the Mississippi River. Warren supervised the building of a bridge over the river at Rock Island in 1870. For the remaining twelve years of his life, Warren supervised engineering projects on rivers, harbors, canals, and bridges along the Atlantic Coast. Warren was recognized as an outstanding engineering scholar. His reports contained new results in engineering science and practices. He was elected a member of the National Academy of Sciences and was a member of several professional societies.

| **USMA 1852** | **Thomas Lincoln Casey** | **Engineer** |

10 May 1831 (Sacketts Harbor, NY) – 25 March 1896 (Washington, DC)
Graduate # 1536 (1st out of 43), listed in *DAB, NCAB, AR* (1896)

Military Service:
1861-1865: Combat and fortification engineer during Civil War
1867-1877: Staff officer for the Office of the Chief of Army Engineers

Professional Service:
1852-1854: Construction engineer on Delaware Bay
1854-1859: Assistant Professor of Engineering, USMA
1859-1861: Construction engineer for Wagon Road from
Vancouver to Oregon
1866-1867: Construction engineer for locomotives for railroad company

1867:   Construction engineer for fortification in ME
1877-1888: Construction engineer for Washington Monument,
                  Jefferson Monument, and Garfield Statue
1888-1895: Chief of Army Engineers
1890:   Member, National Academy of Sciences

T. L. CASEY graduated first in the Military Academy class of 1852 and taught engineering at the Academy for five years. During the Civil War, he oversaw the construction of Maine's coastal fortifications, completing the massive Fort Knox on the Penobscot River. After the war, he headed the division in the Office of the Chief of Engineers responsible for engineer troops, equipment, and fortifications. The Corps' most distinguished builder of monuments and public buildings, Casey headed the Office of Public Buildings and Grounds in Washington, DC from 1877 to 1888. He built the State, War, and Navy Department Buildings and completed the construction work on the Washington Monument. The placing of a sturdy foundation under the partially completed Washington Monument (already 173 feet high) was Casey's greatest engineering accomplishment. He then started construction on the Library of Congress building, dying suddenly just as it was completed. Casey became a member of the National Academy of Sciences in 1890 and was considered a highly skilled construction engineer and technical problem solver.

USMA 1853   **William Robertson Boggs**   **Technologist**

18 March 1829 (Augusta, GA) – 5 September 1911 (Winston-Salem, NC)
Graduate # 1582 (4th out of 52), (ordnance), listed in *NCAB, AR* (1912)

Military Service:
1859:   Combat duty against Mexican marauders in TX
1861-1865: Combat duty for Confederate Army in Civil War (Pensacola, Trans-Mississippi Department)
                  (Brigadier General)

Professional Service:
1853-1854: Engineering duty for railroad company in CA
1854-1857: Ordnance duty at Watervliet Arsenal, NY
1857-1859: Ordnance duty at Baton Rouge, LA
1859-1861: Ordnance duty at Foundry in Pittsburgh, PA
1865-1876: Consulting engineer and architect for various civilian projects, GA, MO
1875-1880: Professor of Technical Mechanics and Drawing, Virginia Agricultural and Mechanical
                  College, Blacksburg, VA (now Virginia Polytechnic Institute)
1880-1900: Consulting engineer for various projects

W. R. BOGGS was commissioned in the Corps of Engineers upon his graduation from West Point in 1853. As a topographic engineer, he was sent to the West to survey routes for the

Pacific Railroad. After one year, he transferred to the Ordnance Corps and returned East to the Watervliet Arsenal, NY. After three years, he moved to the Baton Rouge Arsenal and then to the Army's Fort Pitt Foundry in Pittsburgh, where he helped **Thomas Rodman (USMA 1841)** build the newly designed 8-inch and 10-inch Rodman cannons. At the outbreak of the Civil War, Boggs resigned from the Union Army and entered the Confederate Army as an artillery officer. He spent most of his service in the Trans-Mississippi Department as the Chief of Staff for **Edmund Kirby-Smith (USMA 1845)**. The Confederacy missed a great opportunity to use Boggs' ordnance expertise on the Rodman cannon. After the war, Boggs became a railroad and mining engineer and a building architect in MO and GA. In 1875, he secured the Professor of Technical Mechanics and Drawing position at Virginia Agricultural and Mechanical College in Blacksburg, VA (now Virginia Polytechnic Institute). The President of the school, Charles Minor, had recruited Boggs specifically because of his West Point background. Boggs was one of six professors in 1875 on the faculty. Boggs had a reputation as a patient but demanding teacher, who taught his students in much the same way as he was taught 25 years before at West Point. Through Boggs, the West Point's teaching methods of **Sylvanus Thayer (USMA 1808)** spread to yet another of America's technical schools.

USMA 1853 | **John McAllister Schofield** | **Scientist**

29 September 1831 (Gerry, NY) – 4 March 1906 (St. Augustine, FL)
Graduate # 1585 (7th out of 52), listed in *DAB, ANB, NCAB, AR* (1906)

Military Service:
1853-1855: Garrison duty in SC and FL
1861-1865: Combat duty in Civil War (Wilson's Creek, Lost Mountain, Kulp's Farm, Kenesaw Mountain, Atlanta, Nashville) (Major General)
1866-1868: Commander of Army Forces, Department of Potomac
1868-1869: Secretary of War
1870-1876: Commander of Division of the Pacific
1881-1888: Commander of various Army units
1888-1895: Chief of Staff of the Army (Lieutenant General)

Professional Service:
1855-1860: Professor of Natural and Experimental Philosophy, USMA
1860-1861: Professor of Physics, Washington University, St.Louis, MO
1876-1881: Superintendent, USMA

J. M. SCHOFIELD surveyed land in Wisconsin and taught school there before becoming a cadet. Commissioned in the artillery at graduation, he first served in garrison duty for two years before returning to West Point to teach science and mechanics. Enjoying both teaching and scientific work, Schofield took a leave of absence in 1860 to teach physics at Washington

University in St. Louis. If not for the Civil War, Schofield probably would have continued his career as a science professor. However, he soon found himself an important player in Missouri's role as a border state in the Union. Commanding various units of Missouri volunteers, he was able to keep some measure of stability in the state. President Lincoln supported Schofield's efforts and realized his important contributions to the Union effort. Schofield also proved himself as an outstanding combat commander on several occasions. After the war, Schofield was sent on a diplomatic mission to France involving French interference in Mexico. His negotiations were successful. Back in the states, he oversaw Army reconstruction projects in several southern states until 1868, when he was appointed the Secretary of War. When Ulysses S. Grant (USMA 1843) became President, Schofield was given various assignments out West and handled issues of railroad expansion and conflicts with Native Americans. From 1876 to 1881, Schofield led the Military Academy as its Superintendent. In 1888, he became the Army Chief of Staff and commanded the Army until 1895. Schofield was a bright man, able engineer, and a strong leader. Always sensible and fair, he used his experience and connections to accomplish the mission in all his varied assignments. While always scientifically and technically minded, Schofield never had the opportunity to continue his career in science that he had built before the Civil War.

References:

McDonough, James, *Schofield: Union General in the Civil War and Reconstruction*, Florida State University Press, Tallahassee, 1972.

Weigley, Russell, "Military Thought of John M. Schofield," *Military Affairs* (Summer 1959), pp. 77-84.

USMA 1854 | **George Washington Custis Lee** | **Engineer**

16 September 1832 (Ft Monroe, VA) – 18 February 1913 (Fairfax, VA)
Graduate # 1631 (1st out of 46), listed in *DAB, NCAB, AR* (1913)

Military Service:
1861-1865: Served with Confederate Army (special staff of President Davis) (commanded division at Sayler's Creek) (Major General)

Professional Service:
1854-1861: Engineer for river and harbor improvements
1865-1870: Professor of Military and Civil Engineering, VMI
1871-1897: President, Washington College

G. W. C. LEE was an outstanding student in his West Point class of 1854. He was a skilled civil engineer, who began his military career designing and constructing harbor facilities and river navigation systems, which were two of America's critical infrastructure needs at the time. Like his father **Robert E. Lee**

(USMA 1829), Custis Lee resigned from the United States Army and entered the Confederate Army when Virginia seceded from the Union. He began his work for the Southern forces as an engineer designing fortifications around Richmond, but was soon pulled away to serve other more pressing needs. Selected to be the aide-de-camp for President Jefferson Davis (USMA 1828), he had many special duties. Some of the missions he was assigned during his war-time service included inspection and consulting of the defenses for Norfolk, VA and Wilmington, NC and carrying important messages from the Confederate President to military leaders in the field. He helped with the design and restructure of Army units and their functions. Toward the end of the war, Lee led several units in desperate battles in the final defense of the Confederacy. Despite his personal valor, his entire unit was captured at Sayler's Creek. He was paroled from his war prison in the North to tend to the illness of his mother. When the Civil War ended, Lee became the Professor of Military and Civil Engineering at Virginia Military Institute (VMI). He was an outstanding teacher and a mainstay as the school rebuilt its technically based program. After five years of teaching and upon the death of his father, who was then President of Washington College, Custis Lee was called to serve as his father's successor. As the leader of this new and growing college, Lee built the infrastructure and curricular programs of the college. He used the West Point and VMI models to help institute new programs, as he successfully presided over the school for 26 years. Lee retired in 1897 and lived a quiet life at his estate, "Ravensworth" in Virginia for his last 16 years.

USMA 1854 | **Oliver Otis Howard** | **Mathematician**

8 November 1830 (Leeds, ME) – 26 October 1909 (Burlington, VT)
Graduate # 1634 (4th out of 46), listed in *DAB, ANB, NCAB, AR* (1910)

Military Service:
1854-1857: Ordnance duty at Watervliet Arsenal and Florida
1861-1865: Civil War commander (Manassas, Peninsula, Antietam, Fredericksburg, Chancellorsville, Gettysburg, Chattanooga, March to the Sea) (Major General) (Medal of Honor)
1874-1878: Expeditions against Indians
1881-1894: Command duties at various regional headquarters in the U.S.

Professional Service:
1857-1861: Assistant Professor of Mathematics, USMA
1869-1874: Founder and first President of Howard University
1880-1881: Superintendent, USMA

O. O. HOWARD's technical and educational lives are completely intertwined with his military and humanitarian contributions. This makes Howard a complicated person to comprehend and his technical contributions difficult to ascertain and interpret. Howard graduated from Bowdoin College at age 19 and then entered USMA. Upon his graduation in 1854, he worked on ordnance issues at the Watervliet Arsenal, NY and in FL. For the next four years, he taught mathematics at West Point for department head **Albert Church (USMA 1828)**. Howard resigned his Regular Army commission at the beginning of the Civil War to serve in the volunteers, as a battle commander in many important battles. Even though he lost an arm at the Battle of Fair Oaks, he quickly returned to his field command. Howard's tactical field decisions at Chancellorsville and Gettysburg were criticized, but his personal courage was never questioned. A controversial leader because of his strong religious beliefs, he was often called "the Christian Soldier," "Biblical soldier," or "Havelock of the Army." After the Civil War, Howard was given the unique duty as Director of the Bureau of Refugees, Freedmen, and Abandoned Lands, which was charged with distributing abandoned lands to emancipated slaves and caring for the former slaves by providing food, shelter, medical care, and education. Howard's staff consisted mostly of Army officers, who did not always relish or approve of their mission. He made detailed plans, but many of his efforts were sabotaged by the political leadership, competing priorities in government, staff disinterest, or his own inexperience. The most successful part of Howard's work with the Freedmen's Bureau came in the area of education. The Bureau maintained many successful primary schools in the

South and established several black colleges and normal schools. He was a co-founder of Howard University in Washington, DC and served as its first President from 1869 to 1874. He was able to raise funds, build a viable campus, establish a strong curriculum, and set high standards of study. While many of his actions were controversial in terms of proper use of funds and resources, he was cleared of wrongdoing even though his reputation was clouded by the inquiry. In general, his professional role as an administrator in this important government service effort has been judged as a failure, yet his personal commitment to this humanitarian effort on behalf of African-Americans and racial integration in America has been judged as exceptional. The next phase of Howard's diverse professional life took him back into military service with involvement with a different minority – the Native Americans. In 1872, he went west to negotiate a treaty with Cochise. He followed that mission with military operations against other Indian groups including the Nez Perce and Paiutes. These campaigns have been judged as partial successes, and although Howard had sympathy for the Indians, he never considered this humanitarian work. They were strictly military operations against a hostile enemy. As was usually the case in his career, Howard's next duty was yet another completely different type of activity – the Superintendency of USMA. His tenure in this position (1880-1881) was short and uneventful. After six more years of coordinating operations against Indians, he moved east to New York for his last six years of Army duty as a commander of the regional forces. Upon retirement from the Army, Howard wrote his memoirs and raised money for the Lincoln Memorial University in

Appalachia. Howard's life was certainly both rich and complex, and his contributions were significant in many areas. While history has judged him as a mediocre administrator and military tactician and a controversial figure, he was a good person, who made a difference in the world by serving his fellow people in an honorable and dedicated manner.

References:

Carpenter, John Alcott, *Sword and Olive Branch: Oliver Otis Howard*, Fordham University Press, New York, 1999.

McFeely's William, *Yankee Stepfather: General O. O. Howard and the Freedmen*, Yale University Press, New Haven, CT, 1968.

| USMA 1855 | Junius Brutus Wheeler | Engineer |

1831 (NC) – 15 July 1886 (Lenoir, NC)
Graduate # 1681 (5th out of 34), listed in *AR* (1887)

Military Service:
1855-1858: Frontier duty in TX, OR, WA
1863-1865: Combat duty in Civil War (Red River, Elkins Ferry, Jenkins Ferry)
1870-1871: Duty in Office of Chief of Army Engineers, Washington, DC

Professional Service:
1858-1859: Topographic engineer in OR and WA
1859-1863: Assistant Professor of Mathematics, USMA
1865-1870: Engineer duty to improve harbors on Great Lakes
1871-1884: Professor of Engineering, USMA

J. B. WHEELER began his military career in the cavalry after his West Point graduation in 1855. His first duty was on the frontier in Texas, which was followed by service on the Pacific Coast. Wheeler transferred to the topographical engineers and worked on surveys in WA and OR. In 1859, he returned to USMA to teach mathematics for four years. He entered combat action in the Civil War in 1863. His assignment was with the Army of Arkansas, where he fought in several skirmishes. After the war, he returned to construction duty as a member of the Corps of Engineers, working to improve harbors on the Great Lakes for five years. After one year in staff work at the Office of the Chief of Army Engineers, Wheeler reentered academic duty as the Department Head and Professor of Civil and Military Engineering and the Science of War at USMA. Serving from 1871 to 1884 and succeeding the legendary engineering professor **Dennis Mahan (USMA 1824)**, he had the opportunity to reconstitute the engineering and academic programs at the Academy. As his academic title indicates, he followed his predecessor's hallmark and focused West Point's engineering program on civil engineering and military applications during his professorship. This left the program somewhat out-of-date with the new aspects and disciplines of engineering in the late 19th century. Wheeler's writings also show this perspective. He authored textbooks entitled *Elements of the Art and Science of War* (1878), *Elements of Military Engineering* (1883), and *Elements of Civil Engineering* (1884). While Wheeler was a highly competent and successful engineer, he never had the opportunity to work in the new areas of engineering or visit other schools or programs with new curricula and modern pedagogy. West Point had lost an opportunity to modernize its technical program during Wheeler's tenure at the Academy.

USMA 1855   ## Alexander Stewart Webb   **Mathematician**

15 February 1835 (New York, NY) – 12 February 1911 (Riverdale, NY)
Graduate # 1689 (13th out of 34), listed in *DAB, NCAB, AR* (1911)

Military Service:

1855-1856: Combat duty in Seminole War, FL
1856-1857: Garrison duty in MA and MN
1861-1865: Combat duty in Civil War (Bull Run, Yorktown, Mechanicsville, Richmond, Antietam, Chancellorsville, Gettysburg, Wilderness, Spotsylvania) (Major General)
            (wounded at Gettysburg and Spotsylvania) (Medal of Hoonor-awarded in 1891)

Professional Service:

1857-1861: Assistant Professor of Mathematics, USMA
1866-1868: Assistant Professor of Geography, USMA
1869-1902: President, College of the City of New York

A. S. WEBB entered the artillery upon graduation from West Point in 1855. Almost immediately, he found himself in combat in FL against the Seminole Indians. In 1857, he began a four-year assignment teaching mathematics at West Point, where he developed

cadets as problem solvers and technological leaders. At the start of the Civil War, Webb saw considerable field combat duty in artillery units. Webb was a brave, successful combatant and field leader and was awarded the Medal of Honor for his bravery at the Battle of Gettysburg. He continued his brilliant command at Spottsylvania, where he was severely wounded. Throughout the war, Webb was an inspiring leader and a brave fighter. After the war, Webb taught geography at the Academy for two years before leaving the Army in 1869 to become President of the College of the

City of New York, succeeding the immensely popular and successful first president of the school, **Horace Webster (USMA 1818)**. Webb was a fine administrator and became a popular academic leader. However, Webb's tenure at the college was one of stagnation as he steadfastly maintained the traditional curriculum and rigid academic program (similar to West Point model) that Webster had initiated. Webb left the college in good financial condition when he retired in 1902. Among his numerous academic accolades was an honorary degree from Hobart College, NY.

USMA 1857 | **Edward Porter Alexander** | **Engineer**

26 May 1835 (Washington, GA) – 28 April 1910 (Savannah, GA)
Graduate # 1762 (3rd of 38), (mathematician), listed in *DAB, ANB, NCAB, AR* (1910*)*

Military Service:

1857-1861: U.S. Army service in technical duties
1858: Expedition against the Mormons in Utah
1861-1865: Confederate Army (signal, ordnance, artillery) (Brigadier General) (Manassas, Antietam, Fredericksburg, Chancellorsville, Gettysburg)

Professional Service:

1857-1860: Assistant Professor of Practical Military Engineering, USMA
1859-1860: Designer of wig-wag system of signal flags and lanterns
1860-1861: Construction engineer for fortifications on Alcatraz Island, CA
1866-1869: Professor of Mathematics and Engineering, University of South Carolina
1869-1871: President, Columbia Oil Company (cottonseed oil)
1870-1872: Actuary for insurance company
1871-1892: Superintendent/President of several railroad companies
1885-1887: Government Director of Union Pacific Railroad
1897-1900: Arbitrator of boundary dispute between Nicaragua and Costa Rica

---

E. P. ALEXANDER was the Professor of Mathematics and Engineering at two schools (USMA and University of South Carolina) for a total of six years. In addition to teaching cadets during his first assignment after graduation, he used his creative abilities to help Albert Myer design the wig-wag communication system using signal flags and lanterns. He was a multi-talented, versatile officer, who used his technical skills in engineering, signal communications, ordnance, and artillery on behalf of the Confederate Army during the Civil War. Many of his assignments during the war made direct use of his technical abilities. He helped design several communication systems for the Confederacy and supervised the deployment of the South's only observation balloon, in which he went aloft as the observer. As the Confederate Army's premier artillerist (Longstreet's Chief of Artillery and one of Lee's hand-picked specialists), he directed and designed the cannon fire for many major battles. He is well known as the artillery director for the barrage that preceded the ill-fated

Pickett's charge at Gettysburg. After the Civil War, he used his organizational talents in the railroad business. In that role, he was called "the young Napoleon of the railways." He was a student of the technical aspects of railroading and wrote two publications on the subject, *On Various Railroad Questions* and *Railway Practice*. After retirement from his railroad work, he owned and farmed land on two islands off the coast of South Carolina. President Grover Cleveland hunted ducks on these lands with Alexander and other government dignitaries. Alexander used his sense of judgement in fairness and precision in arbitrating a boundary dispute between Nicaragua and Costa Rica. He also served on a commission to investigate blockages in the flow of the Columbia River. Alexander was prolific in his writings about the Civil War and wrote several important and brilliant essays and two highly acclaimed memoirs, *Fighting for the Confederacy: The Personal Recollections for General Edward Porter Alexander* and *Military Memoirs of a Confederate*. Alexander's life is often compared with that of Joshua Lawrence Chamberlain of the Union Army.

Reference: Kline, Maury, *Edward Porter Alexander*, University of Georgia Press, Athens, 1971.

USMA 1857 || **Henry Martyn Robert** || **Engineer**

2 May 1837 (Robertville, SC) – 1 May 1923 (Hornell, NY)
Graduate # 1763 (4th out of 38), listed in *DAB, ANB, NCAB, AR* (1925)

Military Service:
1858-1860: Frontier duty in WA
1861-1865: Combat engineer in construction of defenses of Washington, DC
1901:   Chief of Army Engineers, Washington, DC

Professional Service:
1857-1858: Assistant Professor of Natural and Experimental Philosophy and of Practical Military
             Engineering, USMA
1865-1867: Assistant Professor of Practical Military Engineering, USMA
1867-1871: Construction engineer for San Francisco harbor and lighthouse
1871-1873: Construction engineer of harbors and lighthouses in WI, MI, NY, IL, OH
1875-1885: Construction engineer for projects on Great Lakes, NY harbor and Gulf of Mexico,
             Cumberland, TX and cities in Mexico
1900-1910: Consulting engineer for Galveston, TX and cities in Mexico

H. M. ROBERT graduated in the Military Academy class of 1857. He chose his commission in the Corps of Engineers and taught science and engineering at the Military Academy after a tour as a combat and construction engineer during the Civil War. Following his academic service, Robert explored routes for wagon roads in the West and engaged in fortification work in Puget Sound, WA. During the Civil War, he worked on the defenses of Washington, DC and Philadelphia, PA. Robert served as a construction engineer of the Army's Division of the Pacific Coast from 1867 to 1871. He then spent two years improving rivers in Oregon and Washington and six years developing the harbors in Wisconsin and Michigan on the Great Lakes. He subsequently improved the facilities and navigation channels of harbors of Oswego, NY and Philadelphia, PA. His next duty was to construct efficient locks and dams on the Cumberland and Tennessee Rivers. As Southwest Division Engineer from 1897 to 1901, Robert studied various methods on how to deepen the Mississippi River for better navigation. He was President of the Army Board of Engineers from 1895 to 1901. Appointed Chief of Army Engineers in 1901, he then retired from the Army three days later. He became famous for his *Pocket Manual of Rules of Order,* a book on parliamentary law published in 1876. It is better known today as *Robert's Rules of Order.* He began work on this document during the Civil War, when he was embarrassed by not knowing the proper procedures for conducting a public meeting. Refining the steps over the course of nearly ten years, his system was designed so that the majority would prevail, but the minority would be heard, all within the bounds of controlled emotions and proper courtesy and respect for one another. His major engineering work was the seawall that protected Galveston Harbor in Texas. Built after a major hurricane in 1900 (the deadliest natural disaster in U.S. history with over 10,000 deaths), this seawall was carefully designed and constructed with state-of-the-art practices to prevent flooding and erosion. He also helped raise the city by filling the low lands with over 16 million cubic yards of sand pumped out of the bay. This feat by the Army Corps of Engineers, combined with the humanitarian aid from the Red Cross led by Clara Barton, was one of the greatest disaster relief efforts in U.S. history. Robert also wrote several technical reports on construction practices for the Corps of Engineers. Robert's ability to organize endeavors, whether an engineering project through his systematic solution process or an organizational meeting through his rules of order, was his hallmark and legacy.

USMA 1859 | **William Emery Merrill** | **Engineer**

11 October 1837 (Fort Howard, WI) – 14 December 1891
Graduate # 1825 (1ˢᵗ out of 22), listed in *DAB, NCAB, AR* (1892)

Military Service:
1861-1865: Combat engineer in Civil War (Prisoner of War 1861-1862) (Penninsular Campaign, Yorktown, Cedar Mountain, Manasses, Tennessee Campaign, Chickamauga, Missionary Ridge)
1865-1867: Various staff engineer in Washington, DC
1867-1870: Staff engineer in Missouri Territory

Professional Service:
1859-1860: Construction engineer at Ft. Pulaski, GA

1860-1861:   Assistant Professor of Engineering, USMA
1870-1878:   Construction engineer for harbors and rivers (Great Lakes, Ohio River, Mississippi River)
1878:   Visit to Europe to study moveable dam construction
1878-1888:   Construction engineer for rivers and canals in various states
1889:   U.S. representation at the Congress of Engineers in Paris

---

W. E. MERRILL attended West Point during the period when the program was five years in duration. The additional year was included in order to add more humanities to the science-dominated curriculum. Neither the science nor humanities caused Merrill great difficulty as he finished first in his class. After a year of construction engineering in the field and a year of teaching engineering at West Point, Merrill became a combat engineer at the outbreak of the Civil War. He served in several areas in various commands and was always valued as a bright, innovative engineer who significantly helped his unit in combat engagements. Merrill was captured and held prisoner for several months, but escaped. After the war, he continued to serve as a military staff engineer for five years before returning to construction aspects of the Corps of Engineers. Post 1870, he worked on rivers, harbors, and canals, becoming America's expert on the construction of locks and dams. Traveling to Europe to study movable dams, he later employed this device on the Ohio River. He lived long enough to see the beginnings of his design work on the Ohio River, but the entire project was not completed for nearly 40 years. Merrill authored many studies on river and canal navigation. In 1870, his book *Iron Truss Bridges for Railroads* was published. In 1889, he represented the United States at the Congress of Engineers in Paris. A brilliant and dedicated engineer, Merrill set the standards of scholarship and service for more than a generation of Corps of Engineer officers.

USMA 1859   Samuel Henry Lockett   Engineer

6 July 1837 (Mecklenburg County, VA) – 12 October 1891 (Bogota, Columbia, South America)
Graduate # 1826 (2nd out of 22), listed in *AR* (1892)

Military Service:

1859-1860:   Military instructor at USMA
1861-1865:   Combat duty in Confederate Army during Civil War (Corinth, Shiloh, Vicksburg, Mobile)
                   (Prisoner of war)
1875-1877:   Engineer Officer in Egyptian Army

Professional Service:

1860-1861:   Construction engineer, Ft. Pulaski, GA and Ft. Clinch, FL
1865-1867:   Professor of Mathematics and Natural Science, Judson Institute, Marion, AL
1867-1873:   Professor of Engineering and Mechanics, Louisiana State University
1869-1873:   Topographic engineer for Survey of Louisiana
1873-1874:   President, Calhoun College, AL
1877-1883:   Professor of Mathematics and Mechanics, East Tennessee State University

1883-1884: Engineer for the construction of the pedestal for the Statue of Liberty, New York Harbor
1884-1888: Construction engineer for water and gas works in various cities in the U.S.
1888-1891: Construction engineer for railroads and public works in Chile and Columbia

S. H. LOCKETT graduated from Howard College before entering USMA. He remained at the Academy after graduation to teach tactics. After one year of construction duty in FL and GA, Lockett resigned from the U.S. Army to join the Confederacy. Serving as a combat engineer in the Mississippi area, he worked for **P. G. T. Beauregard (USMA 1838)** and Joseph E. Johnston (USMA 1829). Lockett was a skillful combat engineer and an innovative military problem solver. After the war, he taught mathematics and sciences in AL and then became Professor of Mechanics and Engineering at Louisiana State University. While there, he conducted geological surveys for the state and produced various maps of the area. After one year as President of Calhoun College, Lockett was appointed an officer in the Egyptian Army through a nomination by General W. T. Sherman (USMA 1840), Commander of the U.S. Army. In 1876, he was in a campaign to Abyssinia where he won accolades for both his military and scientific contributions from the Egyptian government. In 1877, Lockett returned to America and academics as the Professor of Mathematics and Mechanics at East Tennessee University. In 1883, he was enticed into a new endeavor. Lockett partnered with Charles Stone (USMA 1845), who had been his Commanding General in the Egyptian Army. Stone hired Lockett to help him with the construction of the pedestal for the Statue of Liberty. After his work on the statue was complete, Lockett engineered water works and gas works for various cities in the United States. In 1888, he began work on railroad and waterworks projects in Columbia, South America, where he died in 1891. Lockett was a maverick, jumping from one adventure to another, in and out of academics and military service, and moving to many places all over the world.

USMA 1860    **Horace Porter**   **Engineer**

15 April 1837 (Huntingdon, PA) – 29 May 1921 (New York , NY)
Graduate # 1849 (3rd out of 41), (ordnance), listed *ANB, NCAB*

Military Service:
1861-1865: Combat duty in Civil War (Port Royal, Ft. Pulaski, Tennessee Campaign, Antietam, Chickamauga, Chattanooga, Wilderness, Spottsylvania, Cold Harbor, Appomattox) (Medal of Honor for action at Chickamauga) (Brigadier General)
1864-1869: Aide-de-Camp and secretary to Ulysses S. Grant

1869-1873: Secretary to the President of the United States

Professional Service:
1860-1861: Ordnance duty at Watervliet Arsenal, NY
1873-1896: Vice President and engineer, Pullman Car company
1875-1879: Construction engineer for elevated train line in New York City

---

H. Porter attended Lawrence Scientific School at Harvard College for one year before he entered the five-year program at USMA. Upon his graduation in 1860, he was commissioned in Ordnance Corps and served at Watervliet Arsenal for one year before the start of the Civil War. Porter was assigned to the Port Royal Expedition. He played a major role controlling the artillery during the siege of Fort Pulaski, GA. As Chief of Ordnance for his Army, he fought at Antietam and Chattanooga. His efforts to rally and lead fleeing soldiers at Chickamauga gained him the Medal of Honor (awarded 40 years later). Porter had impressed Ulysses S. Grant (USMA 1843) with his knowledge of military operations. Grant as the new General-in-Chief of the Union Army selected Porter as his aide-de-camp in 1864. After the war, Porter remained on Grant's staff. When Grant became President, Porter stayed on active Army duty as the Secretary to the President. Porter resigned from the Army in 1872 and worked as an engineer for elevated rail construction. In 1897, Porter became the United States Ambassador to France. In 1905, he completed his foreign service and returned to the United States. Porter authored many magazine articles and books about his association with Grant. While he was a brilliant scientist, he had little dedicated time to devote to science, given his long tenure in political and public service.

USMA 1860 | **Benjamin F. Sloan, Jr.** | **Scientist**

16 May 1836 (SC) – 19 February 1923 (Biltmore, NC)
Graduate # 1853 (7th out of 41), (mathematician, engineer, educator), listed in *NCAB, AR* (1925)

Military Service:
1860-1861: Frontier duty in NM
1861-1865: Combat duty in the Confederate Army during the Civil War

Professional Service:
1867-1868: Civil Engineer
1876-1880: Professor of Mathematics, Agricultural College of Mississippi
1880-1887: Professor of Mathematics and Civil Engineering, University of South Carolina

1887-1902: Professor of Physics and Civil Engineering, University of South Carolina
1902-1908: President, University of South Carolina

B. SLOAN spent just one year in frontier duty with the Dragoons after graduation from West Point. At that time, he resigned his Army commission to join the military forces of the Confederacy. After the Civil War, Sloan was a practicing civil engineer before taking an academic position in 1876. After teaching mathematics at the Agricultural College in Mississippi for four years, Sloan found his professional home at the University of South Carolina. For 28 years, he either taught mathematics, science, or engineering or led the school as its President. Sloan was a scholar of the top rank at the University. As the University's President, he was a strong and caring educator and visible leader setting the tone for the reconstruction of the academic programs of the South. He was a tough disciplinarian, but the students and faculty members at the University praised him for his character and concern for their development. Sloan presided over the centennial of the University of South Carolina in 1905 and retired from his productive career as a technical educator and academic leader in 1908 at age 72.

USMA 1860 | **John Moulder Wilson** | **Engineer**

8 October 1837 (Washington, DC) – 1 February 1919 (Washington, DC)
Graduate # 1858 (12th out of 41), listed in *NCAB, AR* (1919)

Military Service:
1860-1861: Ordnance duty at Ft. Monroe Arsenal, VA
1861-1865: Combat duty in Civil War (Bull Run, Yorktown, Williamsburg, Gaines' Mill, South Mountain, Malvern Hill, Antietam, Memphis, Vicksburg, Ft. Blakely) (Medal of Honor)
1882-1886: Assistant to the Chief of Army Engineers, Washington, DC
1897-1901: Chief of Army Engineers

Professional Service:
1865-1871: Engineer for improvements on Hudson River
1871-1875: Construction engineer for harbor improvements on Lake Ontario and St. Lawrence River
1875-1882: Construction engineer in the northwest
1885-1889: Supervising engineer for buildings and monuments in Washington, DC
1889-1893: Superintendent, USMA
1893-1899: Construction engineer in Washington, DC and New England, and on the Great Lakes

---

J. M. WILSON graduated from the Military Academy in 1860 and was commissioned in the Artillery Corps. He immediately transferred to the Ordnance Corps and served a year at Fort Monroe Arsenal, VA. Seeing heavy combat action during the Civil War, he transferred to the Corps of Topographical Engineers in 1862 and earned the Medal of Honor for fighting at Malvern Hill, VA. He joined the Corps of Engineers in 1863 and fought in AL. After the

Civil War, Wilson worked on Hudson River improvements and drafted plans for the canal around the cascades of the Columbia River. He improved the facilities and navigation of the Great Lakes harbors of Oswego, NY; Cleveland, OH; and Toledo, OH. Wilson was in charge of public buildings and grounds in Washington, DC during both Grover Cleveland

administrations and was Superintendent of the Military Academy from 1889 to 1893. Among those on his academic staff were **Edgar Bass (USMA 1868)** in mathematics, **Peter Michie (USMA 1863)** in science, and **James Mercur (USMA 1866)** in engineering. Before his appointment as Chief of Army Engineers, he was the Northeast Division Engineer. As the Chief of Army Engineers, Wilson directed the Corps' activities during the Spanish-American War. Retiring in 1901, he still remained a prominent figure in the cultural, political, and military scene of Washington, DC. Among his many tributes were an honorary degree from Columbian University, Washington, DC and memberships in the American Society of Civil Engineers and the Washington Academy of Sciences, which was established in 1898 by Alexander Graham Bell.

USMA May 1861 | **John Whitney Barlow** | **Engineer**

26 June 1838 (Perry, NY) – 27 February 1914 (Jerusalem, Palastine)
Graduate # 1901 (14th out of 45), listed in *DAB, AR* (1915)

Military Service:
1861-1866: Combat and engineering duties in Civil War (Bull Run, Virginia Peninsular Campaign, Yorktown, Williamsburg, Malvern Hill, Gettysburg, Atlanta, Nashville)

Professional Service:
1864:   Assistant Professor of Mathematics, USMA
1865-1869: Construction engineer at Ft. Cinch, FL
1869-1870: Construction engineer at Ft. Montgomery, NY
1870-1874: Construction engineer in Missouri and frontier West
1874-1883: Construction engineer for fortifications and harbors in New England
1883-1886: Construction engineer for harbors and rivers on Great Lakes and various rivers in the West
1886-1890: Chief engineer of Muscle Shoals Canal, AL
1892-1896: Topographic engineer marking the U.S.-Mexico border.
1888-1901: Supervising engineer for projects in the Northwest and in New England
1901:   Chief of Army Engineers for one day
1902-1903: Inspecting engineer for markers along the Mexican border

Upon graduation from West Point, **J. W. Barlow** entered the Civil War as an artillery officer. After several battles, he transferred to the Corps of Engineers and served as a topographic and bridging engineer in several engagements. General George Thomas (USMA 1823) placed him in charge of the defenses of

Nashville, TN. After the war, Barlow was assigned fortification construction duties at several posts before being sent to frontier duty. In 1871, he commanded a detachment of engineers who, along with members of the Geological Survey, explored the Yellowstone Park area. As a result of his detailed reports, Congress made Yellowstone a National Park in 1872. Barlow's report was eventually published by the government. After more construction assignments, Barlow became the chief engineer of the canal around the Muscle Shoals of the Tennessee River. In 1890, this canal opened to shipping traffic. Over a four year span, Barlow supervised the marking of the U.S.-Mexican border. On 2 May 1901, he advanced to Brigadier General and Chief of Army Engineers. On the next day, he retired from the Army. At the request of the State Department, he continued to work after his military retirement with officials from Mexico on the markers and monuments along the border. Barlow died while on a trip to the Holy Lands in 1914. He is remembered as a fine engineer and a bold, adventurous explorer.

| USMA June 1861 | **Alfred Mordecai** | Mathematician |

1841 (PA) – 19 January 1920 (Washington, DC)
Graduate # 1941 (9th out of 34), (ordnance), listed in *NCAB, AR* (1920)

Military Service:
1861-1865: Combat duty in Civil War (Manassas, Morris Island, Ft. Sumter)

Professional Service:
1861-1862: Assistant Professor of Mathematics, USMA
1861-1863: Ordnance duties as inspector and Chief of Ordnance
1865-1869: Assistant Professor of Ordnance, USMA
1869-1874: Ordnance duties in FL, KS, MA
1874-1881: Assistant Professor of Ordnance, USMA
1881-1892: Ordnance duties at Springfield Armory, MA
1898-1899: Ordnance duty at Watervliet Arsenal, NY
1899-1902: Ordnance duty at Benicia Arsenal, CA
1902-1904: Ordnance staff duty at Office of Chief of Ordnance, Washington, DC (Brigadier General)

A. Mordecai graduated from West Point in 1861, 38 years after his father with the same name. Mordecai was commissioned as a topographic engineer, but transferred just two months later to his father's branch, the Ordnance Corps. Mordecai immediately joined in preparation for the Civil War. He fought in the Battle of Bull Run and then returned to West Point to teach mathematics for one year. While there, he served as an inspector of ordnance at the West Point Foundry. Even though Mordecai was inexperienced, the war situation left him as the most senior ordnance officer available in the Ordnance Bureau in Washington, DC. Therefore, Mordecai was the acting Chief of Ordnance for the Army for almost a year during the war. Returning to combat duty in 1864, Mordecai fought in several battles. Transferring back to ordnance duties when the war concluded, Mordecai returned to the

West Point faculty, this time as an Assistant Professor of Ordnance for four years. For five more years, Mordecai commanded arsenals and developed new Army munitions. From 1874 to 1881, Mordecai returned to the classroom at West Point for this third tour at the Academy. Back in the field, Mordecai commanded two large arsenals in New York State until 1892. He chaired commissions to study carbines, rifled cannons, gun manufacturing, fortification design, machine guns, cartridge design, carriage design and weapon testing. In 1892, Mordecai took charge of Springfield Armory, MA. Just six years later, he was back at Watervliet Arsenal, and then a year later, he was reassigned to Benicia Arsenal in CA. His last two years of

military service were back in the Office of the Chief of Ordnance in Washington, DC. Mordecai was considered the most knowledgeable and experienced ordnance officer in the Army since his father.

USMA 1862 **George Lewis Gillespie, Jr.** **Engineer**

7 October 1841 (Kingston, TN) – 27 September 1913 (Saratoga Springs, NY)
Graduate # 1968 (2nd out of 29), listed in *NCAB, AR* (1914)

Military Service:
1862-1865: Combat duty in Civil War (Antietam, Harper's Ferry, Fredericksburg, Chancellorsville, Petersburg, Five Forks, Sailor's Creek, and others; Bethesda Church - Medal of Honor)
1901-1903: Chief of Army Engineers, Washington, DC
1901: Acting Secretary of War (when President McKinley was assassinated)
1902-1903: Special duty carrying out provisions of Spanish-American War
1904-1905: Assistant Chief of Staff, War Department

Professional Service:
1866-1869: Engineer duty in LA, TX, NH, and MA
1869-1873: Engineer duty in constructing lighthouses and improving

harbors on the Great Lakes
1874-1877: Engineer duty for public works in the West
1877-1878: Visit to Europe
1878-1881: Engineer for public works in OR and WA
1881-1890: Engineer duty improving and building New York Harbor
1890-1894: Engineer duty improving harbors and rivers in MA, CT
1894: Visit to Europe representing U.S. at Congress on Navigation, The Netherlands
1894-1897: Engineer for rivers and fortifications in FL and GA
1896-1898: Engineer for projects in Northeast

G. L. GILLESPIE graduated second in the class of 1862 at the Military Academy and was commissioned in the Corps of Engineers. A southerner who remained loyal to the Union, Gillespie joined the Army of the Potomac in September 1862. He commanded engineer units that built fortifications and pontoon bridges throughout the Virginia campaigns until the Appomattox surrender. He received the Medal of Honor for carrying dispatches through enemy lines under withering fire to General Phillip Sheridan (USMA 1853) at the Battle of Bethesda Church. He was Sheridan's chief engineer in latter battles of the war. After the Civil War, Gillespie supervised the improvement of harbor facilities at Cleveland, Chicago, Boston, and New York. Later, he initiated the construction of the canal at the cascades of the Columbia River and built the famous lighthouse on Tillamook Rock off the Oregon Coast. Gillespie served on the Board of Engineers and for six years was President of the Mississippi River Commission, a position of tremendous importance to the Corps of Engineers' efforts in the middle half of the United States. He commanded the Army's Department of the East in 1898. While Chief of Army Engineers from 1901 to 1903, he was acting Secretary of War in August 1901 when President McKinley died and was in charge of the ceremonies at McKinley's funeral. He served as Army Assistant Chief of Staff from 1904 to 1905 with the rank of Major General. Gillespie retired from the Army in 1905.

USMA 1863   ‖ **Peter Smith Michie** ‖   **Scientist**

24 March 1839 (Brechin, Scotland) – 16 February 1901 (West Point, NY)
Graduate # 1996 (2nd out of 25), listed in *DAB, BDAS, AR* (1901)

Military Service:
1863-1865: Combat duty in Civil War (Charleston, Ft. Sumter, Ft. Wagner, Cole's Island, Olustee,

Ft. Harrison, Appomattox) (Brigadier General)

Professional Service:
1867-1871:   Assistant Professor of Engineering, USMA (also teaching military engineering and chemistry)
1871-1901:   Professor of Natural and Experimental Philosophy, USMA
1871-1901:   Member of Board of Overseers of Thayer School of Engineering, Dartmouth College, NH
1882-1900:   Author of numerous scientific textbooks

P. S. MICHIE'S family moved to America in 1843. Michie chose the Corps of Engineers, entering combat duty immediately after graduating in 1863. Michie, along with his West Point classmates, was afforded all four years of the Academy's program despite the need for soldiers to fight in the Civil War. Michie's combat duties took him to the sieges of Charleston, Ft. Sumter, and Ft. Wagner, where he became known for his work in building protected approaches to the forts. He then went on to various combat units, becoming the chief engineer and a valuable staff officer for several major combat units. In just one and a half years after commissioning, he was a brevet Brigadier General. Ulysses S. Grant (USMA 1843) commented that Michie was "one of the most deserving young officers in the service."

After the war, Michie's career turned to academics as he became a professor at West Point for 34 years. From 1867 to 1871, he taught engineering and chemistry. Then in 1871, he was selected to be the Professor of Natural and Experimental Philosophy and Head of the Department. For the next 30 years, Michie set the standards in science for the West Point cadets as engineers-in-training. He wrote textbooks in several areas of science and mechanics – waves, sound, light, analytical mechanics, hydro-mechanics, and seacoast defenses. Michie was a popular academic and military leader at West Point. Dedicated and hard working, he was popular with both cadets and faculty officers. During his tenure, some progress was made in modernizing the Academy's curriculum and pedagogy. The science curriculum evolved to include new topics that were being initiated at other institutions and needed for future engineers. As an outreach to the academic community, Michie was an overseer of the Thayer School of Engineering at Dartmouth College. Among his many honors were degrees from Princeton College, NJ and Dartmouth College, NH.

USMA 1863 | **William Rice King** | **Engineer**

15 December 1839 (Eagle Ridge, NY) – 18 May 1898 (Rock Island, IL)
Graduate # 1999 (5th out of 25), listed in *AR* (1898)

Military Service:
1863-1865: Combat engineer duty in Civil War (VA, NC)
1865-1870: Staff duty with Office of Chief of Army Engineers, Washington, DC

Professional Service:
1870-1876: Engineer duty at Willet's Point, NY
1876-1886: Engineer duty on rivers and harbors of Tennessee and Cumberland Rivers
1886-1895: Commandant of the Engineer School of Application, Willet's Point, NY
1895-1898: Engineer duty to improve the navigation of the Mississippi River, Rock Island, IL

W. R. KING was industrious and mechanically gifted as a youth as evidenced by building a bridge over the Hoosick River, NY and conducting professional land surveys before he entered USMA. Graduating during the Civil War, he went immediately into combat as an engineer for units engaged in NC and VA. After the war, he served in the Office of the Chief of Army Engineers in Washington, DC. During this assignment, he experimented with torpedoes (sea mines), projectiles, and recoil mechanisms. For the 28 years following this staff and research work, King was an active field engineer, building bridges, tunnels, roads, and canals. Designing new types of canal locks and sluices, he improved navigation on several rivers and enhanced the port facilities of several harbors. For nearly ten years of his military career, he had the opportunity to teach engineering students at the Engineer School of Application at Willet's Point, NY. King was a prolific author, among his publications were numerous articles on torpedoes, coast artillery weapons, armor plating of fortifications, and gun carriages. As an energetic and creative engineer, King made tremendous contributions to both America's infrastructure and the weapons of the U.S. Army.

USMA 1863 | **William Henry Harrison Benyaurd** | **Engineer**

17 May 1840 (Philadelphia, PA) – 7 February 1900 (New York, NY)
Graduate # 2000 (6th out of 25), listed in *AR* (1900)

Military Service:
1863-1865: Engineer and combat duty in the Civil War (defense of Pittsburgh, bridges at Rappahannock and Richmond, Siege of Petersburg, Five Forks, VA) (Medal of Honor)
1865-1866: Commander of engineer troops at West Point, NY

Professional Service:
1866-1869: Assistant Professor of Engineering, USMA

1869-1872: Construction engineer for pontoon bridge across the Mississippi River at Rock Island, IL
1872-1882: Engineer for river and harbor improvements in MS, LA, TX, and IL
1884-1889: Construction engineer for fortifications in CA
1890-1895: Civil engineer for improvements of rivers, harbors, and fortifications
1890-1891: Member of Engineer Board for Mining in CA
1891-1895: Construction engineer for fortifications in CA
1895-1899: Civil engineer for improvements of harbors, rivers, and fortifications in FL, GA
1898-1899: Combat engineer for fortifications in Spanish-American War (Key West, FL)
1899-1900: Engineer duty in New York Harbor

W. H. H. Benyaurd entered West Point just before the Civil War and was a cadet during the first two years of America's bloody battles. He went immediately into combat engineering service upon his graduation in 1863. He took part in building pontoon bridges across rivers at several important times during the Civil War. At Five Forks, Benyaurd and **Gouverneur Warren (USMA 1850)** rallied their troops to continue their attacks. Showing tremendous bravery, Benyaurd eventually advanced into the enemy ranks where he captured seven prisoners, earning the Medal of Honor for his actions. After the war, he taught engineering at the Academy before launching into a 30-year career of improving harbors, rivers, and fortifications around the country. Benyaurd was a force of leadership and technical expertise in the Corps of Engineers. In addition to supervising challenging field construction work, he served on several commissions and boards that considered important engineering issues. In 1898, he re-entered combat duty during the Spanish-American War. His final assignment was in New York Harbor where he continued his river and harbor work, when he died while still in active Army service. Benyaurd was both a bold, fearless soldier (as evidenced by his Medal of Honor) and a strong, capable engineer (as evidenced by over 30 years of outstanding accomplishments in fieldwork).

USMA 1864   ‖ **Oswald Herbert Ernst** ‖   **Engineer**

27 June 1842 (Cincinnati, OH) – 21 March 1926 (Washington, DC)
Graduate # 2025 (6th out of 27), listed in *DAB, ANB, NCAB, AR* (1926)

Military Service:
1864-1865: Combat duty in Civil War (Georgia Campaign, Atlanta, Ezra Church)
1898-1899: Combat duty in Spanish-American War (Puerto Rico, Cuba)

Professional Service:
1865-1868: Construction engineer for fortifications in San Francisco, CA

1868-1871: Command at Engineer School of Application, Willet's Point, NY
1871-1878: Assistant Professor of Practical Military Engineering, USMA
1878-1889: Engineer for navigation and harbor improvements on Osage, Mississippi, Ohio, Missouri, and Illinois Rivers
1889-1893: Construction engineer for buildings and monuments in Washington, DC
1893-1898: Superintendent, USMA
1899-1906: Engineer for design of Panama Canal and harbor improvements in Chicago, IL and Baltimore, MD
1906-1916: Consulting engineer on various projects

O. H. ERNST studied at Harvard University for two years before entering West Point. He selected the Corps of Engineers and entered combat duty upon his graduation in 1864. After taking part in the Georgia Campaign, he earned accolades and promotion for his combat service. From 1865 to 1868, Ernst worked on the fortifications in San Francisco. He then had the opportunity to help **Henry Abbot (USMA 1854)** with the development of the Engineer School of Application at Willet's Point, NY for three years. While in that assignment, he went to Spain in 1870 to make observations and measurements of the solar eclipse. Ernst's next seven years were spent teaching cadets military engineering at West Point. During his time at the Academy, Ernst wrote several important scholarly publications – *Manual of Practical Military Engineering* in 1873 and several articles in *Johnson's Cyclopedia* on technical subjects. In 1878, he began a lengthy stretch of working on river and harbor improvements at various locations. He supervised digging a deep-sea channel in the Galveston, TX harbor. In 1889, Ernst moved to Washington, DC to supervise the work on government buildings and monuments. Specifically, his work on the Washington Monument was significant. His five–year tenure as Superintendent was marked with modernization of the academic program, as the Academy prepared to celebrate its centennial and enter the 20th century. Ernst returned to combat during the Spanish-American War, and his field leadership at Coamo and Asamante again earned him accolades and promotion. After the war, Ernst served on several engineering commissions. His work on the Panama Canal, supporting Abbot's recommendation of a lock-based canal, was significant in the later decision to build such a canal. He spent several years traveling and studying in Europe and Panama in order to finalize his recommendations. Retiring from the Army in 1906, he continued his engineering consulting work for various government projects.

USMA 1865   ‖ **Charles Walker Raymond** ‖   **Engineer**

14 January 1842 (Hartford, CT) – 3 May 1913 (Washington, DC)
Graduate # 2047 (1st out of 68), (scientist), listed in *DAB, AR* (1913)

Military Service:
1865-1866: Assistant to Engineering Board, Boston, MA

1866-1871: Assistant to Engineering Board Pacific Coast
1869-1870: Exploration of the Yukon River, Alaska
1871-1872: Command of engineer company, Willet's Point, NY
1881-1883: Command of engineer company, Willet's Point, NY
1886-1888: Assistant to the Chief of Army Engineers, Washington, DC

Professional Service:
1868-1869: Construction engineer on Pacific Coast
1872-1878: Assistant Professor of Natural and Experimental Philosophy, USMA
1874-1875: Command of expedition to Tasmania to observe transit of Venus
1878-1881: Assistant Professor of Military Engineering, USMA
1883-1886: Civil engineer for river and harbor improvements in MA and on the Mississippi River
1888-1889: Construction engineer for Washington, DC
1889-1904: Construction engineer for Philadelphia Harbor, St. Lawrence Seaway, and Great Lakes
1904-1910: Railroad engineer in New York City

C. W. Raymond graduated from Brooklyn Polytechnic Institute before attending West Point in 1861. Raymond was a cadet during the Civil War, and while his program was not reduced in length, he was sent into field duty as a cadet in 1863 to serve as a staff officer during the Gettysburg campaign. When he graduated in 1865 at the top of his class, Raymond chose to enter the Corps of Engineers. After support and administrative duties assisting engineer boards and working on construction jobs on the Pacific Coast, Raymond went on a geological expedition of the Yukon River. Traveling on the first steamboat on the Alaskan River, Raymond mapped the river and established the United States border in the region. His report was published by the Senate. From 1872 to 1881, he was a science and engineering professor at West Point. While still on the faculty, he spent one year in Tasmania observing the transit of Venus. Raymond engineered the construction of new buildings and the creation of a new water supply system for the Academy. During the 1880's, Raymond was in charge of river and harbor improvements in MA, DE, and PA. He supervised the dredging of the Philadelphia Harbor and the construction of the Delaware breakwater. He designed a navigable, deepwater connection of the Great Lakes to Atlantic Ocean although not all of his plan was implemented. Raymond improved, expanded, and modernized the railroad services (tunnels, tracks, and stations) for New York City. As a foremost expert on excavation, he advised **George Goethals (USMA 1880)** on the digging of the Panama Canal. Raymond was an excellent scientist and engineer. His selfless and supportive personality made him a valuable and well-liked member of the Army Corps of Engineers.

USMA 1866 | **James Mercur** | **Engineer**

1843 (PA) – 21 April 1896 (Fort Monroe, VA)
Graduate # 2116 (2nd out of 41), listed in *AR* (1896)

Military Service:
1872-1876: Engineer staff officer at Willet's Point, NY

Professional Service:
1866-1867: Surveyor of the Great Lakes
1867-1872: Assistant Professor of Natural and Experimental Philosophy, USMA
1876-1881: Demolition engineer, Hell Gate, NY
1881-1884: Engineer for river and harbor improvements, VA, NC, SC
1884:   Engineer for New York Harbor
1884-1896: Professor of Civil and Military Engineering, USMA

J. MERCUR excelled at engineering as a cadet and entered the Corps of Engineers upon his graduation in 1866. After surveying duty on the Great Lakes, he returned to the Academy to teach science. He was so outstanding as a teacher that he was allowed to stay five years. Mercur moved down to Willet's Point in New York City for engineering staff duty before a challenging opportunity presented itself to Mercur. He was assigned to assist **John Newton (USMA 1842)** in removing obstructions in the East River at Hell Gate, NY. This was the largest demolition project in the world and Mercur was the expert at charging the mines with explosives and laying down the electrical fuse. In 1881, he finished his demolition duties and moved south to perform river and harbor duties for the Corps of Engineers operations. In 1884, Newton, as head of the Corps of Engineers, sent Mercur back to New York Harbor as a steward for the City's rivers and harbors. However, later that year, Mercur was selected as the Professor of Civil and Military Engineering and Department Head at West Point and assumed his new academic duties replacing **Junius Wheeler (USMA 1855)**. Mercur immediately took on the challenge of modernizing the engineering program. First, he modified the book by **Dennis Mahan (USMA 1824)** on permanent fortifications. Then he modernized the book on the military attack of fortified places. Finally, Mercur's *Elements of the Art of War* was a vastly improved textbook on the science of warfare. It received many accolades as a valuable technical perspective on the subject. In addition to his military engineering knowledge, Mercur was a specialist in steam engines and cement construction and also studied and wrote on astronomy, geology, and botany. After twelve years as professor, he died while in office. Mercur was a famous Army engineer and a distinguished technical educator.

USMA 1866 | **Frank Soulé, Jr.** | **Engineer**

6 August 1845 (Woodville, MS) – 14 February 1913 (Berkeley, CA)
Graduate # 2125 (11th out of 41), (mathematician, ordnance), listed in *AR* (1913)

Military Service:
1866-1870: Various duties in technical positions

Professional Service:
1866-1867: Ordnance duty at Allegheny Arsenal, PA
1867-1869: Assistant Professor of Mathematics, USMA
1869-1872: Professor of Mathematics, University of California at Berkeley
1872-1908: Professor of Civil Engineering and Astronomy, University of California at Berkeley
1884-1908: Dean of the College of Engineers, University of California at Berkeley

F. SOULÉ entered the Ordnance Corps upon graduation from USMA. After one year of service at Allegheny Arsenal, PA, he taught mathematics at West Point. In 1869, he took a leave of absence, moving out to California to study more mathematics. In 1870, Soulé resigned from the Army to become the Professor of Mathematics at the newly formed University of California at Berkeley. Soulé was involved from the very beginning of the technical program at Berkeley, since the college was founded in 1868 as a result of the Morrill Land Grant Act of 1862. university leader Henry Durant needed a
strong faculty leader in mathematics and engineering so he selected Soulé for his professor. No one at the University was disappointed in this choice. In 1872, Soulé switched over to head the Civil Engineering Department. Then in 1884, he became the Dean of Engineering. During the Spanish-American War, he filled in as the military science instructor at the university. At various times, he consulted with state engineers and politicians for civil works projects in CA. His irrigation survey of the San Joaquin Valley in 1900 was an important contribution to the agriculture of the area. He also wrote a report on the Great San Francisco Earthquake and Fire of 1907, for the Department of the Interior. Soulé was a highly respected faculty member at the growing university and had the pleasure of working with **Edward Holden (USMA 1870)**, when Holden served as President of Berkeley. Soulé was a member of the American Society of Civil Engineers and Sigma Xi honorary scientific society. During his long tenure at the university, he saw it grow from a struggling organization to one of the most significant educational institutions in the United States. Soulé's contributions in that growth and development were significant. He built an observatory, led geodetic studies, operated weather stations, and designed engineering laboratories. He was a beloved teacher, and the entire university closed for his funeral services in 1913.

USMA 1866	**Hiero Benjamin Herr**	Engineer

12 November 1842 (Lancaster Country, PA) – 3 September 1920 (Dillsburg, PA)
Graduate # 2129 (15th out of 41), (mathematician, prospector), listed in *NCAB, AR* (1921)

Military Service:
1866-1867: Garrison duty at Ft. Trumbull, CT

Professional Service:
1867-1869: Assistant Professor of Mathematics, USMA
1869-1874: Professor of Engineering, Mathematics, and Astronomy, Lehigh University, PA
1874-1878: Prospector and engineer for silver mine in CO
1878-1883: Engineer for U.S. government improving navigation on the Mississippi River
1883-1884: Professor of Mathematics for University of California at Berkeley
1884-1899 and 1906-1915: Engineer for public works in Chicago, IL
1900-1908: Engineer for diamond mines in Brazil and gold mines in Mexico

---

H. B. HERR attended the Pennsylvania Normal School before entering USMA. Becoming an artillery officer, he served just three years in the Army after his graduation from USMA in 1866. After one year in garrison in CT, he taught mathematics at the Academy for two years. In civilian life, he took the position of the Professor of Engineering, Mathematics, and Astronomy at the highly technical school, Lehigh University, PA. After teaching for five years, he yearned for more practical and active field work. Herr spent the next ten years as a field engineer working on various projects. First he tried his hand in silver mining in CO, and then he spent time serving the government in public works engineering projects on the Mississippi River, working for fellow West Point graduate, **William Benyuard (USMA 1863)**. When Benyaurd was reassigned, Herr found another West Point graduate that needed his help. This time he replaced his West Point classmate, **Frank Soulé** who was taking a sabbatical leave as the Professor of Mathematics at the University of California at Berkeley for one year. Upon moving east in 1884, he returned to construction engineering, building public works in Chicago, IL and several buildings for the World's Fair. This was followed by more adventure in his professional life as he was hired by business firms to study, analyze, and design diamond mines in Brazil and gold mines in Mexico. Finally, back in Chicago in 1908, he settled into more conventional construction work in the city. Herr was a maverick, often turning setbacks into opportunities, but always finding the exciting action involved in engineering and science.

USMA 1866 | **Henry Harrison Chase Dunwoody** | **Scientist**

23 October 1842 (Highland County, OH) – 1 January 1933 (Interlaken, NY)
Graduate # 2133 (19th out of 41), (meteorologist), *AR* (1933)

Military Service:
1866-1870:   Artillery duty at various places
1898-1900:   Combat duty in Cuba as Chief Signal Officer
             during Spanish American War
1901-1904:   Staff/Signal Officer at DC and NY

Professional Service:
1870-1891:   Meteorological duty in Office of Chief of Signal Corps,
             Washington, DC
1891-1898:   Special detail to Weather Bureau, Washington, DC

H. H. C. Dunwoody grew up in Iowa and worked in the law office of the State Senator who appointed Dunwoody to the Academy. He graduated from USMA and was commissioned in the artillery, but soon transferred to the Signal Corps. In 1870, the Signal Corps established a congressionally mandated national weather service. Chief Signal Officer Albert Myer built up a weather service of international acclaim. It was known that weather systems generally moved from west to east across the country. A system was established for taking meteorological observations at military stations and giving notice of the approach and force of storms via a sequence of telegraph offices. Joseph Henry had done this for some time at the Smithsonian Institute. In a few years, the Signal Office included many forms of meteorological observations and made weather predictions for many purposes. The demands of this new agency required officers familiar with meteorology. General Myer added a school of meteorology to his school of telegraphy and military signaling near Washington, DC. Meteorological experts provided the necessary training for the Army officers. After Myer's death, the fort's name was changed to Fort Myer. Dunwoody taught the meteorology course which included meteorology instruments, cartography, meteorology theory, thermodynamics, weather predictions, and topographic surveying. Some civilian scientists were added to the staff because Army officers were subject to reassignment to other duties. Dunwoody became the leader of the nation's meteorological staff with the duties of weather predictions and storm warnings. When the weather bureau moved to the Department of Agriculture in 1891, Dunwoody was assigned to continue his important work in predicting the weather for the country as the chief of forecasting. His system of sending out storm warnings saved many lives, as he continued this crucial work until 1898. With the outbreak of the Spanish-American War, Dunwoody left meteorological service for combat in Cuba and then after the war performed high-level staff duties in the Signal Corps. Dunwoody retired from the Army in 1904. As a capable and expert researcher in both electronic communications and atmospheric sciences, he invented and patented crystal receivers for radios and after his retirement went into the communications business. He was awarded a medal at the World's Exhibition in 1893 for his ground-breaking work on representing graphically meteorological data and analyzing weather patterns.

USMA 1867 | **Lewis Muhlenberg Haupt** | **Engineer**

31 March 1844 (Philadelphia, PA) – 10 March 1937 (Cynwyd, PA)
Graduate # 2162 (7th out of 63), listed in *NCAB, AR* (1937)

Military Service:
1867-1869: Army duty in technical service

Professional Service:
1867-1869: Survey of the Great Lakes
1869-1870: Examiner for U.S. Patent Office
1872-1875: Assistant Professor of Dynamical Engineering, University of Pennsylvania
1875-1892: Professor of Civil Engineering, University of Pennsylvania
1874-1892: Director of Franklin Institute, Philadelphia, PA
1875: Surveyor of PA in service with the Coast Survey
1877-1902: Member of Nicaragua and Panama Canal Commissions
1900-1902: Research engineer for removal of sand bar in oceans
1902-1904: Construction of jetties in Texas
1906-1915: Professor of Civil Engineering, Franklin Institute, University of Pennsylvania, PA

L. M. HAUPT, son of **Herman Haupt (USMA 1835)**, attended the Lawrence Scientific School of Harvard University before entering West Point. After graduation, he entered the Corps of Engineers and conducted surveys of the Great Lakes. He resigned from the Army in 1869 and began similar topographic work as a civilian in PA. After surveying in PA and VA and developing the Fairmont Park area of Philadelphia, he moved to the U.S. Patent Office as a technical specialist for a brief period. He also served as a traffic engineer for the City of Philadelphia, laying out roadways for efficient travel. In 1872, Haupt began his career in academics. First, he taught as an assistant professor teaching engineering at the University of Pennsylvania. In 1875, he became the Professor of Civil and Mechanical Engineering at the university. As the director of Franklin Institute, which was founded in 1824 to promote science, he contributed greatly to the academic and scholarly advancement of the technical disciplines. Haupt continued to perform surveys for the Coast Survey while teaching classes and writing specifications for engineering contracts for the Patent Office. Haupt was appointed to numerous governmental engineering commissions by President McKinley, primarily for canals (Nicaragua and Panama) and for harbor development along the coasts. He served as a technical judge of transportation engineering for the Paris Exposition. Haupt's genius in the field of hydrographics enabled him to design new state-of-the-art breakwaters and jetties. His design won the prestigious Magellanic Premium of the American Philosophical Society (APS) in 1887. Haupt was one of only 32 scientists who have received this prize in the 215 years of eligibility. Writing numerous important papers on engineering and scientific phenomena for canals, roads, rivers, oceans, and harbors, Haupt held memberships in the APS, American Society for Civil Engineers, and the

American Association for the Advancement of Science. Haupt was a highly successful scholar and a research leader in several fields of advanced engineering and science.

USMA 1868   ║ **John George David Knight** ║   **Mathematician**

24 January 1846 (London, England) – 9 June 1919 (NJ)
Graduate # 2220 (2nd out of 54), listed in *AR* (1920)

Military Service:
1890-1895:   Staff duty at Office of Chief of Army Engineers, Washington, DC
1901-1904:   Duty on General Staff, War Department, Washington, DC
1904-1907:   Staff duty in Philippines
1907-1909:   Various leadership duties on staffs of Army departments, engineer districts, and engineer boards
1917-1918:   Active duty during World War I

Professional Service:
1868-1870:   Graduate study in engineering at the Engineer School of Application, Willet's Point, NY
1870-1874:   Construction engineer in New York Harbor
1874-1881:   Assistant Professor of Mathematics, USMA
1882-1885:   Engineer for navigation improvements and levee construction on Mississippi River
1885-1887:   Faculty at Engineer School of Application, Willet's Point, NY
1887-1890:   Engineering faculty at the Infantry and Cavalry School, Ft Leavenworth, KS
1895-1896:   Construction engineer for New York Harbor
1895-1901:   Faculty at Engineer School of Application, Fort Totten, Willet's Point, NY

J. G. D. KNIGHT was an outstanding student at USMA and entered the Corps of Engineers upon graduation in 1868. He immediately undertook two years of graduate schooling at the Engineer School of Application at Willet's Point, NY. Knight next taught mathematics at West Point in 1874. During his seven years on the faculty, he wrote a textbook on determinants for the use of cadets and taught cadets the application of mathematics to their military profession. Knight contributed to the transition from **Albert Church (USMA 1828)** to **Edgar Bass (USMA 1868)** as head of the Mathematics Department. After leaving the Academy, Knight took on three years of engineering field work on the Mississippi River in 1882. Next, he moved back to New York for both construction and academic duties at the Engineer School at Willet's Point. After teaching combat engineering principles to infantry and cavalry officers in Fort Leavenworth, KS, he returned to New York once again as a harbor engineer. Knight was on many engineering and science boards, mostly involving work on submarine mines and torpedoes, range finders, and large artillery weapon systems for coastal defenses. He was involved in the design and construction of an improved water supply system for Washington, DC and providing electric lights to the same city. He retired from the Army in 1910 as a Brigadier General.

USMA 1868   ┌─────────────────────┐
                    │ **Edgar Wales Bass** │   **Mathematician**
                    └─────────────────────┘

30 October 1843 (Prairie du Chien, WI) – 6 November 1918 (New York, NY)
Graduate # 2222 (4th out of 54), listed in *AR* (1919)

Military Service:
1862-1864: Enlisted soldier in action on frontier in Indian Wars

Professional Service:
1869-1874: Assistant Professor of Natural and Experimental Philosophy, USMA
1874-1875: Assistant Astronomer of U.S. Expedition to New Zealand to observe the transit of Venus
1876-1878: Assistant Professor of Natural and Experimental Philosophy, USMA
1878-1898: Professor of Mathematics & Head of Department, USMA

E. W. Bass entered the Army as an enlisted soldier and served in combat against the Sioux

Indians. He then went to USMA as an experienced cadet. Upon graduation, he was commissioned in the Corps of Engineers, serving at Willet's Point, NY for one year before returning to West Point. Back at West Point in 1869, he taught cadets as an Assistant Professor of Natural and Experimental Philosophy. He remained at West Point for five years before participating in an expedition to New Zealand to observe the transit of Venus. Upon the expedition's completion, Bass returned to Willet's Point for a brief period before resuming his teaching duties at West Point. In 1878 he was appointed Professor of Mathematics and Department Head, succeeding **Albert Church (USMA 1828)**, who had been Department Head for 41 years. Bass was not satisfied with the status of the curriculum or Church's textbooks, which were in use in all the courses and presented a perspective on mathematical concepts from a half-century earlier. Bass replaced these older textbooks with newer, modern ones and wrote his own textbook in calculus that he implemented in the courses at the Academy. In 1896, Bass' *Elements of Differential Calculus* replaced Church's text, a book that had been used for nearly 50 years at West Point. Bass also wrote a

successful trigonometry book with **Henry Ludlow (USMA 1876)** which was published in many editions. This book contained tables of many functions and was used at many colleges as a reference book. A demanding, yet fair teacher, Bass was a strong supporter of the West Point educational system. In October 1898, he retired from the Army and his professional service, spending his retirement in Bar Harbor, ME and in New York City, where he died at age 75.

USMA 1868 | **William Louis Marshall** | **Engineer**

11 June 1846 (Washington, KY) – 2 July 1920 (Washington, DC)
Graduate # 2225 (7th out of 54), listed in *DAB, NCAB, AR* (1922)

Military Service:
1872-1876: Frontier duty on exploration of the Rocky Mountains
1908-1910: Chief of Army Engineers, Washington, DC

Professional Service:
1868-1870: Graduate engineering study at the Engineer School of Application, Willet's Point, NY
1870-1871: Assistant Professor of Natural and Experimental Philosophy, USMA
1871-1872: Engineering duty at Willet's Point, NY
1976-1890: Engineering duty for river and harbor improvements in AL, GA, TN, WI, and IL
1890-1899: Engineer duty for Hennepin Canal (IL) and various construction projects
1899-1908: Construction engineer for New York Harbor; Sandy Hook, NJ; and Willet's Point Engineer
            School, NY
1910-1920: Consulting engineer for various hydro-electric projects

---

At age 16, **W. L. MARSHALL** enlisted in the cavalry of the Union Army and fought in the Civil War. He then entered the Military Academy in 1864, graduating in 1868, and was commissioned in the Corps of Engineers. Accompanying George Wheeler's Expedition in the Rocky Mountains, Marshall covered thousands of rugged, frontier miles on foot and horseback and discovered the important passage now called Marshall Pass in central Colorado. He oversaw improvements on the lower Mississippi River and on rivers and canals in several states. As the Chicago District Engineer from 1888 to 1899, he planned and began to build the Hennepin Canal, connecting the Illinois and Mississippi Rivers. Marshall made innovative use of concrete and developed original methods for canal lock construction and movable dams. Stationed in New York City from 1900 to 1908, he worked on the Ambrose Channel project and sought to standardize fortification construction methods. Marshall was the originator and designer of many public works projects in New York City (bridges, canals, waterworks, electric power systems, piers, and wharves). He served as the Chief of Army Engineers from 1908 to 1910. While Chief, he initiated a commission to oversee U.S. highway construction and the development of inland waterways. He retired from the Army in 1910, but his engineering reputation earned him a special appointment from President Taft as consulting engineer to the Secretary of the Interior on hydroelectric power projects. He was the grand nephew of Chief Justice John Marshall and a tremendous contributor to military and construction engineering.

USMA 1868   **Henry Metcalf**   Scientist

29 October 1847 (NY) – 17 August 1927 (NY)
Graduate # 2227 (9th out of 54), (ordnance, inventor, technologist), listed in *NCAB, AR* (1930)

Military Service:
1868-1869: Staff duty in Ordnance Bureau, Washington, DC
1869-1870: Aide-de-camp for Major General Henry Halleck

Professional Service:
1870-1875: Ordnance duty at Springfield Armory, MA
1875-1877: Special duty in charge of the U.S. Army Ordnance
             display at the International Exhibition in Philadelphia, PA
1877-1881: Ordnance duty at Frankford Arsenal, PA
1881-1884: Ordnance duty at Benicia Arsenal, CA
1884-1886: Ordnance duty at Watervliet Arsenal, NY
1886-1893: Assistant Professor of Ordnance and Gunnery, USMA

H. METCALF attended West Point for five years, graduating in 1868. He chose the Ordnance Corps and began his career as a technical staff officer in the Ordnance Bureau. Metcalf served as aide-de-camp for **Henry Halleck (USMA 1839)**, who at that time was commander of the Department of the South. In 1870, Metcalf reported to Springfield Armory, MA to work on designing, testing, and producing armaments. While in this assignment, he inspected small arms manufactured by various companies and in the armory. He was instrumental in coordinating the ordnance exhibit in the international exhibition in Philadelphia in 1876. Metcalf then served at several Army arsenals, insuring top-quality weapons and munitions were being built for Army forces. In 1886, Metcalf became an Assistant Professor of Ordnance and Gunnery at the Academy. Over his seven years in academics, he wrote articles on manufacturing techniques and a complete and modern textbook on ordnance theory and practice for cadets. This book was very technical, including scientific and mathematical presentations, making it the most advanced book on this subject at that time. One of Metcalf's most significant contributions was the invention of the detachable magazine for rifles in 1873. This was a significant advancement in infantry small arms and gave American troops a tremendous advantage on the battlefield. After his retirement in 1893 due to an eye injury, Metcalf was active in his local community of Cold Spring, NY, serving on water and sewer boards and the board of education.

USMA 1868 | **Robert Fletcher** | **Engineer**

23 August 1847 (New York, NY) – 7 January 1936 (Hanover, NH)
Graduate # 2230 (12th out of 54), listed in *DAB, NCAB, AR* (1936)

Military Service:
1868-1869: Frontier duty in Texas

Professional Service:
1869-1870: Assistant Professor of Mathematics, USMA
1871-1918: Professor of Engineering, Thayer School of Engineer, Dartmouth College, NH
1881:   Ph.D. awarded from Dartmouth College
1895:   Member of the National Geographic Society
1901-1902: President, American Society for Engineering Education
1902:   Fellow of the American Association for the Advancement of Science

Having completed three years of study at the New York Free Academy (later College of the City of New York), **R. FLETCHER** had little trouble with the West Point program and graduated high in his scientific studies in the class of 1868. His first duty was on the frontier

for one year. He then returned to teach mathematics at the request of Department Head **Albert Church (USMA 1828)**. After one year of teaching and with Church's recommendation, Fletcher was offered the opportunity to lead the newly established Thayer School of Engineering at Dartmouth College, NH. **Sylvanus Thayer (USMA 1808)** had endowed the new program and sought a young, talented engineering educator to give life and energy to the program. Fletcher filled these requirements and set off to built the program Thayer envisioned. Despite his young age of 23 years, Fletcher was knowledgeable in the fundamentals of mathematics, sciences, and engineering principles, and he also had tremendous insight into the future needs of engineers. At first he was the only professor in the graduate-level program and found himself teaching students all aspects of engineering and technology – astronomy, bridge design, machine design, and materials. While there he continued his own studies and received his Ph.D. from Dartmouth in 1881. Later, he added other faculty members and specialized his own work in construction engineering principles. He remained an active researcher and consulting engineer working on bridges, water works, and sewage systems in New England. For 48 years, he headed the highly selective program, educating hundreds of the finest engineers in America. From 1901 to 1902, he served as President of the American

Society for Engineering Education and was active in America Society of Civil Engineers. Dedicated and wise in the academic culture of engineering education, Fletcher left a legacy of quality technical education leadership in America as a pioneer and a stalwart contributor in America's advancement in technical education.

| USMA 1869 | **Samuel Escue Tillman** | Scientist |

2 October 1847 (Shelbyville, TN) – 24 June 1942 (Southampton, NY)
Graduate # 2275 (3rd out of 39), (chemist, educator), listed in *AS* (January 1943)

Military Service:
1869-1870: Frontier duty at Ft Riley, KS
1873-1874 and 1876-1879: Frontier and topographic duty at Ft. Apache, AZ

Professional Service:
1870-1872: Assistant Professor of Chemistry, Mineralogy and Geology, USMA
1872-1873: Assistant Professor of Engineering, USMA
1874-1875: Astronomical duty on trip to Australia and Tasmania to observe the transit of Venus
1875-1976: Assistant Professor of Natural Philosophy, USMA
1876-1879: Survey work in Western U.S.
1879-1880: Assistant Professor of Chemistry, USMA
1880-1911: Professor of Chemistry, USMA
1917-1919: Superintendent, USMA

S. E. TILLMAN graduated from USMA in 1869 and joined the artillery branch with duty at Ft. Riley, KS. In 1870, he returned to West Point for a three-year tour as a science instructor.

This was the beginning of 36 total years of academic service at the Academy, involving four separate tours and three different academic departments. Between his West Point tours, Tillman served on the frontier in AZ and performed surveying in western United States. He also traveled to Australia and Tasmania to perform astronomical observations of the transit of Venus. Tillman was a versatile scientist, who began teaching chemistry, mineralogy, and geology and later taught engineering and mechanics during two separate tours at the Academy. Through his teaching and research contributions during his academic assignments, Tillman built a strong record of academic contribution and was selected to replace **Henry Kendrick (USMA 1835)** as the Professor of Chemistry and Department Head in 1880. His supporters for the position included astronomer Simon Newcomb and many Army generals. Tillman's contributions as an academic leader included improving the science curriculum, requiring more written exams, building a new academic building for science teaching, and establishing a post for a full-time librarian. Tillman was instrumental in selecting **Edward Holden (USMA 1870)** for the new librarian position. In his department, the new sciences of electricity and x-rays were introduced and taught to cadets. Tillman's textbook writing filled the needs of the new curriculum and included books on heat, rocks, minerals, and general chemistry. While Tillman retired from the Army and his professorship in 1911, he was recalled to military service in 1917 to be Superintendent of the Academy during World War I. Leading the Academy through this difficult time when classes graduated early and programs were in a constant flux, Tillman faithfully fulfilled his final Army mission to develop skilled and educated Army officers for immediate combat duty in Europe.

| USMA 1869 | **Arthur Sherburne Hardy** | Mathematician |

13 August 1847 (Andover, MA) – 13 March 1930 (Woodstock, MA)
Graduate # 2282 (10th out of 39), listed in *DAB, NCAB, AR* (1930)

Military Service:
1869-1870: Artillery duty in FL

Professional Service:
1870-1871: Topographic engineer for railroads
1871-1873: Professor of Mathematics, Grinnell College, IA
1873-1874: Student at Ecole de Pontes et Chaussees, Paris, France
1873-1878: Professor of Civil Engineering, Dartmouth College, NH
1878-1893: Professor of Mathematics, Dartmouth College, NH

A. S. Hardy was educated at private schools in Switzerland, the Phillips Andover Academy in MA, and Amherst College in MA (for one year), before he entered West Point. After serving only one year in the Army after his graduation from West Point 1869, he became a distinguished scholar in many areas, although his contributions in mathematics seem to be his most significant. After a year of surveying and charting for a railroad company, he began his mathematics teaching career teaching at Grinnell College, IA. Hardy then returned to New England in 1878 to become Professor of Civil Engineering in the Thayer School of Engineering at Dartmouth College, NH, working for **Robert Fletcher (USMA 1868)**. During this period, he taught advanced engineering mathematics to the most talented students in America. As an innovator and problem solver, Hardy was one of the first people in America to use new mathematical structures called quaternions to solve complex engineering problems. He authored and translated mathematical treatises and wrote textbooks on surveying, calculus, and analytic geometry. These were the premier works in America on these subjects. His textbooks were popular and well received by faculty and advanced graduate students at several schools. He was an accomplished mathematical scholar and technological leader in America. Hardy also published over two dozen poems and several novels while he continued his mathematical work. His first attempts at literary composition met with mixed success. In 1893, Hardy completely changed the direction of his professional career after failing in his bid to become President of Dartmouth. While he continued to write some mathematical papers, he became the editor of *Cosmopolitan* magazine for two years and then at the request of President McKinley served for a decade as the United States ambassador or minister to several countries (Persia, Greece, Romania, Serbia, Switzerland, and Spain). In his later years, Hardy wrote several more novels and books of poetry; several were best sellers. Even by West Point standards, Hardy was a remarkably versatile savant. Among his many tributes was an honorary degree from Amherst College and election as a Fellow of the American Association for the Advancement of Sciences.

Reference:

Stewart, E. Kate, *Arthur Sherburne Hardy: Man of American Letters*, Scripta Humanistica, Potomac, 1986.

USMA 1869 || **David Alexander Lyle** || **Scientist**

21 January, 1845 (Fairfield County, OH) – 10 October 1937 (St. Davids, PA)
Graduate # 2284 (12th out of 39), (metallurgist, inventor, etymologist), listed in *NCAB*

Military Service:
1869-1870: Garrison and topographic duty in CA
1870-1871: Frontier and survey duty in AK, NV, AZ
1871-1872: Garrison duty in CA
1898-1899: Ordnance officer for Spanish-American war

Professional Service:
1872-1875: Assistant Professor of Natural and Experimental Philosophy, USMA
1875-1882: Ordnance service at Springfield Armory, MA
1883-1884: Science and mining engineering studies at Massachusetts Institute of Technology
1882-1889: Inspector of ordnance and foundry operations
1889: Fellow of American Association for the Advancement of Science
1889-1890: Military representative of U.S. at the Paris Exposition
1890-1902: Inspector of ordnance, Philadelphia, PA
1902-1908: Ordnance officer for the South and Gulf Departments, Augusta Arsenal, GA
1882-1909: Researcher into life-saving apparatus for marine applications

D. A. LYLE was commissioned in the Artillery Corps upon graduation from USMA. After duties in CA and AK, where he learned the Chinook language and mapped the Fort Wrangel area, Lyle went on the Wheeler Expedition to conduct a geographical survey of NV and AZ. As part of his duties, he extensively explored Death Valley, studying the geology and ecology of the region. In 1872, he returned to West Point to teach science for three years. He was a remarkable teacher since he knew the practical uses of science in the life of an Army officer. Joining the Ordnance Corps in 1875, Lyle served at several arsenals, armories, and proving grounds. He became engaged in the science of metallurgy, studying the materials for guns, armor plating, and projectiles as he inspected these items for the Army. To supplement his practical knowledge, he studied at Massachusetts Institute of Technology, receiving a B.S. degree in mining engineering. Lyle traveled in Europe to study and report on the Ordnance operations of European military forces and attended the Paris Exposition in 1889. For many years, Lyle faithfully and expertly served on the Board of Life-Saving Appliances and, as a result of that work, invented the Lyle gun for shooting flares. He wrote many papers (83 in all) on his scientific work, including reports on life-saving apparatus, rockets, leather manufacturing, and geology. After his retirement in 1908, Lyle edited and contributed to dictionaries as an expert etymologist. Lyle was a fellow of the American Association for the Advancement of Sciences and a member of the American Institute of Mining Engineers. Knowledgeable in many areas of science, he selflessly used his knowledge and talents in public service.

USMA 1870   **Winfred Scott Chaplin**   **Engineer**

22 August 1847 (Glenburn, ME) – 12 March 1918 (St. Louis, MO)
Graduate # 2313 (2nd out of 58), listed in *NCAB, AR* (1918)

Military Service:
1870-1872: Garrison duty at Ft. Adams, RI

Professional Service:
1872-1874: Civil engineer in MI, IL
1874-1877: Professor of Mechanics, Maine State University, Orono, ME
1877-1882: Professor of Civil Engineering, Imperial University of Japan, Tokyo
1882-1886: Professor of Mathematics, Union College, NY
1886-1891: Professor of Civil Engineering, Harvard University, MA
1891-1907: Chancellor of Washington University, St. Louis, MO

W. S. CHAPLIN was a bookkeeper before he entered the Academy. He was commissioned in the Artillery Corps and served in Fort Adams, RI, after his graduation in 1870. After two years of Army service, he resigned to find jobs with more pay to support his widowed mother and the rest of his family. After two years in mining and railroad engineering, he moved back to ME to fill the Professor of Mechanics position at the State University of Maine. Once again, to earn more money, Chaplin went to Tokyo, Japan as a Professor of Civil Engineering at the Imperial University. West Point science department heads and President Ulysses Grant (USMA 1843) endorsed him for this position. In 1882, he returned to the United States and soon found a position at Union College in Schenectady, NY as Professor of Mathematics. In 1885, Chaplin was recruited by the President of Harvard, Charles W. Eliot, to be the Dean of the Lawrence Scientific School and Professor of Engineering. After six years of science teaching at Harvard, Chaplin took advantage of another opportunity and became Chancellor of Washington University in St. Louis, MO. He led this major technology school into the 20th century, serving 17 years as its leader and making significant contributions to the university. During his tenure the university grew from 170 students to over 1100. Chaplin was well liked by the students and faculty where he both taught students and administered to the needs of the faculty. Chaplin authored an article in the *Centennial of the United States Military Academy* entitled "On the Services of Graduates in Civil Life, 1802–1902." As one of the leaders of America's technical education community, Chaplin was a Fellow of the American Academy of Arts and Sciences. Among his many accolades were honorary degrees from Union College and Harvard University.

USMA 1873 ║ **William Herbert Bixby** ║ **Engineer**

27 December 1849 (Charlestown, MA) – 29 September 1928 (Washington, DC)
Graduate # 2468 (1st out of 41), listed in *NCAB, AR* (1929)

Military Service:
1910-1913: Chief of Army Engineers, Washington, DC

Professional Service:
1873-1875: Graduate engineering study at Engineer School of Application, Willet's Point, NY
1875-1879: Assistant Professor of Civil and Military Engineering, USMA
1879-1881: Engineering study at Ecole Nationale des Ponts and Chaussees, France
1881-1884: Faculty trainer at Engineer School of Application, Willet's Point, NY
1884-1891: Engineering duty in NC
1891-1910: Engineering duty in RI, PA, OH, MI, and IL
1917-1919: Engineering duty on Mississippi River

W. H. BIXBY graduated first in the Military Academy class of 1873 and was commissioned in the Corps of Engineers. After serving as a student in the Engineering School of Application at Willet's Point and as an Assistant Professor of Engineering at the Military Academy, Bixby attended and graduated with honors from the French military academy for roads and bridges. Bixby worked on engineering projects in North Carolina from 1884 to

1891, where he oversaw improvements on the Cape Fear River, modernized the area's coastal forts, and responded to the construction needs caused by the earthquake that hit Charleston, SC in 1886. Bixby served next on construction projects in Newport, RI. From 1897 to 1902, he oversaw navigation and flood control improvements to the Ohio River and its tributaries from Pittsburgh to Cincinnati. After two years in charge of projects in Detroit, Bixby went to Chicago to work on its harbor facilities. Bixby was President of the Mississippi River Commission for two terms (1908-1910 and 1917-1918).

As Chief of Army Engineers from 1910 to 1913, he oversaw the challenging effort of raising the battleship <u>Maine</u>. He retired in 1913, but was recalled to service in 1917 to work on the Mississippi River while line engineers were sent into combat during World War I. He was an expert in standardizations and specifications for engineering practices, especially river and harbor dredging and distances and loading of suspension bridges. His valuable report on wind pressures on bridges was used by the entire engineering community. Bixby was a member of the American Society of Civil Engineers, both the American and British Associations for the Advancement of Science, American Mathematical Society, and the American Academy of Arts and Sciences.

USMA 1874 | **John Phillip Wisser** | **Technologist**

10 July 1852 (St. Louis, MO) – 19 January 1927
Graduate #2517 (9th out of 41), (scientist), listed in *NCAB, AR* (1927)

Military Service:
1874-1875: Garrison duty in FL
1875-1878: Artillery duty in AM, VA, RI, SC
1882-1884: Artillery instructor, Artillery School for Practice,
Ft. Monroe,VA
1884-1886: Garrison duty in CA and WA
1894-1898: Artillery duty in NY and VA
1904-1906: Inspector General for Pacific Division, CA
1906-1909: Military Attaché, Berlin, Germany
1909-1912: Artillery commander, GA
1915-1918: Commander, Hawaii Department

Professional Service:
1878-1882: Assistant Professor of Chemistry, Mineralogy, and
Geology, USMA
1886-1894: Assistant Professor of Chemistry, Mineralogy, and Geology, USMA

1898-1901:   Instructor of engineering at the Artillery School, Ft. Monroe, VA
1901-1902:   Special duty at the Pan-American Exposition, Buffalo, NY
1902-1904:   Inspector of artillery weapons and training, RI and ME

J. P. WISSER became an artillery officer upon his commissioning in 1874. He spent several years serving in his branch before returning to West Point to teach science in the Department of Chemistry, Mineralogy, and Geology for four years. This department taught science courses to upperclass cadets, and Wisser was an ideal teacher of practical science and technical awareness. Wisser spent two years out West as a staff officer and aide-de-camp for General John Gibbon (USMA 1847). Returning to West Point in 1886, Wisser filled a senior faculty position in his old department. He was Department Head **Samuel Tillman's (USMA 1869)** primary assistant. Again, his passion for science enabled him to inspire both cadets and the junior faculty members. After eight more years of teaching cadets, Wisser was reassigned back to artillery duties. From 1895 to 1901, he served as the editor for the *Artillery Journal.* In 1898, he began teaching engineering at the Artillery School at Ft. Monroe, VA. Wisser earned a reputation as an expert in both artillery weapons and artillery operations. The Army used him in that capacity from 1902 until his retirement in 1918, often calling him to advise artillery commanders and to evaluating artillery training and maneuvers. An expert technologist in sophisticated Army weaponry, Wisser was an important contributor to many levels and aspects of Army technical operations.

USMA 1874 | **Wright Prescott Edgerton** | **Mathematician**

14 November 1852 (Tallmadge, OH) – 24 June 1904 (West Point, NY)
Graduate # 2522 (14th out of 42), listed in *AR* (1905)

Military Service:
1874-1882:   Numerous troop assignments (Ft. Johnston, NC, Ft. Monroe,
             VA, Summerville, SC, Washington Arsenal, DC, San
             Antonio, TX, Ft. McHenry, MD, Willet's Point, NY)
1888:   Quartermaster of hospital at Hot Springs, Arkansas
1898:   Duty in the Puerto Rican campaign

Professional Service:
1882-1887:   Principal Assistant Professor of Mathematics, USMA
1889:   Assistant Professor of Mathematics, USMA
1893-1898:   Associate Professor of Mathematics, USMA
1898-1904:   Professor of Mathematics and Head of the Department,
             USMA

W. P. EDGERTON's childhood days were filled with adventure. In 1863, his father was appointed Chief Justice of Idaho and the family journeyed for four months traveling westward from Omaha, NE to Bannock, ID. This trip was taken during the times of Indian unrest and in the midst of the Civil War. Despite his lack of formal schooling while growing up on the frontier, Edgerton was able to enroll and succeed academically at West Point. After graduating and becoming an artillery officer, he spent eight years in garrison duty at ten different stations located in six states including tours of duty at the Artillery School at Fort Monroe, VA and graduate work at the Engineer School of Applications at Willet's Point, NY. In 1882, Edgerton returned to USMA as the Principal Assistant Professor of Mathematics, where he remained for five years. After a short time away, he returned to West Point and the Mathematics Department. Edgerton was the first person to be given the position and academic rank of Associate Professor at the Academy. Edgerton's next duty was in the Puerto Rican campaign in 1898. After his field duties were completed, he was appointed Professor of Mathematics and Head of the Mathematics Department, succeeding **Edgar Bass (USMA 1868)**. Edgerton held that position until his death in 1904. Edgerton introduced two important changes in the mathematics curriculum at West Point. Prior to 1900, algebra and geometry had been taught in that order; Edgerton had the two subjects covered simultaneously, with recitation in each subject on alternate days. Adopting the new educational methods of the times, Edgerton also implemented written final tests, thereby allowing students proficient in the written tests to be exempt from the final, end-of-semester, oral examinations administered by the Academic Board of Examiners.

USMA 1875  **Engineer**

13 October 1855 (Ellsworth, ME) – 11 April 1907 (Schenectady, NY)
Graduate # 2552 (3rd out of 43) (electrical technologist), listed in *DAB, NCAB, AR* (1908)

Military Service:
1885-1886: Aide-de-camp to General Hancock
1898-1899: Volunteer in combat during Spanish-American War (Cuba, Puerto Rico) (Brigadier General)

Professional Service:
1875-1878: Engineer study at Willet's Point, NY
1878-1880: Topographic engineer for geographical survey of CO, AR, NM, TX
1880-1883: Engineer instructor at Willet's Point, NY
1883-1885: Assistant Professor of Civil and Military Engineering, USMA
1886-1888: Investigator of electricity infrastructure in the United States (governmental study)
1889-1893: Manager and engineer of electric-powered railroad company
1893-1907: Vice President of General Electric

E. GRIFFIN was commissioned in the engineer branch and was stationed as a graduate student at Willet's Point Engineer School of Application after graduation from West Point. Three years later, he had the opportunity to serve on the geographical survey of the West, mapping and charting areas in CO, AR, NM, and TX. He returned to the East, first to teach at Willet's Point and then at West Point in 1883, teaching civil and topographic engineering for two years. Griffin's next assignment was as aide-de-camp to General Winfield Hancock (USMA 1844), while he used his additional time to conduct professional investigations. During this period, Griffin wrote two significant papers on military photography and seacoast defenses.

From 1886 to 1888, Griffin was assigned to the engineer office in Washington, DC. While on a special assignment to investigate the electricity infrastructure of the majors cities of the United States, he studied the status and safety of telephones, telegraphs, lighting, and electrical wires. His foundational report on this important national infrastructure was published by the Senate. Griffin also studied and advocated the use of electric railroads and streetcars in cities. Griffin's work was so outstanding that he received numerous offers for employment in the electricity industry. In 1889, he resigned from the Army and began his career in the electrical industry, first managing a company producing electric railroads. Then in 1892, his company merged with the Edison Company to form General Electric. Griffin was the 1st Vice President of the new and growing company. From his various leadership positions in this technical industry, he directed the electric railway boom in America. In 1904, his article, "The Foundation of the Modern Street Railway" explained the growth of this industry. Griffin was an informed, analytical manager of technology and a bold, aggressive businessman. In the midst of his economic success, he volunteered to serve in the Army during the Spanish-American War and commanded his regiment in combat in Cuba and Puerto Rico. Griffin was a pioneer in the new technology of electricity and led the U.S. to understanding and using its potential as it entered into the 20th century.

USMA 1876      **Technologist**

19 February 1855 (Carrollton, OH) – 10 November 1942 (Washington, DC)
Graduate # 2597 (5th out of 48), (ordnance), listed in *DAB, ANB, NCAB, AS* (January 1944)

Military Service:
1876-1879: Expedition and garrison duty on frontier and in CA (fought against Sioux and Bannock Indians)

1887-1888: Ordnance duty at Office of the Chief of Ordnance, Washington, DC
1889-1892: Ordnance duty at Office of the Chief of Ordnance, Washington, DC
1896-1899: Fortification inspector during Spanish-American War (Luzon)
1899-1900: Combat duty in Philippine insurrection
1900:   Combat duty in Boxer Rebellion, China
1901-1918: Chief of Ordnance, Washington, DC (on duty during World War I on the Supreme
                  War Council) (Major General)
1912-1913: President, Army War College
1917-1919: Supreme War Council (on fact-finding trip to Europe)

Professional Service:
1879-1884: Assistant Professor of Mathematics, USMA
1884-1887: Ordnance duty at Watertown Arsenal, MA
1888-1889: Visit to Europe to study technological improvement of weapons systems
1892-1896: Testing and evaluation duty at Sandy Hook Proving Ground, NJ

W. CROZIER entered the artillery upon his graduation in 1876. His first duties were on the frontier fighting in the Indian Wars. Eventually, Crozier was stationed in garrison in CA before returning to West Point to teach mathematics for five years. Crozier's Department Head at the Academy was **Edgar Bass (USMA 1868)**, who was introducing new textbooks and content to the Academy's program. In 1881, Crozier transferred to the Ordnance Corps and began his intense study of ordnance engineering. His own research centered on artillery, but he was fast becoming an expert in all areas of ordnance. From 1884 to 1887, Crozier was assigned to Watertown Arsenal, MA, where he was able to concentrate his research efforts and author technical papers on ordnance issues. Moving to the Office of the Chief of Ordnance, Crozier traveled to Europe to investigate new weapons technologies. After he returned, Crozier worked with Adelbert Buffington (USMA 1861) on designing a gun carriage to better protect the gun and crew during battle. The new Buffington-Crozier gun carriage that they developed was adopted by the Army in 1894. From 1892 to 1896, Crozier had the perfect opportunity to continue his research at Sandy Hook Proving Ground in NJ, where he was able to test and evaluate his new ideas at the ordnance test center. In 1899, he and naval officer Alfred Thayer Mahan represented the United States at the International Peace Conference at The Hague. Crozier then sought combat assignments and served in the Philippines and in China. Crozier turned down an offer to head the Natural and Experimental Philosophy Department at West Point. Instead, in 1901 he was made Chief of Ordnance and promoted to Brigadier General. Crozier was both effective as an administrator and as a technical expert in ordnance. He was a gifted technical writer, authoring *Notes on the Construction of Ordnance* and other treatises on ordnance engineering, and an inspiring orator. He was a strong supporter of technical skills in army officers and often sided with the technical experts over the wishes of the field commanders. Crozier became deeply embroiled in the politics of war preparations as World War I raged in Europe. However, once the United States entered the war, Crozier's ordnance department was immediately overwhelmed with their mission to provide sufficient modern weapons and equipment to the expanding American Army. Through Herculean efforts by Crozier and the ordnance staff, the situation was rectified and Army ordnance accomplished its challenging wartime mission. As a valuable member of President Wilson's Supreme War Council, he worked with Winston Churchill at Versailles to develop a method to pool ordnance equipment for all the allied forces. Retiring from active duty in 1919, he maintained his high-profile social and political life in Washington, DC. Crozier was a brilliant technologist and a capable administrator. However, he was steadfast in his support of military technologists and never allowed line officers or civilians sufficient influence in the issues of ordnance. Crozier was the most influential and longest-tenured Chief of Ordnance in the Army's history, personally insuring that this highly technical branch accomplished its mission and through advanced technical developments vaulting the U.S. Army into a leadership position in the world.

USMA 1876 | **Henry Hunt Ludlow** | **Mathematician**

1854 (Easton, PA) – 14 August 1926 (Washington, DC)
Graduate # 2598 (6th out of 48), listed in *AR* (1932)

Military Service:
1876-1878: Garrison duty in NY and SC
1883-1884: Garrison duty in FL
1885-1891: Garrison duty in MD, VA, TX, and TN
1891-1893: Garrison duty in Washington, DC
1893-1897: Garrison duty in GA, LA, and CA
1897-1898: Military science instructor, Mississippi Agricultural and Mechanical College
1899-1901: Combat duty in artillery during Philippines War
1901-1903: Garrison duty in CA
1903-1906: Military science instructor, Mississippi Agricultural and Mechanical College
1906-1909: Garrison duty in NY and NC
1909-1912: Garrison duty in NC
1912-1915: Garrison duty in SC
1915-1917: Garrison duty in CA
1918-1919: Military science instructor, George Washington University, Washington, DC

Professional Service:
1878-1879: Surveyor for Wheeler's exploration of the West
1879-1883: Assistant Professor of Mathematics, USMA
1884-1885: Student at Engineer School of Application, Willet's Point, NY

H. H. LUDLOW was commissioned in the artillery after his completion of the program at West Point. He had built a reputation as a brilliant mathematician while still a cadet and helped correct errors in **William Bartlett's (USMA 1826)** *Mechanics* book while studying the course. Serving in garrison until 1878, he was next assigned to Wheeler's exploration of the western frontier. Returning east in 1879, he had the opportunity to teach mathematics at West Point for four years. During his teaching service, he wrote a textbook, *Elements of Trigonometry*. He later added more tables of function values and logarithms with the aid of his Department Head **Edgar Bass (USMA 1868)**. He studied torpedo (sea mine) construction and deployment at the Engineer School of Application. In addition to the numerous field assignments he had during his 43-year career, Ludlow taught military science at universities three separate times and served in combat in the Philippines. Ludlow had the skills and interest to be a remarkable mathematician or scientist, but he sacrificed opportunities to develop these skills for military assignments in service to his country. Despite of this short time actively engaged in science, his contributions were notable.

USMA 1877   **William Brandon Gordon**   **Scientist**

1853 (PA) – 11 January 1938 (FL)
Graduate # 2646 (6th out of 76), (physicist)

Military Service:
1877-1878: Frontier duty in WA and CA
1878-1881: Garrison duty in CA
1881-1884: Ordnance duty at Watervliet Arsenal, NY
1888-1891: Ordnance duty at Watervliet Arsenal, NY
            and member of Army Board for Gun Manufacturing

Professional Service:
1884-1888: Assistant Professor of Natural and Experimental
            Philosophy, USMA
1901-1917: Professor of Natural and Experimental Philosophy,
            USMA

W. B. GORDON selected the artillery branch upon his graduation from West Point in 1877. After four years in the artillery, he transferred to the Ordnance Corps in 1881. He learned his new branch skills at the largest gun testing and manufacturing plant in the Army at Watervliet Arsenal, NY. Gordon then returned to West Point to teach physics and mechanics for four years. After a brief return to Watervliet Arsenal, Gordon assumed the position of Professor and Department Head of Natural and Experimental Philosophy at the Academy, succeeding **Peter Michie (USMA 1863)**. Leading that important science department for the first seventeen years of the 20th century, Gordon was responsible for setting the standards in science for Academy graduates as the Army and nation prepared for World War I.

Unfortunately, Gordon was limited by his lack of academic experience and lack of advanced education. As many of America's programs in science modernized and advanced, West Point maintained a more classical physical science approach put in place by Michie and his predecessor **William Bartlett (USMA 1826)**. Gordon increased the time in the curriculum on astronomy and expanded the laboratory facilities to accommodate large mechanical experiments.

USMA 1877   **Henry Ossian Flipper**   **Engineer**

21 March 1856 (Thomasville, GA) – 3 May 1940 (Atlanta, GA)
Graduate # 2690 (50th out of 76), listed in *ANB, AS* (June 1977)

Military Service:
1878-1881: Frontier duty in Ft. Sill and other western outposts

Professional Service:
1878-1881: Engineer duty as surveyor and construction supervisor on the frontier
1881-1883: Engineering service
1883-1891: Mining and engineering duty in Mexico and AZ
1901-1912: Mining and engineering duty in northern Mexico
1921-1924: Railroad engineering in AK
1924-1930: Construction engineering in Venezuela

H. O. FLIPPER was born into slavery and grew up in GA. Following the Civil War, he attended the American Missionary Association School. Schools like this one were coming available for freed slaves as part of the reconstruction of the South and work of the Freedmen's Bureau under the direction of **Oliver O. Howard (USMA 1854)**. In 1873, Flipper was appointed to West Point and in 1877 he became the first African-American to graduate from USMA. Through his advanced West Point education, Flipper's technical skills and knowledge were highly developed and ready for the challenges of service in the Army. He was commissioned in the cavalry branch and was assigned to frontier duty with an all-black unit. His unit saw action against the Apache Indians. From 1878 until 1881, Flipper's duties included scouting, topographic surveying, draining swamps, building roads, and supervising construction of frontier fortifications in TX and the Indian Territory. Flipper left the Army in 1881 in a controversy involving a court-martial for conduct unbecoming an officer. As a civilian, Flipper went into government and private engineering projects and positions. He performed challenging technical work – map making, surveying, conducting mining operations, laying railroad tracks, and supervising construction for both civil and military engineering projects. Because of his engineering experience and talents, Flipper became the special assistant to the Secretary of the Interior with duties in support of the Alaskan Engineering Commission. He also became an authority on Mexican land and mining law. Flipper wrote several works – an autobiography about his West Point experience and a technical paper for the Department of Justice in 1895 about Mexican land laws. His 48-year career as an engineer on the frontier made him an important contributor to western development and the expansion of the U.S. across the continent. It was not until 1999 that the President and the Army posthumously pardoned Flipper for the incident in 1881 that led to his dismissal from the Army. Fortunately, Flipper had the technical expertise and bravery to continue his contributions in technical fields after his setback in the Army. Having suffered and overcome racial prejudice and discrimination, Flipper became a pioneer for African-Americans and freed slaves in his tremendous life accomplishments, dedicated military service, and productive technical career.

Reference:

Flipper, Henry O., *The Colored Cadet at West Point,* Arno Press, New York, 1969.

USMA 1879   **Gustav Joseph Fiebeger**   **Engineer**

9 May 1858 (Akron, OH) – 18 October 1939 (Washington, DC)
Graduate # 2764 (5th out of 67), listed in *AR* (1940)

Military Service:
1882-1883: Scouting duties as aide-de-camp to General
            George Crook against the Chiricahua Apache
            Indians in AZ

Professional Service:
1879-1882: Graduate studies in civil and military engineering,
            Engineer School of Application, Willet's Point, NY
1883-1888: Assistant Professor of Civil and Military
            Engineering, USMA
1888-1896: Engineer duties for rivers and harbors in VA, NC,
            and DC
1896-1922: Professor of Engineering, USMA

G. J. FIEBEGER was commissioned in the Corps of Engineers upon his graduation from USMA. After three years of graduate study in engineering at Willet's Point, where he developed a close friendship with **George Goethals (USMA 1880)** and studied under

Henry Abbot (USMA 1854), Fiebeger spent a year in field duty in pursuit of the famous Indian chief Geronimo. As General George Crook's (USMA 1852) aide-de-camp, Fiebeger was a scout for the expedition as it traveled about AZ, NM, and Mexico. In 1883, he returned to West Point as an Assistant Professor of Civil and Military Engineering. For five years, he was an outstanding teacher, able to motivate and explain the topics and develop the cadets' thinking skills. For the next eight years, Fiebeger worked on river and harbor improvements and served as an engineer in Washington, DC. In 1896, he became Professor of Engineering at the Academy succeeding **James Mercur (USMA 1866)**, who died while serving in this position. Fiebeger first revised and then rewrote all the textbooks used in his department's courses. The textbooks covered civil engineering, field fortifications, permanent fortifications, elements of military strategy, and campaigns of the Civil War. His *Civil Engineering* book advanced the subject in terms of clarity in symbolism and presentation. His *Campaigns of the American Civil War* contained detailed descriptions of the war's campaigns and was considered his best work. After he observed military operations during World War I, Fiebeger wrote a textbook for cadets entitled *Campaigns of the World War*. As seen by the subjects covered in the department, West Point's engineering had developed a focus on the history of military campaigns and combat engineering. While this historical slant was good motivation and background for many cadets for Army service, it left West Point out of touch with the new developments in the technical aspects of engineering and engineering education. However, Fiebeger's scholarship was substantial. He was an eminent scholar of military history and military engineering. His research work was thorough and his textbook writing superb. Fiebeger was an expert in his field and greatly enhanced West Point's reputation in the military aspects of engineering and technology.

USMA 1881  **Lyman Hall** **Mathematician**

18 February 1859 (Americus, Georgia) – 16 August 1905 (Dansville, NY)
Graduate # 2917 (39th out of 53), listed in *AR* (1906)

Military Service:
none (declined service in the Army)

Professional Service:
1883-1886: Assistant Professor of Mathematics, South Carolina Military College
1886-1888: Professor of Mathematics, Edgewood Military Academy
1888-1896: Professor of Mathematics, Georgia School of Technology
1896-1905: President, Georgia School of Technology

L. HALL attended Mercer University for three years before transferring to West Point, where he struggled some with the academic program. He graduated in the bottom part of his class in 1881. Declining to serve in the Army, he instead became commandant of a military academy in GA. Hall taught mathematics at the Georgia Military Academy at Kirkwood, GA; the South Carolina Military Academy; and Moreland Park Military Academy, GA. Hall was the first Professor of Mathematics at the Georgia School of Technology (now called Georgia Institute of Technology), beginning his teaching in 1888 and writing several algebra textbooks while teaching. When the school needed a President in 1896, Hall was called upon to lead the young college and build its academic program. Hall was known for being strict, disciplined, and aloof. As President of the School, Hall set out to transform Georgia School of Technology from a trade school to a real technological college. Hall had a rigid and unbending nature. In 1901, the senior class refused to return to class as scheduled on December 31, instead arriving two days later. Calling each member of the class to his office, Hall explained that such insubordination was unacceptable and dismissed each one from the college for six weeks. They had to return to school for an additional six weeks in the summer in order to graduate. He was known to the students at Georgia Tech as "Captain Hall." Despite some setbacks, Hall was successful at growing and improving the school as it became a leading engineering institution. As President, he built more dorms; emphasized discipline; established new programs in electrical engineering, civil engineering, and chemical engineering; and sought funding from the state legislature and private benefactors. Enrollment increased from 80 to over 500 students during his nine-year tenure. He served as president until 1905 when his health failed, and he died while on vacation in NY. After his death, the new chemistry building was named in his honor. Hall had also received an honorary degree from Washington and Lee University.

Quotation: By Hall: "In the first place I would put accuracy."

USMA 1882   **John Taliaferro Thompson**   **Technologist**

31 December 1860 (Newport, KY) – 21 June 1940 (Great Neck, NY)
Graduate # 2942 (11th out of 37), (ordnance), listed in *NCAB, AR* (1941)

Military Service:
1882-1888: Garrison duty WA, KY, MD, AR, LA, and AL
1888-1890: Student at Artillery School, Ft Monroe, VA
1898-1899: Ordnance duty during Spanish-American War in Cuba and Tampa, FL
1907-1914: Ordnance duty in Office of Chief of Ordnance, Washington, DC
1917-1919: Ordnance duty in Office of the Chief of Ordnance, Washington, DC

Professional Service:
1890-1891: Ordnance duty at Navy Gun Factory, Washington, DC
1891-1896: Ordnance duty at Rock Island Arsenal, IL; Omaha Ordnance Depot, OK; Chicago, IL

1896-1898: Assistant Professor of Ordnance and Gunnery, USMA
1914-1917: Ordnance engineer for Remington Arms Company
1920-1940: Inventor, engineer, and business leader for small arms manufacturing companies

J. T. THOMPSON attended Indiana State University for one year before entering USMA. He was commissioned in the artillery upon graduation. His first six years of service were in various garrison assignments as an artillery officer. In 1888, he attended the Artillery School. In 1890, the emphasis in his professional life took a turn as he transferred to the Ordnance Corps. He began a series of assignments in gun factories, arsenals, armories, and foundries, working on both cannons and small arms. These assignments gave him a solid foundation in the understanding of the principles of weapon design and manufacture. After an assignment in Cuba during the Spanish-American War, Thompson recognized a need for more firepower for the individual soldier. Thompson began working on ideas to provide that capability through automatic loading through breech mechanisms. He had duty at the Office of the Chief of Ordnance where he could pursue and test his new ideas and inventions. Retiring from the Army in 1914, Thompson worked as an engineer for Remington Arms Company, building a small arms plant in PA. This plant made more rifles than any other during World War I, selling small arms to the U.S., England, and Russia. Thompson was recalled to active duty during the war to supervise small arms manufacturing and deliver small arms to the troops in Europe. After the war, he returned to civilian industry to develop automatic-loading small arms. His research and testing took place in Cleveland, OH. The result of Thompson's work was the Thompson .45 caliber sub-machine gun, which was a major breakthrough in small arms. Portable and automatic, its production involved nearly 300 patents. This "Tommy gun" was immensely popular and soon was being produced in many sizes and models. Thompson continued to invent improvements in small arms, machinery, and airplane parts. He was a productive scholar, writing articles about his gun designs, other small arms, sighting devices, seacoast defenses, torpedoes, and artillery. Thompson was a member of the American Association for the Advancement of Science and other technical societies. Among his many honors was an honorary degree from Indiana State University.

USMA 1884 | **Hiram Martin Chittenden** | **Engineer**

25 October 1858 (Cattaraugas, NY) – 9 October 1917 (Seattle, WA)
Graduate # 3023 (3rd out of 37), listed in *DAB, ANB, NCAB, AR* (1918)

Military Service:
1884-1910: Army duty in technical assignments
1897-1900: Duty during Spanish-American War

Professional Service:

1884-1887: Graduate study at the Army's Engineering School of Application, NY

1887-1888: Mapping an surveying on the frontier

1888-1896: Engineer for river and harbor improvements of the Missouri and Ohio rivers

1891-1893: Construction engineer for roads in Yellowstone National Park

1894-1897: Engineer for reservoir construction for the irrigation of western lands

1900-1906: Engineer on the Missouri River and Yellowstone Park

1904:   Commission to survey and study Yosemite Valley

1906-1910: Construction engineer in Seattle, WA

1910-1915: Port commissioner for Seattle, WA

H. M. CHITTENDEN attended Cornell University, NY for one year before entering West Point. After his graduation, he spent three years in engineering graduate study at the Army's Engineer School. He was transferred to the frontier for a year of mapping and charting, before he began his concentrated work on the Missouri River. During that time, he spent two years building roads and surveying Yellowstone National Park. The result of his work was Chittenden's popular book on the Yellowstone published in 1895. He also contributed articles to *Harper's Weekly* opposing the construction of a railroad through the park. Chittenden then studied the potential for reservoirs to irrigate dry lands of the West. He gained national recognition as a strong advocate for government involvement in designing and building reservoirs by publishing a popular report on his work in 1897. In 1904, Chittenden investigated the Yosemite area in CA. The result of his work was the establishment of Yosemite as a National Park. Chittenden wrote history books on the fur trade and steamboats. He returned to duties in Yellowstone and then became the Corps of Engineers chief engineer in Seattle from 1906 to 1910, building the canal and lock in Seattle Harbor that bear his name today. Retiring from the Army in 1910, his last professional position was commissioner of the Port of Seattle, where he protected the environment and public property from developers. Chittenden was involved in a controversy over the effects of trees and forests on stream flow and flood control. An active member of the American Society of Civil Engineers, he published an article in the *Proceedings of the American Society of Civil Engineers,* which was severely criticized by President Roosevelt. Chittenden's work to preserve Yellowstone and Yosemite, establish reservoirs for irrigation, and to expose the American public to issues of environmental science were important contributions that helped build the culture and economics and preserve the unique ecosystems and natural resources of the American West.

USMA 1890 | **Edgar Jadwin** | **Engineer**

7 August 1865 (Honesdale, PA) – 2 March 1931 (Canal Zone, Panama)
Graduate # 3331 (1st out of 54), liste–d in *DAB, ANB, NCAB, AR* (1931)

Military Service:
1897-1898: Staff duty in Office of the Chief of Army Engineers
1898-1900: Combat and engineering duty in Cuba during the Spanish-American War
1911-1916: Staff duty in Office of the Chief of Army Engineers, Washington, DC
1917-1919: Combat engineering duty in France during World War I
1919-1920: Investigation of conditions in Poland for the President
1926-1929: Chief of Army Engineers, Washington, DC

Professional Service:
1890-1897: Engineering duty for rivers and harbors in East Coast and Mississippi River
1900-1906: Engineering duty for harbors of Los Angeles, CA and Galveston, TX
1907-1911: Engineering duty on Panama Canal
1916-1917: Engineering duty on Ohio River
1920-1924: Engineering duty in SC
1924-1929: Engineering duty along St Lawrence River, designing navigation improvements
            and power generation
1929-1931: Engineering duty in Panama and Nicaragua

E. JADWIN attended Lafayette College for two years before enrolling at West Point. He graduated first in the Military Academy class of 1890 and was commissioned in the Corps of Engineers. He served with engineer troops from 1891 to 1895 and was a combat engineer during the Spanish-American War serving in Cuba. After performing duties as district engineer at the expanding ports of Los Angeles, CA and Galveston, TX, he was selected by **George Goethals (USMA 1880)** as an assistant in the construction of the Panama Canal. His work on that project from 1907 to 1911 was superb. His most important contributions were in digging a deep channel through Gatun Lake and the construction of the Gatun Dam. Returning to the U.S., Jadwin served from 1911 to 1916 in the Office of the Chief of Engineers focusing on bridge and road matters. Upon the United States' entry into World War I in 1917, he recruited a railway construction regiment and led it into service in France. Later in the war, he directed the American construction efforts in France for a year. President Wilson appointed Jadwin to investigate conditions in Poland in 1919. In 1922 to 1924, Jadwin headed the Charleston Engineering District and Southeast Division. He then served two years as the Assistant Chief of Engineers. As the Chief of Army Engineers from 1926 to 1929, he designed a major construction plan for Mississippi River flood control. Jadwin retired as a Lieutenant General in 1929. He died two years later in the Canal Zone while designing improvements for the canal as a civilian engineering consultant.

USMA 1890   ║ **Colden L'Hommedieu Ruggles** ║   **Scientist**

18 March 1869 (Omaha, NE) – 2 April 1933 (Charleston, SC)
Graduate # 3335 (5th out of 54), (ordnance), listed in *AR* (1934)

Military Service:
1890-1893:   Artillery duty at Ft. Columbus, NY and Ft. Monroe, VA
1911-1913:   Commander, Benicia Arsenal, CA
1913-1915:   Commander, Manila Ordnance Depot, Philippines
1915-1918:   Commander Sandy Hook Proving Ground, NJ
1917-1918:   Commander, Aberdeen Proving Ground MD
1918:   Support duty in Europe during World War I
                 (Chief of Technical Staff)

Professional Service:
1896-1900:   Ordnance duty at Frankford Arsenal, PA
1900-1903:   Ordnance inspector at Bethlehem Steel Company, PA
1900-1903:   Electrical engineering study at Leigh University, PA
1903-1908:   Ordnance duty at Watertown Arsenal, MA
1908-1911:   Professor of Ordnance and Gunnery, USMA
1918-1927:   Ordnance duty (manufacturing service) in
                 Washington, DC

C. L'H. RUGGLES was commissioned as an artillery officer
and served in NY and VA for his first military duties after graduation from USMA. In 1893, he transferred to the Ordnance Corps. Ruggles became an expert on manufacturing methods as he studied the systems at the various arsenals where he served. He built a reputation as a talented research scientist as he probed the processes for producing weapons and munitions. While serving as the inspector of the weapons plant at Bethlehem Steel Company in PA, Ruggles attended Lehigh University and received a degree in Electrical Engineering in 1903. While teaching cadets ordnance science at USMA, he wrote a volume on guns and gun carriages for use as a textbook and ordnance reference. Ruggles served in several command positions at arsenals and during World War I, was a technical staff officer in Europe. During his last years of Army service, Ruggles was in charge of the manufacture of all Army weapons and munitions. His contributions to the development of ordnance and general manufacturing industries were substantial. Ruggles was a member of the American Society of Automotive Engineers and the Society of Mechanical Engineers.

USMA 1891 | **Charles Patton Echols** | **Mathematician**

6 September 1867 (Huntsville, AL) – 21 May 1940 (New York, NY)
Graduate # 3387 (3ʳᵈ out of 65), listed in *AR* (1941)

Military Service:
1898:   Commander of Engineer Company in the Philippines Expedition
1918:   Military observer with Allied Armies in France

Professional Service:
1891-1894: Graduate study at the Engineer School of Application at Willet's Point, NY
1895-1898: Instructor and Assistant Professor of Mathematics, USMA
1898-1904: Associate Professor of Mathematics, USMA
1904-1931: Professor of Mathematics and Head of Mathematics Department, USMA

C. P. ECHOLS' father graduated from USMA in 1858 and fought with the Confederacy during the Civil War. Echols spent two years at the University of Virginia before entering West Point in the Class of 1891. After graduation, he studied at the Engineer School of Application at Willet's Point, NY. In 1895, he returned to USMA to teach mathematics. This started his forty-one years of service at the Academy, interrupted only briefly on three occasions. In 1898, he left the Academy for engineering duty at Governors Island, NY and then as Company Commander in the Philippines Expedition. After his combat service, Echols returned to USMA as an Associate Professor of Mathematics and in 1904 was selected as Professor of Mathematics and Head of the Department. In an effort to analyze and critique different teaching techniques and environments in Europe, Echols visited a variety of schools in Europe from 1905 until 1906. During World War I, he participated as a military observer with the Allied Armies in France. Upon his return to USMA, he resumed his duties as Head of the Mathematics Department and remained there until his retirement in 1931. He modernized the curriculum by providing more engineering mathematics to support topics in mechanical and electrical engineering. Echols was affectionately known to generations of Academy graduates as "P" Echols. He was also remembered for his insistence on thorough and rigorous mathematics instruction by his faculty. Stories of his idiosyncrasies became legends at the Academy. Not only was he revered by cadets, but also by his faculty peers and mentors. Described as "a strong link between the old and new West Point", he tried to keep valuable traditions in place while making improvements to modernize the curriculum.

Echols was a modest person and dedicated to the technical education of cadets. Following his retirement, Echols resided in Englewood, NJ, spending much of his time in New York City. In 1940, Echols was brutally murdered in Bryant Park, New York City, at the age of 72.

USMA 1892   **James Postell Jervey**   **Mathematician**

14 November 1869 (Powhatan, VA) – 12 March 1947 (Washington, DC)
Graduate # 3451 (2ⁿᵈ out of 62), (engineer), listed in *AS* (April 1948)

Military Service:
1905-1907:   Command duty with engineers in Philippines
1917-1918:   Combat engineering duty in Europe in World War I (Meuse-Argonne)
1918-1920:   Staff duty at Office of Chief of Army Engineers, Washington, DC

Professional Service:
1892-1895:   Graduate studies in engineering at Engineer School of Application, Willet's Point, NY
1895-1898:   Engineer duties for fortifications and mines in Pensacola Harbor, FL
1898-1905:   Assistant Professor of Practical Military Engineering and Civil Engineering, USMA
1907-1908:   Instructor of Civil Engineering, Engineer School, Washington, DC
1908-1913:   Construction engineer for locks on Panama Canal
1913-1917:   Engineer for public works, VA and WV
1926-1945:   Professor of Mathematics, University of the South, Sewanee, TN

J. P. JERVEY used his brilliant mind and work ethic to succeed as a cadet and graduated second in his class of 62 graduating cadets. Because of his academic accomplishments, he began his career in the Corps of Engineers as a graduate student at the Engineer School of Application. After fieldwork at Pensacola Harbor, FL during the Spanish-American War, Jervey returned to West Point to teach engineering. He was a very good professor and was well-liked by his cadets. He transferred to field duty in the Philippines where his unit worked on the fortifications of Subic Bay. After one year teaching at the Engineer School in Washington, he was sent on a challenging mission to Panama to help **George Goethals (USMA 1880)** build the canal. Jervey's major task was the construction of the Gatun Locks. Using his skill, ingenuity, and determination and coordinating with fellow engineer **Edgar Jadwin (USMA 1890)**, Jervey accomplished his mission. In 1913 to 1917, he performed Corps of Engineer duties in VA and WV. During World War I, he commanded engineers in combat in France, keeping roads clear for rapid movement of supplies and forces to the front and demolishing obstacles blocking the attack. After returning to the U.S. and spending two years in staff and construction work, Jervey retired from the Army in 1920. For the next six years, he served as the city manager for Portsmouth, VA. He was able to use his engineering skills to better perform his civic duties and improve the infrastructure of the city. In 1926, Jervey entered a new career as Professor of Mathematics at University of the South. For 19 years, he taught students and mentored faculty. He was both a fine educator and a scholar. Over the years, he wrote articles on military training, engineering, city management, and mathematics education. Jervey's contributions were varied and plentiful as he finally retired from professional work at age 76.

USMA 1899　　　**Clifton Carroll Carter**　　　**Scientist**

1876 (Fayette, KY) – 20 September 1950 (Washington, DC)
Graduate # 3888 (21st out of 72), listed in *AS* (Janurary 1952)

Military Service:
1899-1901: Combat and support duty in Spanish-American War, Cuba
1901-1902: Staff duty at Ft. Myer, VA
1905-1906: Command duty, Ft. Monroe, VA
1909-1912: Staff duty in HI
1914-1917: Staff duty at USMA

Professional Service:
1903-1905: Instructor of Electricity, Mines, and Mechanisms
　　　　　　at the Artillery School
1906-1907: Student at School of Submarine Defense, Ft. Totten, NY
1908-1909: Student at Massachusetts Institute of Technology
　　　　　　in Electrical Engineering
1912-1914: Special duty studying mine deployment on Chesapeake Bay
1917-1940: Professor of Natural and Experimental Philosophy, USMA

C. C. CARTER graduated from University of Kentucky before attending West Point. He entered the Coast Artillery Corps upon his graduation, which took place a few months early because of the Spanish-American War. Assigned duty in Cuba, he served as General Leonard Wood's aide-de-camp. Carter alternated between schools and service assignments, completing a degree at the Massachusetts Institute of Technology in electrical engineering in less than one year. For three years at West Point, he filled the position of Adjutant of the Academy. In 1917, just as World War I began, Carter was selected to fill the position of Professor of Natural and Experimental Philosophy at the

Academy. His selection was based on his leadership and academic potential, since he had little academic experience or previous opportunity to engage in scholarship as a scientist. Over his 23 years in this position, Carter worked diligently to build laboratories and develop faculty. As an accomplished scholar and successful academic leader, Carter wrote a textbook entitled *Simple Aerodynamics and the Airplane*. A strong believer in the potential of the airplane, Carter make sure that cadets took a rigorous course in the technical principles of air travel and aircraft design. Many technical and engineering schools around the country also used his textbook. Carter was well liked by cadets and showed himself to be a fine scientist and an innovative educator. He was a member of the National Aeronautic Association and the Society for Promotion of Engineering Education.

USMA 1900 | **George Bigelow Pillsbury** | **Engineer**

19 December 1876 (Lowell, MA) – 8 May 1951 (Ross, CA)
Graduate # 3940 (1ˢᵗ out of 54), listed in *AS* (January 1952)

Military Service:
1901-1903: Engineer duty in Philippines
1903-1905: Engineer duty in Washington, DC
1917-1919: Combat engineering duty in World War I (Argonne)
1930-1937: Assistant Chief of Army Engineers, Washington, DC

Professional Service:
1905-1908: Construction engineer in AK
1908-1912: Associate Professor of Mathematics, USMA
1912-1915: Engineer for river and harbor improvements
1915-1917: Construction engineer for forts in CA
1920-1924: Engineer duty in the Office of the Chief of Army Engineers, in charge of all river and harbor work in U.S.
1924-1928: Engineer for charting the Great Lakes and designing the St. Lawrence Seaway navigation channel
1928-1930: Construction engineer in Philadelphia, PA

G. B. PILLSBURY graduated at the top of his West Point class of 1900. He was friends with two other valedictorians at the Academy, **William Mitchell (USMA 1902)** and **Douglas MacArthur (USMA 1903)**. His early assignments in the Philippines and Alaska gave him numerous opportunities to develop his leadership and creativity. In recognition for his contributions to building roads in Alaska, a mountain in the state is named Mt. Pillsbury. His next assignment was teaching mathematics at West Point. This was a rewarding and successful tour for Pillsbury. He was knowledgeable in the subject and was able to motivate the cadets to study and achieve success. After construction and harbor work during tours on both coasts, Pillsbury was sent into combat duty in World War I. After the war, he returned to Washington, DC to supervise the river and harbor work for all the Corps of Engineer projects in the United States. Facing his most challenging project, he completed the charting the Great Lakes and began design of the navigation channel for the St. Lawrence River Waterway. He was tireless in his duties, with tremendous progress made in the plans. In 1928, Pillsbury transferred to construction duty in Philadelphia, PA. Spending his last seven years in the Army as the Assistant Chief of Army Engineers in Washington, DC, Pillsbury retired from the Army in 1937 to travel around the world, eventually settling in CA. He published a substantial reference book entitled *Tidal Hydraulics*. As an expert engineer and a dedicated leader of engineering organizations for the Army, his careful planning helped set the stage for the St. Lawrence River Seaway Project, although no implementation of his plan was executed for a number of years. This 200-mile river rises over 225 feet in elevation, and the final phases of the massive navigation and power project were finally completed in the 1950s.

USMA 1902 ┌─────────────────────────────┐ **Engineer**
│ **William Augustus Mitchell** │
└─────────────────────────────┘

30 November 1877 (Seale, AL) – 6 March 1941 (Tuscumbia, AL)
Graduate #4068 (1ˢᵗ out of 54), listed in *AR* (1941)

Military Service:
1902-1904: Combat engineer in Philippines
1917-1919: Combat engineering duty in World War I
(Soissons, St. Mihiel, Meuse-Argonne, Attigny)

Professional Service:
1904-1906: Graduate student at the Engineer School, Washington, DC
1907-1910: Assistant Professor of Engineering, USMA
1910-1914: Engineering duty for improving rivers and harbors
1919-1922: Instructor of Engineering, General Staff School
1922-1938: Professor of Civil and Military Engineering, USMA

W. A. MITCHELL studied at the Alabama Polytechnic Institute (Auburn) before entering West Point. He graduated first in his class of 1902 (the centennial class of the Academy). As an engineer officer, Mitchell's first assignment was in the Philippines building roads and training troops. After graduate study in engineering, he taught the subject to cadets at USMA. His enthusiasm was contagious with the cadets in his classes; they took to his aggressive style and were eager to learn. After assignments as a construction engineer and military student, Mitchell used his leadership style to organize and train the largest engineer regiment, a forestry regiment of 20,000 soldiers, for service in World War I. As a combat commander, he was highly successful in several important battles of the war. After the war, Mitchell taught engineering at the Staff College before succeeding the famous military engineer and historian **Gustav Fiebeger (USMA 1879)** as Professor of Civil and Military Engineering at West Point. For the next sixteen years, Mitchell taught military engineering and developed cadets as soldiers. He was a fine scholar as well as a dedicated teacher. Among his writings were books and articles about military engineering, civil engineering, mechanical engineering, and military history. During this era, his department included as much military science and history as physical engineering in its curriculum.

USMA 1902 ┌─────────────────────────────┐ **Scientist**
│ **Frederic William Hinrichs, Jr.** │
└─────────────────────────────┘

3 November 1878 (Brooklyn, NY) – 17 February 1944 (Pasadena, CA)
Graduate # 4077 (10ᵗʰ out of 54), listed in *AS* (April 1945)

Military Service:
1902-1904: Garrison duty in NY and NJ
1907-1909: Garrison duty in FL and NM
1909-1910: Staff duty in Office of Chief of Ordnance, Washington, DC

1917-1919: Service during World War I at Watervliet Arsenal, NY and San Antonio Arsenal, TX

Professional Service:
1904-1907: Ordnance duty at Springfield Armory, MA and Frankford Arsenal, PA
1910-1917: Professor of Mechanics, University of Rochester, NY
1921-1944: Professor of Mechanics and Dean, California Institute of Technology

---

F. W. HINRICHS, JR. entered the artillery upon graduation from the Academy during its Centennial Celebration of 1902. After serving in garrison, he transferred first to the Ordnance Corps and then to the Coastal Artillery during his eight-year Army career before he was medically retired in 1910. He entered academics and obtained science degrees from Columbia University, NY and Occidental College, CA.

Coastal artillery in 1913 (from West Point Howitzer)

He taught mechanics at the University of Rochester, NY until the outbreak of World War I. He offered his services to the Army during the war and served in command of ordnance arsenals. After the war, he returned to academics, transferring to the Professor of Mechanics position at the California Institute of Technology. Soon he was also appointed Dean of Upper Classmen. He was an outstanding teacher for the bright, engineering students at the growing technical school. Working for the Institute's President, the famous scientist Robert Millikan, Hinrichs was considered a strong educational leader at the school. While not a research scholar, he built a fine reputation as an expert engineering educator and helped establish the California Institute of Technology as a fine school of engineering. The school grew in both size and reputation during his 23 years on the faculty.

USMA 1902   ‖ **William Howell Williams** ‖   **Scientist**

6 February 1881 (Lancaster, NY) – 11 August 1959 (Berkeley, CA)
Graduate # 4089 (22nd out of 54), (physicist)

Military Service:
1902-1904: Artillery duty in Philippines
1904-1906: Staff duty in Washington, DC
1918-1919: Training duty during World War I
1942-1943: Technical service with National Defense Research Committee

Professional Service:
1916-1917: Science teacher in high school, CA
1919-1949: Professor of Physics, University of California at Berkeley

---

W. H. WILLIAMS entered artillery duty in the Philippines after his graduation. Serving four years in the Army, he resigned to enter civilian life. After working in industry and teaching science at the high school level, he pursued a physics degree at the University of California at Berkeley. Williams served as a training officer during World War I and then returned to his academic work in CA. In 1919, he began his college teaching career with courses in quantum theory, relativity, thermodynamics, and kinetics at the University of California at Berkeley. Williams was promoted to full Professor of Physics in 1928. He conducted research from 1927 to 1928 at the University of Göttingen in Germany. Williams' research was in modern physics, relativity, and quantum theory, which he also taught to the physics students at the university. Mentoring hundreds of bright science students, Williams set the cultural tone for science education at the university. An active member of the American Physical Society, he contributed to the advancement of science teaching at the national level. During World War II, Williams served on the National Defense Research Committee in Washington, DC. In 1949, he retired from teaching as an emeritus professor. Williams played important roles as both a researcher and dedicated educator for a new generation of physicists.

USMA 1903    **Douglas MacArthur**   **Technologist**

26 January 1880 (Little Rock, AR) – 5 April 1964 (Washington, DC)
Graduate # 4122 (1st out of 94), (engineer, systems analyst), listed in *DAB, ANB, NCAB, AS* (Spring 1964)

Military Service:
1913-1917: Staff duty in Washington, DC
1914:   Combat duty in the occupation of Vera Cruz, Mexico
1918-1919: Combat duty during World War I (Champagne-Marne, St. Mihiel, Meuse-Argonne, Sedan)
1928-1930: Commander in Philippines Islands
1930-1935: Chief of Staff of the Army
1935-1941: Military advisor to the Philippines
1941-1945: Combat duty as Commander of Pacific Forces during World War II (Medal of Honor)
                (General of the Army)
1945-1951: Military Governor in Japan
1950-1951: Combat Commander during Korean War

Professional Service:
1903-1912: Engineer duty in U.S., Philippines, and Panama
1919-1922: Superintendent, USMA

D. MacArthur was a brilliant cadet, studying a rigorous and intensive program of engineering, science, and applied mathematics from an array of classic (from West Point authors) and modern textbooks, such as **Charles Davies' (USMA 1815)** *Geometry*, **Henry Ludlow's (USMA 1876)** *Trigonometry*, C. Smith's *Conic Sections*, C. Smith's *Algebra*, Johnson's *Surveying*, Johnson's *Theory of Errors and Least Squares*, **Albert Church's (USMA 1826)** *Descriptive Geometry*, **Edgar Bass' (USMA 1868)** *Differential Calculus*, and Murray's *Integral Calculus*. After graduation, he entered the engineer branch where he excelled in early construction and combat assignments in the U.S., Philippines, and Panama. Appointed USMA's Superintendent from 1919 to 1922, he instituted

reforms in the academic program that reduced in-class time, increased out-of-class requirements, and modified the curriculum. Initially, his initiatives met with mixed reviews as some considered them as lowering the academic standards of the Academy, but ultimately they proved to be successful changes in the Academy's development of independent thinkers and complex problem solvers for the future Army. MacArthur used his analytic and problem solving abilities throughout his military career. As Army Chief of Staff from 1930 to 1935, he often developed quantitative analysis for major issues of Army preparedness and technological development. His engineering talent helped him establish support for the Civilian Conservation Corps and Works Projects Administration as part of the military's support of President Roosevelt's New Deal and America's recovery from the Great Depression. His ability to understand and leverage technology gave his forces advantages throughout his combat service.

Quotations:

By **Omar Bradley (USMA 1915),** who was teaching mathematics when MacArthur was Superintendent: "On the whole, I approved of MacArthur's liberalization of West Point academics, even if it did somewhat curtail the study of my specialty, mathematics."

By MacArthur in his famous "Duty-Honor-Country" speech in accepting the Thayer Award (his view of the future): "You now face a new world – a world of change. The thrust into outer space of the satellite, spheres, and missiles marked the beginning of another epoch in the long story of mankind – the chapter of the space age. In the five or more billions of years the scientists tell us it has taken to form the earth, in the three

or more billion years of development of the human race, there has never been a greater, a more abrupt or staggering evolution. We deal now not with things of this world alone, but with the illimitable distances and as yet unfathomed mysteries of the universe. We are reaching out for a new and boundless frontier. We speak in strange terms: of harnessing the cosmic energy; of making winds and tides work for us; of creating unheard synthetic materials to supplement or even replace our old standard basics; of purifying sea water for our drink; of mining ocean floors for new fields of wealth and food; of disease preventatives to expand life into the hundred of years; of controlling the weather for a more equitable distribution of heat and cold, of rain and shine; of space ships to the moon; of the primary target in war, no longer limited to the armed forces of the enemy, but instead to include his civil populations; of ultimate conflict between a united human race and the sinister forces of some other planetary galaxy; of such dreams and fantasies as to make life the most exciting of all time."

References:

James, D. Clayton, *Years of MacArthur*, 3 vols. Houghton Mifflin, Boston, 1970-1985.

Korn, Bernard, "MacArthur Goes to West Point," *Historical Messenger of the Milwaukee Historical Society*, (Autumn 1974).

Perret, Geoffrey, *Old Soldiers Never Die: The Life of Douglas MacArthur*, Random House, New York, 1996.

Wintraub, Stanley, *MacArthur's War: Korea and the Undoing of an American Hero*, Free Press, New York, 2000.

USMA 1903   **Thomas Etholen Selfridge**   **Technologist**

2 February 1882 (San Francisco, CA) – 17 September 1908 (Fort Myer, VA)
Graduate # 4152 (31st out of 94), (aviator), listed in *AR* (1909)

Military Service:
1903-1906: Artillery duty in CA

Professional Service:
1906-1907: Assistant Professor of Ordnance and Gunnery,
                   USMA
1907-1908: Aeronautic duty in Nova Scotia, Hammandsport,
                   NY and Fort Myers, VA

T. E. SELFRIDGE was a classmate of **Douglas MacArthur** in the USMA Class of 1903. He entered the artillery and served in garrison in CA for his first assignment. In 1906, he helped with the relief effort of the great San Francisco earthquake. In that same year, he returned to the Academy to teach in the Department of Ordnance and Gunnery. By the end of his year, Selfridge had decided on a career in aeronautics and requested duty with the famous Wright Brothers, who had flown the first aeroplane at Kitty Hawk, NC on 17 December 1903, just after Selfridge's graduation. While not able to work with the Wright brothers that summer, Selfridge did obtain an invitation through the efforts of the West Point Librarian **Edward Holden (USMA 1870)** to work with Alexander Graham Bell on his aviation work. The two researchers, Bell and Selfridge, built tetrahedral kites, allowing Selfridge to make his first ascent using a kite. That flight ended in a severe crash, but he survived. Selfridge also flew in two aeroplanes during that summer. When Bell took his flying operations to Hammondsport, NY to join with Glenn Curtiss, Selfridge went along as the Army's representative. The three aviators and aircraft inventors, Curtis, Bell, and Selfridge built and tested engines, aircraft, and new apparatus. When the War Department established an aviation department as part of the Signal Corps at Fort Myer, VA, Selfridge joined with Orville Wright and Captain Baldwin to test balloons and aircraft. On 18 September 1908, Selfridge finally had the opportunity to fly with Orville Wright. With a large number of spectators watching, they ascended and circled the field several times before the propeller blade failed at a height of 150 feet. Wright managed to glide the craft to 75 feet before it dropped from the sky and crashed. Orville Wright survived but Selfridge died from his injuries. Selfridge was the first military casualty of flight, and the world had lost its finest aviation navigator and aeronautic engineer.

References:

Crouch, Tom, *Bishop's Boys: A Life of Wilbur and Orville Wright*, W. W. Norton, New York, 1989.

Hennessy, Juliette, *U.S. Army Air Arm, April 1861 to April 1917*, Office of Air Force History, Washington, 1985.

Roseberry, Cecil, *Glen Curtiss: Pioneer of Flight*, Doubleday, Garden City, NY, 1972.

USMA 1904 | **Charles Roberts Pettis** | **Scientist**

21 May 1880 (Oxford, MS) – 10 January 1969 (Ellisville, MS)
Graduate # 4215 (1st out of 124), (hydrologist, civil engineer, mathematician), listed in *AS* (Winter 1970)

Military Service:
1904-1906: Engineer duty in Philippines
1913-1916: Engineer duty in Philippines (fortifications and roads in Corregidor)
1917-1919: Combat engineer duty in France during World War I
1920-1924: Staff duty in Office of Secretary of War
1929-1932: Engineer troop duty in CO
1941-1943: Military science instructor, Ohio State University

Professional Service:
1906-1909: Construction engineer
1909-1913: Assistant Professor of Mathematics, USMA
1925-1928: Construction engineer in Baltimore Harbor
1932-1936: Construction engineer in OH

1936-1938: Engineer for Great Lakes survey
1938-1939: Construction engineer for Detroit, MI
1939-1941: Professor of Mathematics, Mississippi State College
1944-1950: Professor of Mathematics, Mississippi State College

---

C. R. Pettis graduated from the University of Mississippi before attending West Point. He was valedictorian of his Class of 1904, following **Douglas MacArthur (USMA 1903)** who received the top honor the year before. Pettis chose the engineer branch with duty in the Philippines. After working construction during a tour at Puget Sound in WA, Pettis returned to West Point to teach mathematics. Following his teaching assignment, Pettis returned to the Philippines as an engineer for roadways on Corregidor. During World War I, he saw combat duty in France. Following his combat assignment, Pettis worked in the Office of the Secretary of War and then built harbor facilities in Baltimore. After troop leading in CO and supervising construction in OH, Pettis faced the challenge of charting the Great Lakes in 1936. His analysis of water levels on the lakes was so thorough and innovative that Pettis was allowed to use this work as part of his Ph.D. thesis at the University of Michigan in hydrology (civil engineering). His work was substantial in developing an understanding of the drainage and forces at work in the Great Lakes basin. In 1939, Pettis retired from the Army to become Professor of Mathematics at Mississippi State College. Except for a two-year stint as a military science instructor during World War II, Pettis taught mathematics at the school until 1950. A productive scholar with authorship of articles on hydrology that appeared in several engineering journals, Pettis was a Fellow of the American Association for the Advancement of Science and a member of the American Society for Civil Engineers and the American Geophysical Union. Pettis was a bright, dedicated scientist who accomplished a great deal for the Army and his disciplines of hydrology and mathematics.

USMA 1904   **Chauncey Lee Fenton**   **Scientist**

14 January 1880 (Edinboro, PA) – 8 February 1962 (Fort Sam Houston, TX)
Graduate # 4229 (15th out of 124), listed in *AS* (Summer 1962)

Military Service:
1904-1906: Artillery duties
1910-1917: Command and staff artillery duties (coast artillery at Fort Totten, NY)
1917-1919: Combat service on General Staff in World War I (Cambrai, Aisne-Marne, Meuse-Argonne, Somme)
1919-1922: Staff duties in Washington, DC

Professional Service:
1906-1910: Assistant Professor of Mathematics, USMA
1924-1927: Associate Professor of Mathematics, USMA

1928-1946: Professor of Chemistry and Electricity, USMA

C. L. FENTON headed off to artillery duties after graduating in 1904. In 1906, he returned to West Point to teach mathematics for four years. He was a tremendous instructor, who enjoyed teaching the subject and working with cadets. From 1910 to the beginning of World War I, Fenton served in various staff and command positions in the artillery and his new branch of coastal artillery at Fort Totten, NY. During World War I, Fenton was detailed to a combat staff position and later became Chief of Artillery. After the war, he performed personnel and staff work until he returned to the Mathematics Department at West Point in 1924. As the Associate Professor, he led faculty training and supervised the courses offered by the department. At the urging of Superintendent William Smith (USMA 1892), Fenton accepted the position of Professor of Chemistry and Electricity, succeeding **Wirt Robinson (USMA 1887)** and led the department for the next 18 years. He attended Columbia University in electrical engineering to build his disciplinary expertise. He modernized the program by building laboratories for electrical and chemical experiments. He introduced new topics in electronics and communications and adopted new textbooks for the courses. After his mandatory retirement in 1944, the Superintendent had him recalled to active duty to complete wartime initiatives and post-war planning for the Academy. Because of Fenton, West Point's science program maintained high standards as it prepared to adjust to the technological advances instituted by society and the military during the war. After his retirement, Fenton remained in the West Point area. He was chair of the Sesquicentennial Steering Committee for the Academy and made sure the 150th anniversary celebration was as memorable as the Centennial Celebration that he had witnessed as a cadet.

USMA 1907   **Richard Robert Somers**   **Mathematician**

8 December 1881 (Mantua, NJ) – 22 January 1957 (Woodbury, NJ)
Graduate #4538 (8th out of 111), (ordnance)

Military Service:
1907-1909: Garrison duty at Ft. Strong, Boston, MA
1917-1919: Commandant of Ordnance School, Aberdeen Proving Ground, MD
1920-1924, 1932-1936, and 1940-1942: Staff duty in the Office of the Chief of Ordnance

Professional Service:
1907-1914: Ordnance duty at Sandy Hook Proving Ground, NJ
1914-1916: Assistant Professor of Ordnance and Gunnery, USMA
1924-1932: Ordnance duty at Panama Canal and Watervliet Arsenal, NY
1922-1925 and 1942-1945: Editor of the *Army Ordnance Journal*
1945-1951: Assistant Professor of Mathematics, University of New Hampshire

---

R. R. SOMERS taught school for two years before attending West Point and entering the Coastal Artillery Corps upon graduation. After two years of duty at Fort Strong in Boston, Somers transferred to the Ordnance Corps. His initial ordnance assignment was at Sandy Hook Proving Ground, NJ. However, the Army needed a larger, more remote site for testing and evaluating its weapons. Somers was given the mission to find the location. The Army approved his selection for the Ordnance Corps new testing facility at Aberdeen Proving Ground, MD. Somers was appointed Commandant of the new Ordnance School during World War I. He was in charge of training ordnance officers and soldiers as the Army built up its wartime strength. After the war and follow-on duties in the Office of the Chief of Ordnance and Watervliet Arsenal, Somers taught at the Army Industrial College. He graduated from the Ordnance School of Technology and received an MBA from Harvard University. He enjoyed his duties so much as editor of the *Army Ordnance Journal*, he took on that position after he retired from the Army in 1942. In 1945, he entered academe as a Professor of Mathematics, first at Dartmouth College and then at the University of New Hampshire. Somers was a fine teacher and a dedicated mathematical researcher. Over his 33 years in ordnance, he built a reputation as a superb applied mathematician. After Somers retired, he continued his mathematical research in his specialty of number theory. For many years, right up until the day he died, Somers worked to discover a proof of Fermat's Last Theorem. Many mathematicians had worked on this problem since Pierre Fermat's death in 1665, and Somers hoped to find the obscure path to unlock this mystery, but the resolution to this mathematical puzzle was unknown for another 38 years after Somers died, when the theorem was finally proved by Andrew Wiles of Princeton in 1995.

USMA 1907   **Henry Harley Arnold**   **Technologist**

25 June 1886 (Gladwyn, PA) – 15 January 1950 (Sonoma, CA)
Graduate # 4596 (66th out of 111), listed in *DAB, ANB, AS* (April 1951)

Military Service:
1907-1911: Infantry duty in the Philippines
1911-1913: Aviation training and duty flight instructor, OH and MD
             (received Mackay Trophy)
1913-1916: Infantry duty in the Philippines
1916-1917: Aviation duty in CA and Panama
1917-1918: Staff duty in Washington, DC during World War I
1918-1919: Aviation duty in Europe

1933-1936:   Aviation duty, CA (received second Mackay Trophy)
1936-1938:   Staff duty as Assistant Chief of Air Corps, Washington, DC
1938-1946:   Chief of the Army Air Corps, Washington, DC

Professional Service:
1920-1925:   Aviation duty developing new utilization of aircraft
1925-1929:   Professional schooling
1931-1933:   Aviation research with scientists at California Institute of
             Technology

H. H. "HAP" ARNOLD graduated in the middle of his West Point class as an infantry officer. He spent four years in the infantry in the Philippines before volunteering for aviation duty.

After being taught to fly by the Wright brothers, Arnold joined the Army's first cadre of aviators in 1911. He was an excellent aviator and in 1912 established a world altitude record of 6,540 feet. This feat earned him the Mackay Trophy for aviation excellence. He helped pioneer aerial reconnaissance by being the first to use a radio to report observations to ground stations. A near-fatal crash and losses of friends to aircraft accidents temporarily sent him back to the infantry. Arnold served with George C. Marshall as they became lifelong friends. Resuming flying in 1916, he supervised the training of pilots as the U.S. entered World War I. He volunteered for combat service, but was kept in a staff position in Washington, DC. Arriving in Europe after the war, he assessed the status of wartime aviation and inspected the aviation facilities. During the 1920s, Arnold always managed to place himself at the forefront of developments in the Air Force by performing a number of record-breaking flights. He wrote six books about the U.S. Air Corps, helped Hollywood in producing several films promoting aviation, and testified on behalf of his mentor, Billy Mitchell, during a controversial court-martial in 1928. While stationed at March Field in CA, Arnold spent considerable time with the scientists at the California Institute of Technology learning the technical aspects of aviation. In 1934, Arnold led a flight of ten B-10 bombers on a 5,290-mile round trip flight from Washington, DC to Fairbanks, AK.

This spectacular flight led to an understanding of aviation capabilities in strategic bombing and further built his reputation. He received his second Mackay Trophy for this flight. In 1938, Arnold rose to Chief of the Army Air Corps. Assisted by his friend Marshall, then Chief of Staff of the Army, Arnold efficiently managed a rapid increase in airplane and pilot production prior to 1941. Using his technological knowledge and contacts within the aircraft industry, Arnold expertly led a huge increase in production and training. When the United States entered World War II, it possessed a respectable air force and a strong technical foundation. Arnold faced many production, technological and administrative challenges, but by virtue of his technical expertise, he coordinated the massive armament effort for the Air Force. The Air Force grew from 22,000 men and 3,500 aircraft in 1941 to nearly 2.5

million personnel and 64,000 warplanes by 1945. Arnold spearheaded production of the P-51 *Mustang* for Europe and the B-29 *Superfortress* for Asia. Arnold became a five-star General in 1945. Retiring from the Army in 1946, he wrote his memoirs entitled *Global Mission*. In 1947, the Air Force was made a separate branch of service. Arnold's career seemed to parallel the development of American military aviation as he personally contributed to many milestones in the history of aviation. As the most technologically astute aviator, he worked with scientists like Theodore von Karman and **Roscoe "Bim" Wilson (USMA 1928)** and insured that other aviation officers were educated in aeronautics and other technical aspects of flying. Arnold used both his leadership and his technical knowledge to build the world's largest and most advanced air force.

References:

Coffey, Thomas, *Hap: Military Aviator, the Story of the U.S. Air Force and the Man who Built it: General Henry H. "Hap" Arnold*, Viking Press, New York, 1982.

Daso, Dik Alan, *Hap Arnold and the Evolution of American Airpower*, Smithsonian Institution Press, Washington, 2000.

USMA 1911   ‖ **Raymond Albert Wheeler** ‖   **Engineer**

31 July 1885 (Peoria, IL) – 8 February 1974 (Washington, DC)
Graduate # 4940 (5ᵗʰ out of 82), listed in *AS* (December 1974)

Military Service:
1914:   Veracruz Expedition
1918:   Combat duty in World War I with the American Expeditionary Force
1918-1923: Duty with American Forces in Germany
1941-1942: Combat duty in World War II (Persia, China-Burma-India, Southeast Asia Command)
1945-1949: Chief of Army Engineers, Washington, DC

Professional Service:
1924-1940: Engineer duty in Newport, RI; Wilmington, NC; and Rock Island, IL
1956-1957: Engineer duty clearing the Suez Canal

R. A. WHEELER was commissioned in the Corps of Engineers after graduating from the Military Academy in the class of 1911. After serving with the Veracruz Expedition in 1914, he went to France in 1918 to fight in World War I. He was awarded decorations for his actions in the campaign and, by the end of World War I, had assumed command of his regiment. Between the two world wars, Wheeler served as the district engineer in Newport, RI; Wilmington, NC; and Rock Island, IL. In 1941, he was appointed chief of the U.S.

Military Iranian Mission. A year later, Wheeler transferred to the China-Burma-India Theater as Commanding General of the Services of Supply. In 1943, he was assigned to Lord Mountbatten's Asia Command as the principal administrative officer and Deputy Supreme Commander. Before the end of World War II, he was Commander of the India-Burma Theater. He represented the United States at the Japanese surrender in Singapore. As Chief of Army Engineers from 1945 to 1949, Wheeler initiated the construction of the Missouri River dams project. After his Army retirement in 1947, he worked for the United Nations and the International Bank for Reconstruction and Development on Asian and African development projects. He oversaw the clearing of the Suez Canal in 1956 to 1957. He was made an honorary Knight of the British Empire. Wheeler was the consummate engineer and military officer -- dedicated, skilled, and highly successful in his challenging endeavors.

USMA 1914   ‖ **Allen Parker Cowgill** ‖   **Mathematician**

17 July 1890 (Paducah, KY) – 27 February 1955 (Syracuse, NY)
Graduate # 5216 (11th out of 107), listed in *AS* (Winter 1958)

Military Service:
1914-1915: Duty on Mexican Border
1916-1918: Duty on Mexican boarder and railroad construction in VA
1919-1921: Construction engineer in Philippines

Professional Service:
1915-1916: Student at engineering School in Washington, DC
1918-1919: Assistant Professor of Practical Military Engineering and
            Assistant Professor of Mathematics, USMA
1921-1926: Civil engineering projects in Nebraska
1926-1935: Student at University of Nebraska, earning Ph.D.
            in Mathematics and Civil Engineering
1936-1938: Professor of Mathematics, Indiana Technical College
1938-1947: Professor of Engineering and Mathematics, Syracuse
            University, NY

A. P. COWGILL studied mechanical engineering at the University of Nebraska for two years before entering West Point. He was commissioned as an engineer upon graduation and was sent to perform duties along the Mexican border. Working for Ulysses S. Grant III (USMA 1903), he learned field engineering and survived a major hurricane and flood while in Galveston, TX. He studied at the Engineer School in Washington, DC for a year and then was ordered back to TX. His unit built a 22-mile forbidding road through harsh terrain and numerous rocks near San Antonio, which was later named Cowgill Road. He was an ideal candidate for his next assignment, teaching at West Point. First, he taught Practical Military

Engineering, but soon transferred to the Mathematics Department. This subject was his passion, and Cowgill was in his element as a teacher. After leaving the Academy for duty in the Philippines as an engineer, Cowgill left the Army to try his hand at civil works projects back in Nebraska. After a short time, he entered University of Nebraska as a part time student. He obtained a degree in Mathematics and Astronomy and later a Ph.D. in Mathematics and Civil Engineering. Cowgill taught for eleven years at Indiana Technical College and Syracuse University. He was a patient and inspiring teacher, along with being a fine researcher. He had work published in mathematics journals and was a member of the American Mathematical Society and Sigma Xi. Cornwell retired in the Syracuse area, living on Lake Ontario during the summers. As a contributor to both science and student development, he was always determined to act on principle and to work to his maximum potential.

USMA 1915   Omar Nelson Bradley   Mathematician

12 February 1893 (Clark, MO) – 8 April 1981 (New York, NY)
Graduate # 5356 (44th out of 164), (operations research analyst), listed in ANB,
AS (September 1970), AS (June 1981)

Military Service:
1915-1917: Garrison duty in Spokane, WA and AZ
1917-1918: Guard duty in Montana
1919-1920: ROTC duty in MN and SD
1925-1927: Staff duty in HI
1929-1933: Infantry instructor at Ft. Benning, GA
1934-1938: Tactics instructor at West Point, NY
1941-1942: Commandant, Infantry School, Ft. Benning, GA
1942-1945: Combat Commander during World War II (Mediterranean,
         Europe, Overlord, Division-Corps-Army-Group Commander)
1945-1947: Administrator of Veterans Administration
1948-1949: Chief of Staff, U.S. Army
1949-1953: Chairman, Joint Chiefs of Staff (General of the Army)

Professional Service:
1920-1924: Assistant Professor of Mathematics, USMA
1938-1941: Operations Research duty for the Army Chief of Staff

Described as "calculative" in high school, **O.N. BRADLEY** arrived at the Academy with advanced mathematics abilities. He was a member of West Point's class of 1915, called "the class that stars fell on" with 59 of the 164 graduates becoming generals. He had several assignments with troops and several others as an instructor, both in various infantry training schools and in mathematics education at West Point. In total, 13 years of his first 23 years in the Army were as an instructor. Bradley enjoyed his assignment in the Mathematics

Department at West Point, claiming it was pivotal in his development as an officer and problem solver. Serving beyond his expected 3-year tour by staying an additional year to develop and use his talents in teaching and mathematics, he educated and trained new instructors in the department. He was an outstanding role model for junior instructors because of his ability to teach cadets how to apply mathematics and quantitative modeling to military duties and logical decision making. From 1938 to 1941, he worked on mobilization planning, production modeling, and optimizing the Army branch and unit mix for his mentor, Chief of Staff of the Army, George Marshall. Bradley was an outstanding technical analyst, able to combine his mathematics experience with his common sense to find solutions to complex quantitative issues facing the Army in preparation for World War Il. During World War II, he successfully commanded divisions, corps, and eventually the largest Army ever deployed by the U.S., earning him the title of the "GI's General." After the war, he headed the Veteran's Administration and then in 1948 became Chief of Staff of the Army. In 1949, he was appointed the first-ever Chairman of the Joint Chief of Staff. Once again, his quantitative talents enabled him to solve problems by aligning budgets between the services. He led the nation's military forces during the Korean War and at the beginning of the nuclear expansion of the Cold War. Leaving military service in 1953, Bradley joined the leadership of Bulova Watch Company. He was an expert operations research analyst (before that term was coined) and a strong supporter of technical education for Army officers.

Quotations:

By Bradley, related to his mathematics teaching: "I taught all morning six days a week. In the afternoon I attended math refresher . ... In the evenings I studied the work I would teach plebes the following day."

By Bradley, after his successful Army Command in World War II: "Whatever the case, I know I benefited from this prolonged immersion in math . ... In later years, when I was faced with infinitely complex problems, ... mathematics helped me think more clearly and logically."

By Bradley at the West Point Sesquicentennial (March 1952) as Chairman of the Joints Chiefs of Staff "I do not intend- to emphasize science and engineering to West Pointers in order to urge the Academy to produce outstanding scientists . ... A good working knowledge of the various fields of science will be necessary to relate the latest scientific discoveries to the military problems we have."

By Bradley at Founders Day in 1978, "For 176 years the Long Gray Line has met the needs of our changing society while remaining an impregnable bastion of those ideals upon which our country was founded."

References:
Bradley, Omar, *A General's Life*, Simon & Schuster, 1983.

West Point's Scientific 200

Bradley, Omar, *Soldier's Story*, Rand McNally, Chicago, 1978.

Reeder, Red, *Omar Nelson Bradley: The Soldier's General*. Garrard Pub. Co., Champaign, IL, 1969.

USMA 1915 | **Dwight David Eisenhower** | **Mathematician**

14 October 1890 (Denison, TX) – 28 March 1969 (Washington, DC)
Graduate # 5373 (61st out of 164), (operations research analyst), listed in DAB, ANB, AS (Spring 1968)

Military Service:

1915-1918:	Garrison duty at Ft. Sam Houston, TX
1918-1919:	Training duty during World War I
1919-1921:	Armor duty at Camp Meade, MD
1935-1938:	Duty in the Philippines (Advisor to General MacArthur)
1940-1941:	Division Chief of Staff for the Louisiana Maneuvers
1942:	Chief of War Plans, Army Staff, Washington, DC
1942-1945:	Combat Commander during World War II (Europe, NATO, AEF)
1945-1948:	Chief of Staff, U.S. Army
1951-1952:	Commander in Europe and planning NATO

Professional Service:

1929-1935:	Operations research analyst in the War Department
1948-1950:	President of Columbia University, NY

D. D. EISENHOWER proved himself as a gifted writer and athlete while attending USMA, graduating in 1915 in one of the most celebrated Academy classes. A total of 59 of his classmates, including fellow General of the Army, **Omar Bradley**, wore stars before their careers were over. While he did not see combat action in World War I, he was able to work with George Patton (USMA 1909) on developing Armor tactics and with General John Pershing (USMA 1886) on analyzing World War I battle sites. Eisenhower worked on the War Department staff on the technical aspects of mobilization plans, the enlargement and support of military research and development, and the technical issues relating to the military-industrial complex for Chief of Staff of the Army **Douglas MacArthur (USMA 1903)**. This duty in the War Department set the tone for more analytical and quantitative studies by the department and military organizations as the Army prepared for World Wax II. He followed MacArthur to the Philippines to serve as an advisor and continued to fill the role of technical writer for MacArthur's numerous initiatives and studies. From his outstanding performance at the Louisiana Maneuvers in 1941, Eisenhower was labeled as a strong leader with an analytical mind and a collegial personality. Eisenhower became the commander of all allied forces in Europe during World War II and proved himself to be a master at leveraging technology, executing coalition warfare, and coordinating strategic planning. Working with balky allies and headstrong subordinate commanders, he was able to unite their efforts into an allied victory in Europe. After the war, Eisenhower replaced George Marshall as Chief of Staff and began the draw-down of the wartime Army. After leaving military service in 1948, he served as the President of Columbia University for two years

before returning to Army command in Europe. In 1952, he successfully ran for President of the United States and quickly ended the Korean War. While President, he was able to build technologies in America through numerous government programs, such as the Science Advisory Committee and NASA. Eisenhower spent just a short time in positions dedicated to analytic work, but he was a superb problem solver and a strong supporter of technological development and education.

References:

Ambrose, Stephen, *Eisenhower: 1890-1952*, Simon & Schuster, New York, 1983.

Hughes, David, *Ike at West Point*, Wayne Co., Poughkeepsie, NY, 1958.

Lyon, Peter, *Eisenhower: Portrait of the Hero*, Little, Brown and Co., Boston, 1974.

Perret, Geoffrey, *Eisenhower*, Random House, New York, 2000.

USMA April 1917      **Mathematician**

16 September 1892 (Torrington, CT) – 1 July 1977 (Asheville, NC)
Graduate # 5602 (1st out of 139), listed in AS (June 1978)

Military Service:
1918:   Commander, Combat Engineer Company, attached to British and U.S. Forces, World War I
1923-1926:   Engineer duty, Fort Bliss, Texas
1926-1928:   Assistant Director of Public Buildings and Parks, Washington, DC
1928-1931:   American Battle Monuments Commission, Paris, France

Professional Service:
1918-1922:   Assistant Professor, Department of Mathematics, USMA
1922-1923:   Student, Massachusetts Institute of Technology
1931-1947:   Professor of Mathematics, Head of the Department, USMA

1947-1956:   Dean of the Academic Board, USMA

H. Jones attended Harvard on an engineering scholarship for two years before deciding to enroll at West Point, where he was an outstanding mathematics student. Upon early graduation because of World War I, Jones trained for combat duty as an engineer, traveling to France with his unit. Attached to the British Fifth Army for bridging operations on the Somme River, his engineer company saw combat in response to two large German attacks. Jones earned the Distinguished Service Cross for his

gallant actions in the campaign as he and his men were among the first United States soldiers to see action with the Allied Forces in France. In June 1918, his company joined the arriving American forces to the east of Chateau Thierry, where he saw duty in the Second Battle of the Marne. After completing his combat duties, Jones returned to the United States and was assigned to West Point as an instructor and assistant professor of mathematics. He taught at USMA until 1922, when he left to attend the Massachusetts Institute of Technology, completing a B.S. degree in Civil Engineering. For the next three years, Jones served on an engineer staff at Fort Bliss, TX. Then for two years, he worked in Washington, DC helping with construction of government buildings. His next three years were spent on duties with the American Battle Monuments Commission. Jones returned to USMA in 1931 as the Professor of Mathematics and Head of the Mathematics Department. For 16 years, Jones served the Academy with unfailing common sense and enlightened leadership. While his technical expertise was dated, Jones was a dedicated and talented educator and strong technical mentor. During Jones' tenure a number of new textbooks were used in new courses and, perhaps most significantly, the slide rule was introduced for performing calculations. In 1947, Jones was appointed Dean of the Academic Board and served in that position for nine years. During his tenure, he initiated many policies to improve the academic standards of the Academy.

USMA August 1917   **Gerald Alford Counts**   **Scientist**

24 September 1895 (Ranger, TX) – 30 July 1964 (San Francisco, CA)
Graduate # 5742 (2nd out of 151), (physicist), listed in AS (Spring 1965)

Military Service:
1917-1919:   Combat duty in World War I

1919-1920:   Staff duty in Germany
1944-1945:   Combat duty in World War II

Professional Service:
1920-1921:   Student in Civil Engineering at Massachusetts Institute of
             Technology
1921-1923:   Engineer duty on rivers and harbors in CA
1923-1925:   Engineer duty for dredging ship channel, Galveston, TX
1925-1930:   Assistant Professor of Mathematics, USMA
1930-1931:   Student at California Institute of Technology
1931-1946:   Professor and Department Head of Physics, USMA
1946-1957:   Professor and Department Head of Physics and Chemistry,
             USMA
1957-1959:   Dean, USMA

G. A. COUNTS attended the University of California at Berkeley for one year before entering West Point. Because of the severe need for officers in the field during World War I, his class graduated a year early in August 1917. Counts was sent into combat service in France as an engineer and participated in the MeuseArgonne offensive. After the war, he stayed in Europe until 1920. Returning to the U.S., he attended Massachusetts Institute of Technology studying civil engineering. The next four years were spent using his engineering expertise to improve harbors and dig a shipping channel in Galveston Harbor, TX. In 1925,

Counts began his 33-year tenure as an academic leader at West Point. He spent five years teaching mathematics, twenty-six years as the Head of the Physics Department (later Physics and Chemistry), and two years as Dean. His other duties during that period were one year of studying mathematics and physics at the California Institute of Technology and two years in combat service during World War II, where Counts served in staff engineering positions in North Africa, the Mediterranean, and Europe. During Counts' long service at the Academy, he worked under sixteen different Superintendents and saw the Academy grow from 600 to 2500 students. He was an able administrator, strong leader, and a dedicated, successful teacher. During this era, several of USMA's science leaders were highly skilled teachers, but not active scholars. As the world and the military became more technical in the years after World War II, the science program at West Point began to modernize and improve.

Reference:
Bartlett, Boyd, "Physics at the United States Military Academy," *American Journal of Physics*, Vol. 12, 1944, pp. 78-91.

USMA August 1917   │ **Bartley Marcus Harloe** │   Engineer

16 February 1897 (Brooklyn, NY) – 20 July 1974 (Monterey, CA)
Graduate # 5748 (8th out of 151), (mathematician), listed in AS (September 1975)

Military Service:
1917-1919: Combat duty in World War 1
19191921:   Engineer duty in Philippines
1929-1931: Engineer duty in Nicaragua
1941-1945: Combat and support duty in World War II (North Africa, NATO)

Professional Service:
1921-1922: Studies in Civil Engineering at Rensselaer Polytechnic Institute, NY
1923-1928: Assistant Professor of Mathematics, USMA
1931-1940: Engineer duties with Works Projects Administration (WPA)
1946-1948: Engineer duties in Memphis, TN
1948-1950: Construction duty in HI building Tripler Army Hospital
1950-1963: Professor of Engineering, University of Hawaii
1963-1964: City Manager of Honolulu, HI

B. M. HARLOE entered the Corps of Engineers upon graduation, immediately transferring to the European Threatre to fight in World War I. His assignment after the war was in the Philippines. After attending Rensselaer Polytechnic Institute, NY, Harloe returned to teach mathematics at the Academy. He was such a successful teacher that he stayed two additional years after his normal three-year tour. During the decade of the 1930s, Harloe had a series of assignments with the Works Project Administration. First, he directed the civil works construction projects in the Western United States, and then he was the chief engineer for the national program. This civil works project of President Roosevelt was a major effort, challenging Harloe's talents and creativity as millions of workers involved in the projects needed to stay productive and safe. During World War II, Harloe served as chief of staff for logistics and supply units in North Africa and Europe. From 1946 to 1950, he ran projects for the Corps of Engineers in TN and later in HI. After retiring from the Army in 1950, Harloe became the Professor of Engineering at the University of Hawaii. He also directed the school's management program, becoming engaged in the subject of operations research. Harloe was a valuable contributor and leader in this new program and new discipline of science. As an experienced engineer, he was able to motivate his students and provide them examples of actual engineering projects.

USMA 1920 | William Weston Bessell, Jr. | Mathematics

17 May 1901 (San Juan, Puerto Rico) – 13 January 1977 (West Point, NY)
Graduate # 6545 (6th out of 271)

Military Service:

1923-1928: Professor of Military Science, Rose Polytechnic Institute, Terre Haute, IN

1936-1939: American Battle Monuments Commission, Paris, France

1940-1942: Chief of Military Personnel for the Engineer Branch, Washington, DC

1943-1946: Army Director, Joint War Plans Committee

1946-1947: Commanding General, Antilles Department, San Juan, Puerto Rico

Professional Service:

1921-1922: Student, Rensselaer Polytechnic Institute, Troy, NY

1928-1932: Assistant Professor of Mathematics, USMA

1947-1959: Professor of Mathematics, Head of the Mathematics Department, USMA

1959-1965: Dean of the Academic Board, USMA

W. W. BESSELL was born into a military family. Because of World War 1, Bessell graduated after being at West Point for just two years. Bessell's first assignment was at Camp Humphreys, VA, as a supply officer. Next, he attended Rensselaer Polytechnic Institute, receiving a B.S. degree in Civil Engineering. After two years of engineering duty at Camp Travis, TX, he was assigned as a military science professor to the Reserve Officers Training Corps at Rose Polytechnic Institute, IN. In 1928 he became an Assistant Professor of Mathematics at West Point and was in charge of the mathematics courses for the third class (yearlings). Bessell's next assignments were engineering duty in Hawaii and Zanesville, OH, where he was in charge of the survey and design of the Bolivar Dam. Working with the American Battle Monuments Commission, he supervised construction and maintenance of the eleven World War I monuments and memorials and eight military cemeteries where American soldiers were buried throughout Europe. He was assigned as a staff officer in units engaged in the Fort Benning and Louisiana Maneuvers. In 1940, Bessell performed personnel management duties in Washington, DC. At the outbreak of World War II, he was involved in several positions where he performed operations research duties. First, he was tasked to implement a program that would create the structure and train the soldiers for the engineer amphibious brigades. These units would ultimately prove vital to the island hopping campaigns in the Pacific and in the invasions of Africa, Italy, and France. During the war, Bessell directed the Army component of the Joint War Plans Committee, preparing campaign plans and conducting long-range planning. After the war, he chaired the Postwar Personnel Planning Board, a committee tasked to recommend the strength, composition, and location of the postwar Army and Air Force units. Bessell commanded a station at San Juan, PR for two years before transferring to West Point for a second time, this time as Head of the Mathematics Department. One of Bessell's first actions was to require a course in Probability and Statistics for all cadets, rather than just upper-section cadets as had been done previously. Valuing modern educational technology and audio-visual aids in teaching, he provided each mathematics classrooms with an overhead projector and mechanical computer. His outreach to the Mathematical Association of America helped the Academy's mathematics program serve the needs of science and engineering disciplines, while keeping abreast of the developments in the teaching of mathematics. While inexperienced in academics, Bessell was a dynamic, popular teacher and faculty leader. He managed the conversion of Thayer Hall to an academic building and was instrumental in the Academy's decision to adopt the College Board Placement Test for admissions evaluations in place of the previously used West Point Qualification Test. He served for three years on the College Entrance Examination Board. In 1959, Bessell became the fifth Dean of the Academic Board. As the Dean for six years, he revised the curriculum to allow for some elective courses and provided incoming faculty the opportunity for advanced studies at civilian universities. He established a state-of-the-art academic computer center and improved library holdings. Throughout his career, Bessell showed exceptional leadership and technical excellence.

USMA 1920   **Edward Clinton Gillette, Jr.**   **Scientist**

25 July 1900 (Philadelphia, PA) - 14 March 1986 (Nashville, TN)
Graduate # 6635 (96th out of 271), (chemist, physicist, electrical engineer)

Military Service:

1920-1923:	Artillery duty at Fort Ethan Allan, VT
1923-1927:	Signal and artillery duty in HI
1927-1929:	Artillery duty at Fort Snelling, MN
1937-1941:	Artillery duty at Washington, DC; Ft Lewis, WA; and Ft. Sill, OK
1943-1944:	Staff duty in the Office of the Chief Signal Officer, Washington, DC
1944-1945:	Combat signal duty in World War 11 (OVERLORD, VARSITY, Berlin)
1945-1946:	Staff duty in Office of the Chief Signal Officer, Washington, DC

Professional Service:

1929-1931:	Graduate study in electrical engineering (M.S.) at Purdue University, IN
1931-1937:	Assistant Professor of Electricity, USMA
1941-1943:	Associate Professor of Electricity, USMA
1946-1957:	Professor of Physics and Chemistry, USMA
1957-1964:	Professor and Head of Physics and Chemistry, USMA

E. C. GILLETTE was a cadet during World War I and graduated after only two years of study, even though the war had ended by his graduation day. His first assignment was in hischosen branch of artillery in Vermont. He transferred to HI where he studied signal communications, worked in communications positions, and taught a signal course. Gillette thoroughly enjoyed electronics and kept an active interest as both his scholarship and a hobby. After two more years in artillery duty in MN, Gillette was sent to graduate school in electrical engineering at Purdue University, IN. Arriving at West Point's Department of Chemistry and Electricity to teach his favorite subject of electronics, he quickly became a successful teacher-full of energy and knowledge. His cadets benefited greatly. Gillette spent the next four years in artillery assignments before returning to his former department at West Point in 1941. After two years of teaching at the Academy during World War II, Gillette went to Washington, DC to work on war requirements. After one year, he transferred to Europe to coordinate signal and communication requirements for Operation OVERLORD (Normandy) and Operation

VARSITY (crossing the Rhine River). After working on the communication needs of the Potsdam Conference to conclude the war in Europe, Gillette returned to the United States. In 1946, he was selected to be a Professor and Deputy Department Head in the new Department of Physics and Chemistry as West Point reorganized its program to include the advances brought on by World War II. His duties involved building courses to cover both physics and chemistry and to recruit and educate faculty to teach those courses. Working for Department Head **Gerald Counts (USMA August 1917)**, Gillette accomplished his mission and adopted the modern techniques of instruction available in science coursework. In 1957, he became the Department Head when Counts became the Dean. Gillette retired from the Army in 1964. His scholarship was primarily in electronics; however, he did write teaching articles for the Journal of Chemical Education. He was also a member of the American Society for Engineering Education. Gillette was instrumental in modernizing the Academy's science program after World War II.

USMA 1920 | **Lawrence Edward Schick** | **Technologist**

20 September 1897 (Chicago, IL) – 14 October 1967 (Carmel, CA)
Graduate # 6674 (135th out of 271), (draftsman, graphic artist, earth scientist), listed in *AS* (Spring 1968)

Military Service:
1917-1918: Enlisted soldier during World War I
1920-1923: Cavalry duty at Ft. Riley, KS and Monterey, CA
1923-1925: Cavalry duty in the Philippines
1930-1933: Cavalry duty at Ft. Riley, KS
1938-1941: Staff duty in TX, GA, KY
1941-1945: Combat and support duty during World War II
             (Aleutians, Okinawa)
1945-1946: Staff duty in Korea

Professional Service:
1925-1928: Instructor of Drawing, USMA
1933-1934: Graduate study at Ohio State University
1934-1938: Assistant Professor of Drawing, USMA
1946-1961: Professor of Military Topography, USMA

L. E. SCHICK attended Ponoma College for one year before enlisting in the Army at the
outbreak of World War I. He won an Army appointment to USMA in 1918, graduating in two years due to the war. Schick became a cavalry officer and served at Ft. Riley, KS and Monterey, CA. After a stint in the Philippines, Schick returned to the Academy to teach drawing for three years. More cavalry duty followed, until his selection for graduate school in preparation for another tour at West Point. Schick's second tour at the Academy lasted four years as Department Head Roger Alexander's (USMA 1907)

Drafting class in 1948 (from West Point Howitzer)

primary assistant. Switching to the Adjutant General Corps, Schick served in several locations before landing in Alaska as World War II began. He participated in the Aleutian Campaign and made tremendous contributions to the planning and execution of the invasion of Okinawa. At the conclusion of the war, Schick was in Korea setting up the Provisional Military Government of Korea. In 1946, Schick was selected to replace Alexander as the Department Head, becoming the Professor of Military Topography and Graphics. The department was in the midst of dramatic change and a new name – Department of Earth, Space, and Graphic Sciences. Schick transformed the department from a graphics emphasis to one organized to teach the new fields of science, which were growing in importance after World War II. In particular, he established programs in environmental and physical geography, astronomy, astronautics, computing, and engineering fundamentals, along with modernizing the graphics program and reducing the surveying course. Schick was a versatile scientist – perfectly suited to lead such a program. He also took a leadership role in the construction projects at the Academy, insuring architectural concerns were considered and included in the building plans.

USMA 1923 | **Kenner Fisher Hertford** | **Scientist**

25 September 1900 (Galveston, TX) – 27 April 1995 (Albuquerque, NM)
Graduate # 6964 (5th out of 262), (mathematician, engineer, technologist), listed in *AS* (July 1996)

Military Service:
1923-1926: Engineer duty at Fort Sam Houston, TX
1927-1930: Garrison duty in SC
1938-1940: Interpreter for General Pershing in France
1941-1945: Staff duties during World War II
1945-1947: Military advisor to peace conferences
1947-1948: Military advisor to the United Nations

Professional Service:
1926-1927: Civil engineering study at Cornell University, NY
1931-1932: Surveyor for Interoceanic Canal in Nicaragua
1932-1936: Assistant Professor of Mathematics, USMA
1936-1938: Construction engineer for Okeechobee Canal, FL
1948-1952: Deputy commander, Special Weapons Project, Sandia, NM
1952-1955: Chief of Army Research and Development, Washington, DC

K. F. HERTFORD was a gifted student at West Point with great interest in the sciences and mathematics. Selecting the engineer branch, he served in Texas as a field engineer before attending Cornell University to obtain a degree in Civil Engineering. After garrison duty, Hertford was sent to Nicaragua to survey routes for another interoceanic canal. Returning to West Point, he taught mathematics for four years, and while there, he and fellow mathematics colleague **Charles Nicholas (USMA 1925)** won a new car by making the best guess for the number of pennies in a jar in a store window. The two mathematicians used survey instruments and detailed mathematical modeling to make their guess. Back with the Corps of Engineers after leaving West Point, Hertford worked on the construction of the Okeechobee Canal in Florida. From 1938 to 1940, he was stationed in France serving as General Pershing's (USMA 1886) interpreter. During World War II, Hertford filled high-level technical staff positions. After the war, he became an advisor for diplomats at peace conferences and engaged in the establishment of the United Nations. In 1948, Hertford helped lead the Special Weapons Project in science and technology for the development of nuclear weapons. For three years, he headed the Army Research and Development Staff

Office in the Pentagon before retiring from the Army. In civilian life, he continued his work in the nuclear energy field by managing an office of the Atomic Energy Commission.

USMA 1924   ⎿ **Leslie Earl Simon** ⏌   **Technologist**

11 August 1900 (Memphis, TN) – 28 October 1983 (Winter Park, FL)
Graduate # 7292 (72nd out of 405), (ordnance), listed in *AS* (December 1986)

Military Service:
1944-1945:   Combat mission in Europe and North Africa during World War II
1949-1955:   Assistant Chief of Ordnance, Washington, DC (Major General)

Professional Service:
1933-1937:   Ordnance duty at Picatinny Arsenal, NJ
1937-1949:   Director, Ballistics Research Laboratory, Aberdeen Proving Ground, MD
1955-1965:   Scientific consultant

L. E. Simon graduated from the United States Military Academy in 1924. He was an excellent example of a West Point graduate as an accomplished soldier-scientist. Under his directorship, the Ballistic Research Laboratory (BRL) at Aberdeen Proving Ground, MD became a world-renowned group of technical laboratories with research programs in basic and applied areas of science. It became one of the leading scientific institutions not only in the Army but also in the country. Under Simon's direction, BRL developed the country's first supersonic wind tunnels. This type of aerodynamic equipment was in high demand for the design and testing of early guided missiles of the Army, Navy, and Air Force. The world's first long-range telescopes and radars for tracking guided missiles were developed while he was directing BRL. He oversaw the creation (along with professors from the University of Pennsylvania) of the ENIAC, the first high-speed digital computer, which led to the electronic computing industry.

USMA 1925 | Charles Parsons Nicholas | Mathematician

15 September 1903 (Shelbyville, KY) – 4 September 1985 (Louisville, KY)
Graduate # 7670 (45th out of 245), listed in *AS* (February 1989)

Military Service:
1947-1948: Deputy Assistant Director of Central Intelligence, National Security Council

Professional Service:
1927-1928: Instructor USMA Preparatory School, Hawaii
1930-1935: Instructor of Mathematics, USMA
1941-1942: Associate Professor of Mathematics, USMA
1948-1959: Professor of Mathematics, Deputy Head of Mathematics Department, USMA
1959-1967: Professor of Mathematics, Head of Mathematics Department, USMA

C. P. Nicholas was commissioned in the Field Artillery upon his graduation from West Point. For five years, Nicholas served in artillery units at Fort Benjamin Harrison, IN; Schofield Barracks, HI; and Fort Sill, OK with a one-year stint as an Instructor in English at the USMA Preparatory School in Hawaii. In 1930, Nicholas began his mathematical career as an Instructor in the Department of Mathematics at West Point. Nicholas was a dedicated teacher, able to explain fundamental concepts in a clear manner. He emphasized the essential simplicity of mathematical reasoning in a way that left a lasting impression on his students. During his tour at the Academy, he was assigned as one of the coaches for the mathematics squad that participated in the 1933 competition between Harvard and USMA (see the essay on USMA's MSE Program). West Point won the competition, and Nicholas, among others, received praise from Army leaders. In another activity, Nicholas and a colleague, **Kenner Hertford (USMA 1923)**, used mathematics and surveying to ascertain the number of pennies in a glass bowl in the window of a local store. They won the contest and a new automobile for their efforts. Nicholas returned to Fort Sill as an instructor at the artillery school. In 1940, he was assigned to the Army Maneuvers in Louisiana and then served on the staff at Camp Jackson, SC, prior to returning to West Point as an Associate Professor of Mathematics. When World War II began, Nicholas reported to the War Department Staff for duty in the Military Intelligence Division. His specialty was scientific intelligence, whereby he helped determine the characteristics of enemy weapons while still in their developmental stages. Nicholas led the efforts of many technical researchers in state-of-the-art mathematics, science, and engineering. In 1946, he was selected to serve as a member of the original organizing team for the Central Intelligence Agency and served as the Deputy Assistant Director of Central Intelligence until 1948. Returning to West Point, he served as Professor and Deputy Head of the Department of Mathematics and in 1959 became Department Head. Nicholas' tenure was dynamic and highly successful time for the department, as he developed a program to meet the demands of modern science, engineering, and management. An expert in the educational needs of the military, he instituted methods and advances that raised the mathematics program to national prominence and was a prolific author of textbooks and articles on various educational issues. In addition to the many professional articles appearing in *American Mathematical Monthly* and *Transactions on Education of the Institute of Electrical and Electronic Engineering*, Nicholas' 1600-page textbook on Analytical Geometry and Calculus was a major part of the West Point education system for a decade. Nicholas worked with the Mathematical Association of America Committee on Undergraduate Programs in Mathematics and was able to initiate a sequence of changes in the mathematics course offerings and structure designed to keep USMA in the vanguard nationally. Under his leadership, West Point instituted its first program of mathematics electives. As the architect of these curricular and pedagogical changes, Nicholas provided the Academy with a modern, science-based curriculum and an up-to-date program enhanced by electronic computation. Nicholas retired in 1967 after serving and contributing in field artillery positions, national-level strategic intelligence positions, and as an expert technical educator. Some of Nicholas' publications in the *American Mathematical Monthly* include: "Taylor's Theorem in a First Course" (1951), "Normal and Tangential Acceleration" (1951), "More on Taylor's Theorem in a First Course" (1953), and "Another Look at the Probability Integral" (1957).

USMA 1926   ## Holger Nelson Toftoy   **Technologist**

31 October 1902 (IL) – 19 April 1967 (Washington, DC)
Graduate # 7923 (54th out of 153), (ordnance), listed in *AS* (Winter 1968)

Military Service:
1944-1945: Ordnance duty in Europe during World War II
1958-1960: Commander, Aberdeen Proving Grounds, MD (Major General)

Professional Service:
1945-1952: Researcher on Rocket technology, Office of Chief of
            Ordnance, Washington, DC
1952-1954: Director of Missile Laboratory, Redstone Arsenal, AL
1954-1958: Director of Explorer I Satellite Project

H.N. TOFTOY graduated from West Point and entered the Artillery Corps. Later Toftoy transferred into the Ordnance Corps, where he sought to work on more technical aspects of the Army. He was directly associated with the Army's Guided Missile Program from its inception and was responsible during World War II for bringing

V-2 rocket parts and German missile scientists to the United States to participate in the U.S. Rocket Program. As chief of the Rocket Branch in the Ordnance Department from 1945 through 1952, Toftoy was supervised and directed the scientific efforts of the Army Guided Missile Research and Development Program. His duties included the development of new Army missiles, among them the Nike, Corporal, Honest John, and Super Bazooka. Toftoy established the White Sands Proving Ground and Missile Range in NM as the principal

Army missile test site and arranged for the technical facilities involved in the operation of the range. He also established Redstone Arsenal, AL in the role of applied research for this program. Toftoy hired the scientists and engineers involved in the designing and evaluating the Army's rockets and guided missiles. Moving to Redstone Arsenal, he served as the Director of the Ordnance Missile Laboratories. His technical group at Redstone was responsible for designing and building the Jupiter-C rocket, which lifted into orbit the first American satellite, Explorer I, on 31 January 1958. Working with the famous German scientist Wernher von Braun on this Army project, Toftoy completed his mission with the successful launch of this satellite that discovered the Van Allen radiation belts around Earth. Toftoy retired from the Army in 1960.

USMA 1927   **Theodore Addison Weyher**   **Engineer**

6 May 1905 (Whitewater, WI) – 31 July 31 1999 (St. Petersburg, FL)
Graduate # 8027 (5th out of 203), (ordnance)

Military Service:
1930-1936: Staff engineering duty
1940-1945: Ordnance staff officer, Office of Chief of Ordnance,
                   Washington, DC
1945-1946: Military attaché to Switzerland
1949-1954: Ordnance duty at Frankford Arsenal and Rock Island Depot
1954-1957: Commanding General, Ordnance Weapons Command

Professional Service:
1927-1929: Engineering construction duty in KY and NC
1929-1930: Engineering study at Cornell University, NY
1936-1937: Engineering study at Massachusetts Institute of Technology,
                   M.S. degree
1937-1940: Ordnance researcher at Aberdeen Proving Ground, MD
1957-1965:   Dean of Engineering, University of Miami, FL

T. A. WEYHER studied at the University of Wisconsin for one year before attending the U.S. Military Academy. He entered the Corps of Engineers, undertaking construction assignments for two years before studying engineering at Cornell University. After more engineering duties, Weyher transferred to the Ordnance Corps. He completed his M.S. degree at Massachusetts Institute of Technology in 1937. Weyher's initiation into ordnance duties occurred at Aberdeen Proving Grounds, MD. Then during World War II, Weyher worked as Chief of the Carriage Branch in the Chief of Ordnance Office. He entered the European Theatre in 1944, overseeing parts supplies and technical support. After the war, he spent a year as the military attaché to Switzerland. From 1946 to 1954, Weyher performed various staff, command, and research duties in the Ordnance Corps, building expertise in the utilization of atomic weapons and new materials. Weyher's last assignment was Commanding General of the Ordnance Weapons Command. Retiring in 1957, Weyher became the second Dean of Engineering at the University of Miami, FL. As dean of this fast growing program, Weyher oversaw undergraduate and graduate programs in mechanical, electrical, industrial, civil, and architectural engineering with a student enrollment of over 1500.

USMA 1927 | **James Wilson Green, Jr.** | **Technologist**

18 February 1906 (Little Rock, AR) – 29 December 1990 (Spanish Fort, AL)
Graduate # 8063 (41st out of 203), (electrical engineer, radar expert), listed in *AS* (July 1992)

Military Service:
1928-1931: Signal and communication duty on Corregidor, Philippines
1942-1944: Commandant and head trainer for Radar School, FL
1944-1946: Combat signal duty in the Philippines in World War II

Professional Service:
1927-1928: Graduate study in electrical engineering (MS) at Yale, CT
1932-1935: Assistant Professor of Electricity, USMA
1939-1941: Researcher at the Signal School, Ft. Monmouth, NJ
1947-1957: Professor of Electricity, USMA
1958-1968: Professor of Electrical Engineering, University of Arkansas

J. W. GREEN developed both interest and skill in building, repairing, and operating machines before entering West Point. When he graduated in 1927, he chose the Signal Corps so he could attend graduate school and work on modern, electronic machines. After a year at Yale studying electronics, Greene was sent to the Philippines, staffing the isolated Corregidor outpost. After three years of this rugged, lonely duty, Green taught electricity at the Academy for three years. He was an ideal teacher for the cadets, given his enthusiasm and practical knowledge in electronics, communications, and signal work. Green's next rewarding assignment was at Fort Monmouth where he wrote the technical and training manuals for the Signal Corps as the branch prepared itself for war. When World War II started, Green was in charge of the radar department at Fort Monmouth. Soon afterward, he transferred to the radar school in Florida where he put his innovations on radar equipment and operations into practice. His new methods and techniques of using radars to locate aircraft were quickly implemented throughout the Army in the field. For the last two years of the war, Green went into combat as a signal staff officer in Australia and the Philippines. After the war, he returned to West Point as the Professor of Electricity and deputy to the Department Head and accomplished scholar

Boyd Bartlett (USMA 1919). He brought many new ideas to the curriculum and helped Bartlett modernize the department with the technological advances made during the war. While at the Academy, Green earned his Ph.D. from Purdue University, IN. Green retired from the Army in 1957 to teach electrical engineering at the University of Arkansas. He also served as the university's vice president. Green was an expert technologist, able to understand the needs of solving practical problems and the limitations of physical equipment in the field. He shared his innovative ideas with students and other faculty, keeping alive his contributions to the advancement of science and technology.

USMA 1928 | **James Laffeter Green** | **Engineer**

14 March 1905 (AL) – 25 November 1990 (Princeton, NJ)
Graduate # 8227 (2nd out of 261), listed in *AS* (January 1992)

Military Service:
1928-1939: Garrison and troop duty
1942-1945: Combat engineer duty in World War II (Attu; Memphis, TN; Germany -- Elbe River crossing)
1945-1947: Staff duty in Office of the Chief of Army Engineers

Professional Service:
1930-1935: Engineer duty on rivers and harbors (Louisville, KY and St Louis, MO)
1939-1942: Research duty to design new engineer equipment for Corps of Engineers
1947-1949: Engineer construction duty for base in Okinawa, Japan
1950-1955: Research and development coordinator for the Secretary of the Army, Washington, DC
1955-1971: Associate Professor of Civil Engineering, Princeton University, NJ

J. L. GREEN was a highly successful student at the Academy, finishing second in his class of 261 graduating cadets. Choosing the Corps of Engineers, his early assignments included both garrison duty with troops and engineering positions along the Mississippi and Ohio Rivers. Green also obtained an M.S. degree in civil engineering from the University of California at Berkeley. In 1939, he worked on a project to design and develop new engineering equipment for the U.S. Army and allied armies in preparation for the war. During World War II, Green served in both the Pacific and European Theatres. After the war, he did more engineering research and development work in Washington, DC, before supervising the construction of a new military base in Okinawa. During the last five years of his Army career, he oversaw the research and development program for the Secretary of the Army. During that time, he obtained an M.S. in mathematics from George Washington University. Never having taught at the Military Academy, Green finally had an opportunity to teach students as a civilian. He retired in 1955 to become an Associate Professor of Civil Engineering at Princeton University, NJ. He built a research laboratory and taught subjects involving water resources. One of his students was Gerald Galloway (USMA 1957), who later became the Dean at West Point. Green was a superb teacher and an expert engineer.

USMA 1928   **John Dabney Billingsley**   **Engineer**

4 November 1904 (Fredricksburg, VA) – 23 May 1976 (Washington, DC)
Graduate # 8341 (116th out of 261), (ordnance), listed in *AS* (September 1977)

Military Service:
1928-1932:   Artillery duties
1932-1943:   Ordnance staff duties
1943-1944:   General staff officer, War Department,
                    Washington, DC
1944-1945:   Ordnance duty in Italy during World War II
1950-1951:   Ordnance duty in Korean War

Professional Service:
1951-1968:   Professor of Ordnance, USMA

J. D. BILLINGSLEY graduated from the United States Military Academy in 1928. His association with ordnance science began in 1932 when he transferred to the Ordnance Corps. During his career, he fought in World War II, commanded the Ordnance School, and participated in the Inchon landing in Korea as the senior Ordnance Officer. He contributed to the technical education of cadets through service as the Professor and Head of the Department of Ordnance at the Academy from 1951 to 1968. Early in his tenure as Professor

of Ordnance, he transformed two Ordnance courses into Ordnance Engineering courses by applying principles of engineering, science, and mathematics to the subject. The two course textbooks, which were prepared under his guidance, were highly acclaimed and frequently used by governmental, industrial, military, and educational institutions. These texts became the basis for Ordnance Engineering courses around the world. His foresight in upgrading the courses to an engineering-based presentation enhanced the technical understanding of cadets. Billingsley was instrumental in making other significant changes to the curriculum at the Military Academy, such as the introduction of other Ordnance Engineering courses as electives and involving faculty and cadets in ordnance research programs. Billingsley's insights as an educator had a profound influence on the minds of thousands of cadets and Ordnance officers. Shortly after Billingsley's departure from the Academy, the Academy reorganized its academic structure and abolished the Ordnance Department. Many of the courses Billingsley had designed moved to the Engineering Department, where cadets studied military engineering from the fruits of Billingsley's legacy.

USMA 1930 | **John Henderson Dudley** | **Engineer**

25 September 1907 (Oakland, CA) – 2 October 1994 (Fairfax, VA)
Graduate # 8813 (28th out of 241), listed in *AS* (September 1997)

Military Service:
1944-1946: Engineer Aviation Commander in Philippines
1946-1951: Garrison duty in VA, KS, and DC
1954-1960: Engineer field duty and training, Germany, MO, and VA (Brigadier General)

Professional Service:
1937-1938: Graduate study in Civil Engineering at Massachusetts Institute of Technology
1939-1941: Engineering duty in NY
1941-1945: Engineer for Manhattan Project

1951-1954: Research planning on staff in Washington, DC
1960-1978: Professor of Engineering, California State University at Long Beach

---

J. H. DUDLEY graduated from USMA in 1930 and entered the cavalry branch. In a few years,

he transferred to the Corps of Engineers and went to graduate school in civil engineering at Massachusetts Institute of Technology. He served both as a field engineer and on military staffs until World War II. During the war, he was a construction engineer for various facilities of the Manhattan Project, which secretly built the atomic bomb. Dudley's wife also worked on the Project. After the war, Dudley was given assignments involved in training engineering soldiers and leading engineering units. He served for three years as a Research and Development Staff Officer in the Pentagon. After he retired from the Army in 1960, Dudley became a respected and productive Professor of Civil Engineering at Long Beach State University in CA. He was one of the founding faculty members of the department, where he built and directed the Soil Mechanics Laboratory. The department library was named for him. Dudley contributed significantly to both applied engineering work in the Army and to educating future engineers at his university.

USMA 1931   **Howard Minter Parker**   **Mathematician**

19 June 1909 (West Point, NY) – 11 October 1984 (Washington, DC)
Graduate # 9041 (15th out of 297), (operations researcher, systems analyst, systems engineer), listed in
AS (September 1986)

Military Service:
1934-1936: Engineer troop duty in Ft Riley, KS
1941-1945: Combat duty in World War II (Aleutians, Alaska, Mediterranean, Okinawa)

Professional Service:
1931-1934: Graduate study at Oxford as Rhodes Scholar (philosophy, politics, economics)
1936-1937: Graduate study in engineering (MS) at Princeton University, NJ
1937-1940: Student and faculty duties at Engineer School, Ft Belvoir, VA
1940-1941: Engineer construction duty for MacDill Airfield, FL
1946-1949: Professor of Civil Engineering and Hydraulics, State University of Iowa
1949-1962: Senior Analyst, Operations Research Office, Johns Hopkins University, MD
1962-1965: Senior Analyst, Institute of Defense Analyses

H. M. "NED" PARKER received a Rhodes Scholarship upon graduation from USMA. After studying social science at Oxford for three years, he transferred to troop duty at Fort Riley, KS. Next, he continued his schooling by obtaining an M.S. degree in Civil Engineering from Princeton University, NJ, before teaching at the Engineer School at Fort Belvoir, VA. After a year constructing an airfield in Florida, Parker and his unit were transferred to the Aleutian Islands outpost in Alaska. Parker was located in this bleak and hazardous location for three years of World War II. He was reassigned as a demolition officer to the Mediterranean. After a few months in the European Theatre, Parker joined the planning team in the Pacific Theatre for the attack on Okinawa. However, his health faltered and he was medically retired in 1946. Parker spent the next three years teaching civil engineering and hydraulics at Iowa State University. Parker then changed careers as he became an operations research system analyst. Working for Johns Hopkins University, he studied many technical issues including analyzing data on the air support in the Korean War and defensive needs of the military in Turkey. As a senior analyst for the Institute of Defense Analyses from 1963 to 1965, Parker wrote numerous reports and articles, which influenced high-level defense decision-makers. He also authored textbooks on the new subject of operations research. In 1965, Parker retired from his professional work. In addition to his engineering contributions, Parker was an early pioneer in operations research and performed groundbreaking work in this discipline.

USMA 1937 || **Ellis Edmund Wilhoyt, Jr.** || **Scientist**

22 May 1915 (Carmi, IL) – 10 October 1996 (Washington, DC)
Graduate # 10760 (25th out of 298), (engineer), listed in *AS* (November 1997)

Military Service:
1942-1942: Construction engineer duty in Burma during World War II
1952-1954: Commander, Engineer units in Europe
1965-1967: Commander, Engineer Division, Pacific Coast

Professional Service:
1937-1939: Engineering duty in CA
1939-1941: Graduate study at University of California at Berkeley
1945-1952: Special duty with the Manhattan Project, Los Alamos, NM;
            and Atomic Energy Commission, Washington, DC
1962-1963: Construction engineer of ICBM sites for the Air Force
1963-1965: Construction engineer for NASA at Cape Kennedy, FL;
            Huntsville, AL; and Houston, TX
1967-1969: Construction engineer for San Francisco Bay Area Rapid Transit System

1969-1976: Construction engineer for Washington Metro Area Transit Authority

---

E. E. WILHOYT, JR. displayed outstanding leadership and scholarship during his four years as a cadet. Commissioned into the Corps of Engineers upon graduation in 1937, Wilhoyt went to Los Angeles to start his military engineering career. Two years later, he studied mechanical engineering at the University of California at Berkeley. At the outbreak of World War II, Wilhoyt had the opportunity to train his engineer battalion for a special duty. After the intense training, the unit spent two grueling years building the Burma Road in China. This was one of the most challenging engineering missions of the war, because of the terrain, weather, and remote location. After the war, Wilhoyt was selected for the Manhattan Project. For the next seven years, he was involved with the military uses of atomic energy science. His work at Los Alamos and Sandia was significant in this effort. In 1952, Wilhoyt went back to construction engineering, first in GA, then in Europe and back to Leonard Wood, MO. From 1962 to 1965, Wilhoyt's construction talents were used by the Air Force and NASA to design and build ICBM sites, buildings, and support structures for space transportation. After retiring from the Army in 1967, Wilhoyt used his construction skills to build mass transit systems in San Francisco, CA and Washington, DC. Wilhoyt contributed to several national level technical programs. He was both a talented scientist for atomic energy issues, and a skilled engineer for projects like the Burma Road, missile silos, space infrastructure, and rapid transit. Wilhoyt was a member of the American Society of Civil Engineers and other professions organizations.

USMA 1938   ‖ **John Robert Jannarone** ‖   **Scientist**

3 July 1914 (Newark, NJ) – 14 May 1995 (Montrose, NY)
Graduate # 11034 (1ˢᵗ out of 301), (physicist), listed in *AS* (September 1995), *AS* (July 2000)

Military Service:
1938-1941: Engineer duties
1941-1945: Combat duty during World War II (New Guinea, Philippines, Japan)
1955-1957: Staff duty in Washington, DC

Professional Service:
1945-1947: Research and administrative assistant for the Manhattan Project
1947-1950: Assistant Professor of Physics, USMA
1950-1952: Engineer duty in Los Angeles, CA
1952-1955: Engineer duty to improve navigation on Arkansas, White, and Red Rivers
1957-1965: Professor of Physics and Chemistry, USMA
1965-1973: Dean of the Academic Board, USMA

J. R. JANNARONE attended Montclair State Teachers College, NJ, before entering West Point. He was a bright, high-performing cadet, finishing first in his class, while playing three intercollegiate sports. After selecting the engineer branch, he commanded and performed engineer staff duties in World War II in the South Pacific Theatre. At the war's end, Jannarone was part of **Douglas MacArthur's (USMA 1903)** initial cadre in Japan before being called back to the U. S. to assist **Leslie Groves (USMA Nov 1918)** on the post-war activities of the Manhattan Project. In 1947, Jannarone returned to the Academy to teach physics. After the conclusion of a productive and successful three-year tour at USMA, Jannarone worked on engineering projects for the Corps of Engineers in Los Angeles, CA and on the Arkansas, White, and Red Rivers. After a short assignment in the Office of the Chief of Staff of the Army, Jannarone became the Professor of Physics and Chemistry at the Academy, replacing **Edward Gillette (USMA 1920)**. Jannarone's decision to return to academics took him away from opportunities to lead at the highest levels of the Army. However, it provided him the opportunity to develop the character and technical abilities of a generation of future leaders. In 1965, Jannarone was appointed Dean at the Academy. He led the Academy's expansion with new facilities and modern academic programs to serve the doubling of the size of the Corps of Cadets. Undertaking the modifications necessary to keep USMA at the forefront of technical education in the modern world, Jannarone established himself as an integral part of the Academy's legacy in American science.

USMA 1939 · Nicholas Paraska · Engineer

19 January 1915 (Butler, PA) – 1 June 1998 (Butler, PA)
Graduate # 11362 (28th out of 456), listed in *AS* (September 1999)

Military Service:
1933-1935: Soldier in Army Air Corps
1939-1942: Engineer duty in Panama
1942-1945: Combat engineering duty in Europe during World War II
(bridging of the Roer River)
1946-1960: Engineer duty in various districts and staffs

Professional Service:
1945-1946: Graduate study at Texas A & M
1960-1964: Associate Professor of Engineering, Youngstown State University, OH
1967: Ph.D. from Carnegie Mellon University, PA
1967-1982: Dean of College of Applied Science and Technology, Youngstown State University, OH

N. Paraska was an enlisted soldier for two years before he entered West Point. Upon graduation in 1939, he was commissioned in the Corps of Engineers. Paraska's first assignment sent him to Panama. At the start of World War II, he helped train engineer soldiers and units before finally taking his own combat engineer unit to Europe. Serving in action throughout the campaigns in Europe, Paraska was decorated for his role in bridging the Roer River. After the war, Paraska received a master's degree from Texas A&M before embarking on various assignments as a district engineer, construction engineer, and staff engineer in the Offices of the Chief of Army Engineers. In 1960, Paraska retired from the Army to begin an academic career. He began as an Associate Professor of Engineering at Youngstown State University. After obtaining a Ph.D. from Carnegie Mellon University in 1967, he was appointed Dean of the College of Applied Science and Technology at Youngstown State. Paraska was in charge of curricular development, creating new courses in several technical disciplines, and setting policies for the university's growing program in science and technology.

USMA 1940   ╔════════════════════════╗
                       ║   **John Anthony Graf**   ║   **Engineer**
                       ╚════════════════════════╝

3 April 1917 (Toledo, OH) – 25 April 1996 (Melbourne, FL)
Graduate # 11795 (4th out of 449), listed in *AS* (September 1998)

Military Service:

1940-1942: Training duty for engineer soldiers
1942-1945: Combat engineering duty in World War II
1950-1951: Combat engineering duty in Korean War
1951-1960: Engineering staff and command duty in CA, Turkey, and Ohio River
1966-1967: Combat engineering and logistics staff work, Vietnam

Professional Service:

1945-1947: Graduate study in engineering (M.S.) at California Institute of Technology
1947-1950: Assistant Professor of Engineering, USMA
1960-1964: Research and development coordinator
1964-1966: Engineer for mobility and transportation systems, Warren, MI
1967-1968: Engineer for navigation on Ohio River
1968-1969: Graduate study in general engineering, Pennsylvania State University
1969-1983: Professor of Engineering, State Technical Institute of Memphis, TN

J. A. Graf studied engineering at the University of Michigan before entering West Point. Upon graduation in 1940, he chose the Corps of Engineers. His first assignment was to train a special unit to conceive, build, and deploy subterfuge to deceive the enemy about the strengths and intentions of allied troops. Once in combat in Europe in World War II, Graf was a valuable combat engineer, given commands and promotions. Just four years after graduation, he was a Colonel. When he returned to the United States, Graf attended California Institute of Technology, earning an M.S. degree in engineering and spending the next three years teaching cadets at West Point. He was an excellent teacher and enjoyed his tour immensely. Spending another year back in combat in Korea, graf re–established himself as a combat leader. Following the war, he performed engineering staff, command, and training duties for the rest of the decade. In 1960, Graf had the opportunity to serve in the Army's Research and Development Offices where he could use his creativity and intellect to full effect. Utilizing his engineering skills in the Mobility Command, he worked on several important transportation projects. In 1966, Graf entered his third war as he served as a logistics officer in Vietnam. In 1968, he retired from the Army and returned to academics. After receiving an engineering degree from Pennsylvania State University, Graf began his second career teaching engineering at the State Technical Institute of Memphis, TN. He enjoyed returning to this rewarding profession. A gifted teacher and a dedicated scholar, he was advanced to full Professor and chair of his department. He retired for a second time in 1983. Graf showed himself as a successful professional in military leadership, engineering production, and technical teaching.

USMA 1941 | **William Charles Gribble, Jr.** | **Engineer**

24 May 1917 (Ironwood, MI) – 2 June 1979 (Ft. Belvoir, VA)
Graduate # 12250 (11th out of 424), (scientist), listed in *AS* (June 1981)

Military Service:
1944-1945: Combat duty in Pacific during World War II
1953-1954: Duty with Office of Chief of Engineers, Washington, DC
1961-1963: Duty with Office of Chief of Engineers, Washington, DC
1971:   Commandant of Engineers School, Ft. Belvoir, VA
1973-1976: Chief of Army Engineers, Washington, DC

Professional Service:
1946-1948: M.S. degree University of Chicago
1948-1953: Armed Forces Special Weapons Project, Sandia Base, NM
1954-1956: Atomic Energy Commission
1956-1960: Engineer in Alaska
1964-1966: Director of Research and Development,
            Army Material Command
1966-1967: Deputy Chief of Research and Development for U.S. Army
1971-1973: Chief of Research and Development for U.S. Army
            (Lieutenant General)
1976-1979: Consulting engineer

After **W. C. GRIBBLE, JR.** graduated from the Military Academy in 1941, he was commissioned in the Corps of Engineers. During World War II, he served with construction engineers building a section of the Alaskan Highway in western Canada. Later, he was sent into combat as an engineer to assist **Douglas MacArthur's (USMA 1903)** drive in New Guinea and the Philippines. At the end of the war, he commanded an engineer combat battalion. Gribble then worked in the Los Alamos Laboratory and in the Reactor Development Division of the Atomic Energy Commission. As Alaska District Engineer, he oversaw construction of a nuclear power plant at Fort Greely, AK. He headed the Army's nuclear power construction program from 1960 to 1961. In 1963, he was the North Central Division Engineer. Gribble's scientific skills led to his service as the Director of Research and Development in the Army Materiel Command from 1964 to 1966, and as the Army's Chief of Research and Development from 1971 to 1973. For two years, he commanded the Army Engineer Center at Fort Belvoir, VA, and was Commandant of the Army Engineer School. He became Chief of Army Engineers, serving from 1973 to 1976. In 1976, Gribble received an M.S. degree in physical science from the University of Chicago and in 1978 an honorary doctorate in engineering from Michigan Technological University. He was an honorary member of the United Kingdom's Institute of Royal Engineers.

USMA 1941 | **Joseph Ingram Gurfein** | **Engineer**

28 May 1918 (NY) – 5 June 1997 (Alexandria, VA)
Graduate # 12289 (50th out of 424), listed in *AS* (November 1998)

Military Service:
1941-1945: Combat duty in World War II
1950-1952: Combat duty in Korean War (Inchon, Heartbreak Ridge, Chosin Reservoir)
1961-1963: Commander, Chinon Depot
1963-1967: Staff duty for Army Materiel Command
1964-1965: Combat duty in Vietnam

Professional Service:
1946-1947: Graduate study at Harvard University (M.S.)
1964-1965: Construction engineer for pier in Cam Ranh Bay, Vietnam
1967-1970: Dean of Academics, Federal City College (later University of the District of Columbia)
1972-1974: Construction engineer for expansion of George Mason University, MD
1970s: Assistant Professor of Mathematics and Engineering, George Mason University, MD
1979:   Ph.D. from Pacific Western University

J. I. Gurfein helped many of his classmates learn mathematics, science, and engineering while he was a cadet, foreshadowing an outstanding career in technical teaching. Graduating in 1941 and joining the engineer branch, Gurfein saw combat service in World War II and the Korean War. He was a brave combat leader, receiving awards for rallying troops and saving the lives of his soldiers. In 1947, he received an M.S. degree in engineering from Harvard University. During the Vietnam War, Gurfein oversaw the construction of the huge, state-of-the-art naval pier at Cam Ranh Bay. After his retirement from the Army in 1967, Gurfein entered academic service. He built the academic program at Federal City College as the Dean of the College. Moving to another Washington area school, he helped build academic facilities at George Mason University in VA. Gurfein was a highly successful instructor while serving as a Professor of Mathematics and Engineering at the university. In his honor and memory, George Mason University now bestows an award in his name for outstanding engineering students. A passionate scholar and dedicated researcher, he loved both learning and teaching. He contributed greatly to the advancement of knowledge and the development of his students.

USMA 1946 **William Herbert McMaster** **Scientist**

16 April 1926 (Fort Lewis, WA) – December 1990 (Livermore, CA)
Graduate # 15308 (22nd out of 875), (physicist), listed in *AS* (May 1993)

Military Service:
1946-1950: Troop duty in Germany

Professional Service:
1950-1954: Graduate study in physics (MS and Ph.D.), University of Virginia
1954-1958: Research duty at Lawrence Livermore National
Laboratory, CA
1958-1984: Researcher at Lawrence Livermore National Laboratory,
CA

W. H. McMaster attended West Point during World War II, graduating from an accelerated three-year program in 1946. Among his classmates were Wesley Posvar (Rhodes Scholar and former President of University of Pittsburgh), Amos Jordan (Rhodes Scholar and former Head of USMA's Social Sciences Department), and Edward Saunders (former Head of USMA's Physics Department). McMaster went to

Germany for his first assignment in the cavalry branch. Upon return to the United States, he attended the University of Virginia, studying physics and receiving an M.S. degree in 1952 and a Ph.D. in 1954. His thesis work received a research award and was published in physics journals. After brief duty at Sandia Base, NM, McMaster arrived for research duty at Lawrence Livermore National Laboratory, CA. He would be part of this important scientific center for the next 30 years (four years while in the Army and 26 years as a civilian). McMaster began using the computer to support experiments and collect data. He wrote several important computer systems to diagnose reactions and photo-disintegrations. His contributions were significant for understanding the basic scientific principles of nuclear reactions. In 1958, he left the Army to become a civilian scientist and remained at the Laboratory. Involved in planning several nuclear detonation tests, monitoring explosion sites, and conducting simulations of nuclear reactions, his contributions to the major projects of the laboratory were immense. He was a consummate scientific scholar, a deep thinker with tremendous insights and creativity. McMaster's scientific contributions helped the world understand nuclear reactions and their forces.

USMA 1946   **Alfred Carl Haussman, Jr.**   **Scientist**

26 August 1924 (Geneva, NY) – 11 July 1998 (Livermore, CA)
Graduate # 15688 (402nd out of 875), (physicist), listed in *AS* (September 1999)

Military Service:
1946-1955: Military service in technical assignments

Professional Service:

1950-1952: Nuclear supervisor at Sandia National Laboratory, NM
1952-1953: Army researcher on hydrogen bomb, Princeton, NJ
1953-1955: Army research at Lawrence Livermore National
            Laboratory in nuclear weapons design
1955-1959: Thermonuclear Explosive Physics Group Leader,
            Lawrence Livermore, CA
1959-1962: Chief, Thermonuclear Group, Lawrence Livermore, CA
1962-1968: Associate Director, Military Application Group,
            Lawrence Livermore, CA
1969-1971: Director of Plans, Lawrence Livermore, CA
1971-1975: Director of Laser Program, Lawrence Livermore, CA
1975-1988: Associate Director, Lawrence Livermore, CA
1988:   Co-founder of nChip

A. C. HAUSSMAN, JR. attended Hobart College, NY for a year before attending and graduating from West Point in 1946. His first years in the Army were spent in graduate school studying physics. He did his graduate work at California Institute of Technology, Naval Postgraduate School, and Pennsylvania State University. Attending the Nuclear

Weapons Supervisor School, he served as a nuclear weapons supervisor for two years. In his next assignment, Haussman succeeded in important research duty at Princeton to design the hydrogen bomb's main detonation stage. Following that achievement, his talents were needed at the newly-created Lawrence Livermore National Laboratory in CA. Leaving the Army in 1955, he became a full-time physics researcher at the laboratory. At Livermore, Haussman continued his research work in thermonuclear design, eventually leading projects and supervising all the laboratory's military applications. He was a planning director for a few years and the leader of Livermore's laser development work. In 1975, he became the associate director of the laboratory, where he contributed his scholarship and leadership to the breadth of Lawrence Livermore's science initiatives. One of his mentors was Edward Teller, the laboratory director, who credits Haussman with being one of the "founders" of the lab and the originator of many effective ideas on the construction and delivery methods (submarine and aircraft launching) of the hydrogen bomb. Haussman was the crucial figure in many of Livermore's most productive efforts on the nuclear bomb, ballistic missiles, laser weapons, and basic science research. In many ways, he was a major contributor to both the science and military ethics of the cold war.

USMA 1948 **Gerald William Medsger** **Engineer**

18 August 1927 (CA) – 18 September 1978 (Red Bank, NJ)
Graduate # 16477 (6th out of 301), (operations research), listed in *AS* (June 1990)

Military Service:
1948-1949: Garrison duty at Ft. Riley, KS
1952-1953: Instructor at Engineer School
1953-1955: Garrison duty at Ft. Bragg, NC
1957-1959: ROTC instructor, University of Missouri
1960-1962: Combat engineer duty in Germany

Professional Service:

1949-1952: Construction engineer for military airport in Germany
1955-1956: Construction engineer for radar station in Labrador, Canada
1956-1957: Graduate study at California Institute of Technology (M.S in Civil Engineering)
1963-1965: Research duty with Technical Warfare Board at Ft. Bragg, NC
1965-1969: Assistant and Associate Professor of Mathematics, USMA
1968: Graduate study at New York University (M.S. in Physics)
1969-1975: Director of Institutional Research, USMA
1975-1978: Dean, United States Military Academy Preparatory School (USMAPS)

G. W. MEDSGER was only 16 years old when he arrived at West Point. He had graduated from high school a year earlier, spending the year teaching mathematics at a prep school in CA. Still too young to officially enter the Academy, he had to wait until the end of the summer to be sworn in as a cadet. Academically gifted, Medsger completed his course work near the top of his class and selected engineers as his branch. Serving challenging tours as a construction engineer for an airport facility in Germany and a radar site in Canada, he met the challenges and exceeded expectations. He next taught at military schools and ROTC programs between combat engineering field assignments. Medsger used his advanced degree in engineering to help with his research duties as Chief of the Electronics and Special Warfare Board at Ft Bragg, NC. Medsger uncovered his passion for technical teaching as he spent 1965 to 1969 as an Assistant and Associate Professor in the Mathematics Department at USMA. Always a scholar, Medsger completed the M.S. program at New York University in Physics while teaching full time at the Academy. In 1969, he transferred to an important research position at the Academy – Director of Institutional Research. There he ran studies, performed statistical analysis, and tendered technical advice. Medsger was an active scholar, publishing 14 technical papers and was actively involved in many technical professional societies. He served a term as Director of the Military Operations Research Society. Retiring from the Army in 1975, Medsger continued his interest in technical education by becoming Dean of the USMA Preparatory School for three years before passing away. Medsger had a fine scholarly reputation as an expert in operations research and computer technology.

USMA 1948 | **William Mason Kaula** | **Engineer**

19 May 1926 (Australia) – 1 April 2000 (Los Angeles, CA)
Graduate # 16486 (15th out of 301), (topographer), listed in *AS* (September 2000)

Military Service:
1948-1952: Engineer duty, Germany
1955-1957: Engineer duty, Ft. Benning, GA

Professional Service:
1954-1955: Director, topographic survey of New Guinea
1957-1960: Army civilian researcher on variations in Earth's gravity
1960-1963: NASA Scientist on geodetic satellite project
1963-1986: Professor, UCLA
1986-1989: Chief, National Geodetic Survey
1987:   Elected to the National Academy of Science

W. M. KAULA utilized his West Point education to become a military engineer, but after completing a graduate program at Ohio State in geodesy, he found his calling as a topographic engineer. While the Army used his talents and satisfied his scholarly interests in conducting a topographic survey of New Guinea, Kaula realized that he would have to leave commissioned service in order to continue to work in his technical discipline of interest. Kaula's first position after leaving the Army in 1957 was working as an Army civilian scientist in the Army Mapping Service. There he investigated the variations of the

Earth's gravitational field and its effects on inertial guidance. Kaula moved on to NASA to continue his research and work on a geodetic satellite project. He was a prolific author of technical papers on satellite geodesy. Kaula continued his technical interests and growth as a Professor at University of California at Los Angeles (UCLA). He wrote two advanced technical books, *Theory of Satellite Geodesy* (1966) and *Introduction to Planetary Physics* (1968). Kaula was an active member and leader of his university, serving as department chair and chairing various academic committees. While at UCLA, he continued his research and support of NASA. He designed and implemented several significant science projects on Apollo 15, 16, and 17. In addition, Kaula chaired important NASA advisory committees and panels and contributed his expertise to the National Research Council's Space Science Board. The American Geophysical Union benefited from Kaula's contributions as editor and committee chair. Kaula kept current with his discipline's technical revolution and led an important effort by the National Geodetic Survey as it transitioned to the new GPS-based technology. For all his outstanding contributions, Kaula was elected to the National Academy of Science in 1987.

USMA 1949 | **John Harold Saxon, Jr.** | **Mathematician**

10 December 1923 (Moultrie, GA) – 17 October 1996 (Norman, OK)
Graduate # 17267 (495th out of 574), listed in *AS* (January 1998)

Military Service:
1943-1945: Combat aircraft pilot in World War II
1949-1951: Flight instructor pilot, Vance Air Base, OK
1951-1953: Combat aircraft pilot in Korean War (55 missions)
1957: Experimental Test Pilot School
1966-1968: Air Proving Ground, Elgin Air Base, FL
1968-1969: Tactical fighter duty in Thailand during Vietnam War

Professional Service:
1953: Aeronautical engineering studies at Air Force Institute of Technology, OH
1960: Electrical engineering study at the University of Oklahoma
1963: Assistant Professor Electrical Engineering, USAFA, CO
1970 Professor of Mathematics, Rose State College, OK
1970-1990: Author of numerous mathematics textbooks for school and college students

---

J. H. SAXON, JR. had two years of study at the University of Georgia and two years of combat service as a B-17 pilot in World War II before he entered West Point in 1945. Upon graduation from USMA and entry into the Army Air Corps, he became a flight instructor for B-25s at Vance Air Force Base, OH. Soon he was off to the Korean War to fly B-26 combat missions. After completing 55 missions, Saxon pursued technical studies at the Air Force Institute of Technology, OH. Surviving a crash while there, Saxon went on to further training as a test pilot and graduate study at the University of Oklahoma, earning an M.S. in Electrical Engineering. For his next assignment, he became a popular engineering professor at the Air Force Academy. After tours at the Air Proving Ground in Florida and in Thailand, he retired from the Air Force in 1970. The second phase of his life began as a mathematics professor at Rose State College, OK. Finding that students there were struggling with their textbooks, Saxon began writing textbooks to help students with their understanding and skill development. He formed his own publishing company and eventually wrote thirteen textbooks for school programs and two college texts (calculus and physics). Highly successful in his work, but also controversial in the national mathematics education community, Saxon was often featured in the media for his efforts and became a nationally known speaker on the topic of mathematics education.

USMA 1950 | **Monty Dale Coffin** | **Mathematician**

25 October 1927 (Bedford, KY) – 31 January 2000 (Dayton, OH)
Graduate # 17351 (5th out of 670), (mechanist, engineer)

Military Service:
1950-1951: Pilot training
1952-1953: Combat duty in Korean War
1971-1972: Staff duty in Turkey

Professional Service:
1955-1958: Assistant Professor of Mechanics, USMA
1958-1960: Graduate study at California Institute of Technology
1960-1963: Researcher for Atlas Weapon System, CA
1963-1967: Researcher at Lawrence Livermore Radiation Laboratory, CA
1967-1971: Professor of Mathematics and Department Head, USAFA
1972-1980: Research Director, Air Force Missile Laboratory, OH
1980-1996: Professor of Mechanical Engineering Clark Technical
            College, OH

M. D. Coffin, like many other of his classmates including Frank Borman, entered the Air Force upon graduation. After flight training and combat flying in the Korean War, Coffin attended the Massachusetts Institute of Technology, receiving an M.S. degree in mechanical engineering. He returned to West Point to teach mechanics for three years. After more graduate schooling at California Institute of Technology, Coffin performed research on the Atlas Rocket and in nuclear weapons at Lawrence Livermore Laboratory, CA. In 1967, Coffin completed his Ph.D. at the University of California at Berkeley. His research work in aeronautics was published in technical journals. He next spent four years as the Professor of Mathematics and Department Head, U.S. Air Force Academy, CO. Coffin went to Turkey for military staff duties before returning to further research challenges at Wright Patterson

Air Base in OH, where his work involved missile design and aeronautical engineering. After a 30-year Air Force career with 29 combat missions, Coffin retired to further academic pursuits. Becoming the Director of the Mechanical Engineering Program and Professor at Clark Technical College, OH, he taught courses in civil, mechanical, and electrical engineering; mathematics; and physics. Coffin was a versatile applied scientist, who contributed his talents in both academic areas of teaching and research. As a member of the Mathematical Association of America, American Society of Engineering Education, and the American Institute of Aeronautics and Astronautics, Coffin was a versatile technician with tremendous interest, expertise, and contributions in mathematics, science, and engineering.

USMA 1952 | **Robert Simpson Tickle** | **Scientist**

31 July 1930 (Norfolk, VA) – 4 July 2000 (Ann Arbor, MI)
Graduate # 18614 (123rd out of 527), (physicist), listed in *AS* (July 2001)

Military Service:
1952-1954: Combat duty in Korean War
1954-1956: Garrison duty at Fort Polk, LA

Professional Service:
1956-1960: Graduate student at University of Virginia (Ph.D. in Physics)
1960-1968: Assistant and Associate Professor of Physics, University of Michigan
1968-1995: Professor of Physics, University of Michigan

R. S. Tickle attended the College of William and Mary before entering West Point. At the Academy, he excelled in science. Upon graduation, he selected the armor branch and deployed to Korea to serve in combat. He returned to garrison duty at Fort Polk, LA. Unable to attend graduate school or work in science in the Army, Tickle resigned his commission in 1956 to attend the University of Virginia. He obtained his Ph.D. in physics in 1960 and joined the physics faculty at the University of Michigan, where he became an outstanding teacher and scholar. He was versatile in his research, making contributions both in theory and application – designing the University's cyclotron and using it to conduct experiments in reactions of particles. He worked with scientists throughout the world and was a leading collaborator with scientists at Lawrence Berkeley Laboratory. Tickle was also an environmentalist and through concern for his area's environment entered local politics, where he was successful at using his scientific background to affect the environmental policies of his area. Tickle was a highly respected scientist, making numerous contributions to his field of physics and to his students at the University of Michigan.

USMA 1952	**Edward Higgins White II**	**Technologist**

14 November 1930 (San Antonio, TX) – 27 January 1967 (Cape Kennedy, FL)
Graduate # 18619 (128th out of 527), (aeronautical engineer, astronaut), listed in *AS* (Summer 1971)

Military Service:
1952-1953: Pilot training in FL and TX
1954-1957: Aviation duty in Germany

Professional Service:
1957-1959: Graduate study in aeronautical engineer at
                   University of Michigan
1959-1962: Test pilot and researcher at Wright Patterson
                   Air Base, OH
1962-1967: Astronaut for NASA (Gemini 4)
                   (1st American to walk in space)

E. H. WHITE was the son of Air Force Major General and aviator, Edward White (USMA 1924). He went to high school in Washington, DC and then came to West Point in the class of 1952. He was both a successful student and athlete, achieving All-American status in track and playing soccer. After graduating from the Academy, White joined the Air Force, receiving flight training in FL and TX and his pilot wings in 1953. Following a three-year

Army aviation training in 1954

tour as a fighter pilot in Germany, he studied aeronautical engineering at the University of Michigan, earning an M.S. degree in 1959. White was then assigned to Wright-Patterson Air Force Base, OH, as a test pilot conducting weapons systems development, writing technical reports, and recommending improvements in aircraft design and construction. White was a pioneer and innovator in his field and sought a position where he could see and experience his form of aeronautical science. Continuing as a test pilot until 1962, he applied and was selected to become an astronaut in the NASA program as part of the second group of astronauts. During his first space mission in June 1965 on Gemini 4 (flying with McDivitt on the 8th U.S. space flight), White became the first American to walk in space (extra vehicular activity). White floated freely in space, attached to the space capsule by a cord bringing him oxygen and communications. Maneuvering himself around the outside of the space capsule with a device that shot bursts of compressed oxygen, White *spacewalked* for 21 minutes, during which time he became a national hero. He was named the senior pilot for the first manned mission of the Apollo Project. In preparing for this flight, he died in a tragic accident at Cape Kennedy (now Cape Canaveral), FL. During a training session, a spark started a fire in the space capsule while it was on the launching pad. White, along with fellow astronauts Gus Grissom and Roger Chaffee, died in the fire. During his short professional life, White received many honors and awards including an honorary degree from University of Michigan. He started a fund to build a youth center, which has been completed through other donations and successfully serving the community over the years. Edward White was one of several West Point graduates who have become astronauts. Among this group of modern scientific pioneers and space explorers are: James Adamson (USMA 1969), Buzz Aldrin (USMA 1951), Frank Borman (USMA 1950), Michael Clifford (USMA 1974), Michael Collins (USMA 1952), Patrick Forrester (USMA 1979), Charles Gemar (USMA 1979), Timothy Kopra (USMA 1985), William McArthur (USMA 1973), Richard Mullane (USMA 1967), Donald Peterson (USMA 1955), David Scott (USMA 1954), Sherwood Spring (USMA 1967), Douglas Wheelock (USMA 1983), Jeffrey Williams (USMA 1980), and Alfred Worden (USMA 1955).

Quotation: By Edward White in a speech at the United Nations: "There are no boundaries on this earth when you look down from 100 miles."

USMA 1955   **Robert Lee LaFrenz**   **Scientist**

20 May 1932 (Center, NE) – 24 February 2000 (LaMesa, CA)
Graduate # 20242 (79th out of 470), (nuclear engineer), listed in *AS* (July 2001)

Military Service:
1955-1958: Engineer duty in Germany
1961-1962: Engineer duty in South Korea
1967-1968: Combat engineer duty in Vietnam War

Professional Service:
1963-1967: Assistant Professor of Physics, USMA
1968-1972: Laboratory director for Lawrence Livermore
           National Laboratory, CA
1971-1977: Associate Professor of Physics, USMA
1977-1979: Professor of Physics, USMA
1980-2000: Engineer and executive of various technology companies

R. L. LaFrenz studied for one year at Wayne State before attending the Academy. He was a strong student and selected the Corps of Engineers as his branch. His first assignment was in Germany. He returned to the United States three years later to attend Iowa State University, where he received an M.S. degree in nuclear engineering and later his Ph.D. He spent from 1961 to 1962 in South Korea commanding an engineering bridging company. In 1963, LaFrenz returned to West Point to teach physics. After four successful and enjoyable years in academics, LaFrenz was deployed to Vietnam to construct roads and airfields in the combat zone. In 1969, he was assigned to the Army's Explosive Excavation Group at Lawrence Livermore National Laboratory. This group studied the use of conventional explosives for excavation work. In 1972, LaFrenz returned to the Physics Department at West Point to continue his academic work. He advanced to Professor and was involved in both successful research scholarship and cadet development. In 1979, he retired from the Army to work in industrial science. Starting as a research scientist, he quickly became a technical manager and executive in a scientific company. He formed his own company in CA involved in high technology water treatment. He was active as a consultant, advisor, and member of several technology-based societies. LaFrenz was a talented scientist and military officer, who also became a successful entrepreneur.

USMA 1956 | **John Michael Kallfelz** | **Engineer**

21 November 1934 (Atlanta, GA) – 9 September 1997 (Geneva, Switzerland)
Graduate # 20678 (45th out of 480), (nuclear scientist), listed in *AS* (November 1998)

Military Service:
1956-1961: Engineer duty in Germany

Professional Service:
1968-1993: Professor, Georgia Institute of Technology
1993-1997: Researcher, Switzerland

J. M. KALLFELZ graduated from USMA and entered the Corps of Engineers. He began his career as a dedicated science educator and researcher. After fulfilling his military obligation performing engineering work in Germany, he attended the California Institute of Technology for an M.S. degree and University of Karlsuhe, Germany for his Ph.D. in nuclear engineering. During his 25-year career as a professor at Georgia Institute of Technology, he was a Fulbright Scholar, an international educational consultant, prolific technical author, respected teacher, and journal editor. His fields of expertise were the technically important areas of reactor physics and nuclear energy production. He made

tremendous contributions to these fields as they related to safety and efficiency in generating nuclear power. He earned many honors for his research accomplishments. After leaving

Georgia Tech, he moved to Switzerland to work at the Paul Scherrer Institute, which was a productive laboratory facility with a large, highly-skilled staff. Even at such a prestigious research facility, Kallfelz stood out as a technical and managerial leader of the laboratory. In addition to his science, Kallfelz contributed to society through his work with Amnesty

---

USMA 1959   **John Paul Porter**   **Technologist**

3 July 1936 (Spokane, WA) – 18 August 1999 (University Place, WA)
Graduate # 22676 (444th out of 499), listed in AS (September 2000)

Military Service:
1959:   Entered commissioned service in Air Force
1960-1964: ICBM operations officer
1970-1971: Staff duty in Vietnam

Profession Service:
1964-1965: Missile course at Air Force Institute of Technology
1965-1970: Technical support for NASA for Gemini and Apollo projects (recovery duty for Apollo 13)
1972-1974: Program Director for Air Force Space Program, (CA and HI)
1974-1977: Space and Missile Systems Organization, Los Angeles, CA
1977:   Graduate study at University of Southern California (M.S.)
1977-1979: Space Shuttle development, Vandenberg, CA
1980-1985: Program director for NAVSTAR, global positioning system
1985-1997: Construction engineer for offshore oil platforms, Super
                   Collider, and space launch towers

J. P. PORTER opted for Air Force commissioning upon his graduation from West Point in 1959. His first assignments were in ICBM operations. After missile schooling, he was assigned special duty with NASA on the Gemini and Apollo projects, performing support duties for the manned lunar missions and the recovery of Apollo 13. After a tour in Vietnam as a senior staff officer, Porter returned to duties with the U.S. Air Force space program. He was a program director for the Expendable Launch Vehicle development at the Los Angeles Air Station and commanded the Kaena Point Tracking Station in HI. In 1979, Porter supervised the Space Shuttle Launch Facility development at Vandenberg Air Force Base, CA. Porter's final military assignment was to direct the NAVSTAR Global positioning program. Retiring from the Air Force in 1986 and launching his civilian career, Porter helped build offshore oil platforms, the Super Collider, and mobile rocket towers. Porter was a versatile engineer and accomplished scientist, who made many significant contributions to the technologies of America's space program.

Honorable Mentions

As in any selection, there were many difficult choices on who to include in ***The 200***. There are many others who deserve to be recognized for their science contributions. This entry contains a brief mention of some of those. There are, no doubt, many more. There are three categories of people mentioned in this section: 1) West Point graduates who did not get listed; 2) former West Point cadets who did considerable scientific work, but did not graduate; and 3) West Point faculty members whose scientific contributions were substantial, but were not USMA graduates.

One famous graduate wanted a career in science, but never had the opportunity. During his Army time after graduation until 1854, Ulysses S. Grant (USMA 1843) sought an assignment teaching mathematics. While he stood 21st in his class overall, he was a better student in mathematics. However, he was not good enough in the eyes of the Department Head, **Albert Church (USMA 1828)**, who denied Grant's requests. Not obtaining this opportunity, Grant resigned from the Army. He re-entered Army service during the Civil War. Grant never got his opportunity to become a mathematician, but his technical talents helped him in other areas of his life. "It was never my intention to remain in the Army," wrote Grant, "but to prepare myself for a professorship in some college. I wrote Professor Church requesting him to ask my designation as his assistant."[10]

Some of the other outstanding West Point-educated scientists from the 19th century are: James Cobb (USMA 1811), teacher of college-level science; Samuel Stanhope Smith (USMA 1818), a mathematics professor at USMA; Thomas Ingalls (USMA 1822), President of Jefferson College; Henry Gird (USMA 1822), mathematics professor and President of the University of Louisiana; Thomas Twiss (USMA 1826), engineering professor at South Carolina College; Frederick Smith (USMA 1833), engineering professor at USMA; William Bliss (USMA 1833), mathematics professor at USMA; Daniel Woodbury (USMA 1836), bridge engineer and technical writer; Edwin Morgan (USMA 1837), professor at Lehigh College; Israel Vogdes (USMA 1837), mathematics professor at USMA; Bushrod Johnson (USMA 1840), chancellor of the University of Nashville; Thomas "Stonewall" Jackson, Civil War hero and science professor at Virginia Military Institute; Charles Blunt (USMA 1846), harbor engineer; William Welcker (USMA 1851), professor at University of California at Berkeley; William Nicodemus (USMA 1858), professor at University of Wisconsin; Calvin Esterly (USMA 1877), professor and president at Louisiana University; John Bigelow (USMA 1877), professor at Massachusetts Institute of Technology; Oberlin Carter (USMA 1880), Panama Canal engineer; John Biddle (USMA 1881), Superintendent at USMA; Charles Summerall (USMA 1892), Chief of Staff of the Army and the President of the Citadel; and George Blakely (USMA 1892), mathematics professor at USMA.

---

[9] Grant, *Memoirs*, p. 51.

During the 20th century, West Point continued to produce strong scientific contributors. Among those graduates are: Dorsey Rodney (USMA 1903), dean at Michigan State University; Jay Benedict (USMA 1904), professor and Superintendent at USMA; Robert Eddy (USMA 1905), professor at USMA and Massachusetts Institute of Technology; Roger Alexander (USMA 1907), dean at USMA; Oscar Gatchell (USMA 1912), mechanics professor at USMA; Douglas Greene (USMA 1913), President of Drexel Institute of Technology; Louis Rada (foreign cadet in USMA April 1917); John Weishampel (USMA April 1917), mechanics professor at Lafayette College; James Marshall (USMA June 1918), organizer of the Manhattan Project; Lawrence Leonard (USMA 1922), mathematics professor at William and Mary; Charles Mason (USMA 1925), engineering professor at Virginia Institute of Technology; Vincent Esposito (USMA 1925), engineering professor at USMA; Elvin Heiberg (USMA 1926), mechanics professor at USMA; Winfred Sisson (USMA 1930), professor at USMA and University of California; William Dickinson (USMA 1930), professor at USMA and University of Arkansas; Ellsworth Davis (USMA 1932), Mississippi River engineer; Alfred Starbird (USMA 1933), nuclear weapons expert; Charles Broshous (USMA 1933), engineering and science professor at USMA; John Bristor (USMA 1935), professor at University of Florida; Arthur Overbeck (USMA 1937), nuclear weapons expert; Edward Jacunski (USMA 1938), engineering educator at University of Florida; Edward Gallagher (USMA 1939), Great Lakes surveyor; Harold Brown (USMA 1940), nuclear weapons engineer and systems analyst; Edward Podufaly (USMA 1940), topographer and oceanographer; George Dixon, (USMA 1940), hydraulic engineer; and John Lowry (USMA 1947), mathematics professor University of California Polytechnic.

Several West Point graduates made substantial contributions to the field of ordnance. Some of these noteworthy contributors are: gun carriage designer Adelbert Buffington (USMA 1861); Medal of Honor winner William Beebe (USMA 1863); metallurgist Tracy Dickson (USMA 1892); founder of the Ballistic Research Laboratory, William Tschappat (USMA 1896); ordnance production leader James Burns (USMA 1904); weapon developer George Eddy (USMA 1918); leader in microelectronics John Hinrichs (USMA 1928); and ordnance production leader Floyd Hansen (USMA 1932).

Several others served in important leadership positions, such as Chief of Army Engineers, and had great influence on America's development. West Point graduates in this category are: Charles Gratiot (USMA 1806), William Craighill (USMA 1853), Alexander Mackenzie (USMA 1864), William Rossell (USMA 1873), Dan Kingman (USMA 1875), William Black (USMA 1877), Lansing Beach (USMA 1882), Harry Taylor (USMA 1884), Lytle Brown (USMA 1898), Edward Markham (USMA 1899), Julian Schley (USMA 1903), Raymond Wheeler (USMA 1911), Samuel Sturgis (USMA 1918), and Walter Wilson (USMA 1929).

Several former cadets, who did not graduate, used their technical talents and education at in scientific work. Two such people are famous for other activities, but nonetheless had special talents in scientific disciplines. Edgar Allan Poe (ex-1834), who in addition to his writing talents was a talented mathematician, applied his technical skills to the science of ciphering. Poe had a fascination with cryptography, often referring to *secret writings* in his poems and stories. He conducted a cryptographic challenge in the *Weekly Messenger* in 1839. Poe challenged readers to submit cryptographs for him to solve. He published his solutions to the ciphers submitted by readers and wrote an article in *Graham's Magazine about cryptography*. James Abbott McNeill Whistler (ex-1855) was the son of **George W. Whistler (USMA 1819)** and a famous artist. A brief glimpse of his technical work as an engraver is provided in the essay on the U.S. Coast Survey given later in this volume. Other scientific contributors who attended, but did not graduate from the Academy, were John Latrobe (ex-1822), technical patent lawyer and aid to Samuel Morse as he developed the telegraph; George Hughes (ex-1827), Army surveyor and railroad engineer; Johnson Camden (ex-1851), railroad engineer and U.S. Senator; Thomas Rosser (ex-1861), railroad engineer; Charles Thompson (ex-1875), civil engineer and miner in ND; William Holabird (ex-1877), architectural engineer who originated skeleton steel construction for high-rise buildings; Frank Osborn (ex-1879), civil and construction engineer in Cleveland, OH; Johnson Whittaker (ex-1880), African-American and former slave who taught at South Carolina State University; and Samuel Townsend (ex-1885), inventor of machinery.

The following paragraphs provide information on West Point science faculty members, who were not graduates of the Academy. If they had graduated from USMA, they would have been strong candidates for *The Scientific 200*.

Jonathan Williams

Jonathan Williams was the first Superintendent and an accomplished scientist. He collaborated with his great uncle Benjamin Franklin and was a member of the American Philosophical Society (APS) (see the essay on APS). He established the United States Military Philosophical Society (USMPS) (see the essay on USMPS).

Jared Mansfield (Yale College 1777) was the author of the first book of original mathematical research in America. His work and reputation as a "man of science" so impressed Thomas Jefferson that the President appointed him the first professor at the Academy. From 1803 to 1812 Mansfield was the Surveyor-General of the Northwest Territory before returning to the Academy to teach science for 16 years.

William Barron (Harvard College 1787) was a classmate of John Quincy Adams. He was a capable scientist and teacher. Barron taught mathematics at the Academy for five years, but was charged with neglect and other misdeeds before resigning his commission in 1807.

Ferdinand Hassler immigrated to the United States in 1805 from Switzerland. He taught mathematics at West Point for just three years before moving on to other scientific duties as a professor at Union College, Superintendent of the U.S. Coast Survey, and Head of U.S. Standards of Weights and Measures.

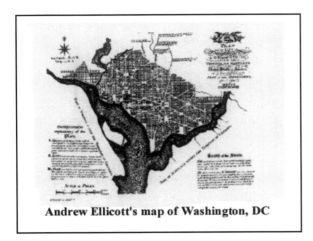

Andrew Ellicott's map of Washington, DC

Andrew Ellicott was a famous surveyor and astronomer who taught mathematics at the Academy from 1813 to 1820. He was the recipient of many awards and honors for his scientific work in Europe. His work in laying out and mapping Washington, DC built his reputation (see figure of Ellicott's map).

Claudius Crozet (École polytechnique 1807) brought state-of-the-art engineering and technology education to America from the École in France. He had served as an engineer for Napoleon and knew how technology could support military operations. He helped establish the substantial mathematics requirement for the engineering education at West Point where he taught from 1816 to 1823.

David Douglass (Yale College 1813) was a progressive and talented professor. At various times, he taught mathematics, science, and engineering at the Academy. He was instrumental in implementing many of Thayer's reform initiatives. Douglass later taught at the University of the City of New York, Kenyon College, and Hobart College.

Robert Yates in 1955 (from West Point Howitzer)

Robert Carl Yates (Virginia Military Academy 1924) had taught at several schools before he returned to active duty during World War II to back-fill for officers who left the faculty for combat duties. He developed faculty and modernized the pedagogy in the mathematics program at the Academy from 1942 to 1954. Yates was a prolific author and wrote several successful textbooks and numerous technical articles.

Reference:
Grant, U. S., *Personal Memoirs of U. Grant*, Bonanza, New York, 1885.

Technical Education Community in America[10]

American science and technology were far behind their European counterparts in 1776. As the nineteenth century began, the science community entered a period of haphazard development that culminated at the end of the century with an educated society of professionals that challenged and, in some ways, surpassed the established bastions of European knowledge and discovery. There were several factors involved in this transformation: the genius and ingenuity of several scientific leaders, the technological need

---
[10] Research help for this section was provided by David Greene.

for expanding into the continent and developing its vast natural resources, the support of enlightened government leaders like Thomas Jefferson, James Madison, James Monroe, and Abraham Lincoln, and the rapid maturation of America's education system through the contributions of technical schools like Yale College, United States Military Academy, and Rensselaer Polytechnic Institute. Evolving from a culture that first produced basic scientific understanding from the arts and crafts, a climate emerged that valued measurement in navigation, surveying, and mapping. From this meager beginning, science and engineering became the means to improve commerce, build infrastructure, modernize technology, and create a prosperous nation. Eventually science became an acceptable and valued occupation in both the private and public domains.

The early institutions of higher learning, circa 1800, were largely devoted to the mastery of the languages, art, literature, and culture. Education was mostly a social opportunity for the wealthy. Colleges such as Harvard, Yale, William and Mary, Brown, Dartmouth, and Princeton were concerned with producing educated clergy, politicians, and lawyers, but not highly trained technologists to solve the problems that were challenging the establishment of the new Republic. Soon, however, this need for technological problem solving was addressed. Yale College advanced the establishment of science as a profession by appointing young Benjamin Silliman in 1802 to educate a generation of men to build and expand the American territory. He was forced to go slowly and to chart his way into the unnavigated waters of American technical education. Silliman was responsible for attracting men to professions that grew in importance for improving agriculture, mercantilism, and eventually, more science. In the same year, President Jefferson and Congress established West Point to build the nation's military and transportation systems. **Sylvanus Thayer (USMA 1808)** accomplished the Military Academy's educational breakthrough as he studied the French system at the École polytechnique in 1815. While there, he obtained over 1000 books to form an outstanding technical library at the Academy. Silliman's breakthrough and revelation came while attending classes in Edinburgh, Scotland in 1805, while visiting Europe to buy books for Yale's library. By 1818, Silliman had established a technical program of study and founded the *American Journal of Science and Arts* (Silliman's *Journal*), and Thayer had put in place a rigorous engineering program with a new pedagogy and a science-centered academic culture. Silliman had the backing of an influential American college willing to take a risk in science, and Thayer had the United States government as his supporter and benefactor. America was late at entering science education, but through good fortune, it began to catch up with these two people and their organizations leading the way.

Alexander Bache

Numerous scientific leaders of historical significance emerged such as Joseph Henry, the world's foremost experimenter with electricity; Amos Eaton, founder of Rensselaer Polytechnic Institute (RPI) in 1824; and **Alexander Dallas Bache (USMA 1825)**, Superintendent of the U. S. Coast Survey. Henry had the good fortune of living in Albany, where the booming economy of America had created a favorable environment for industrialization and education. Studying at the Albany Academy and the

Albany Institute and with support from Amos Eaton, whose technical institute (RPI) was just across the Hudson River, Henry spent six years conducting the best science that the American continent had experienced up to that time. Investigating and experimenting with electricity, he built advanced electric motors and surpassed the Europeans' knowledge of this subject. Soon he had a professorship at Princeton collaborating with scientific colleagues. Fortunately, his best friend and life-long colleague was Bache. Bache and Henry made a good team. They helped each other in science, education, science leadership, and politics. They had a vision of American science leading the world. As they traveled together in Europe, they assimilated European technical and educational expertise and sought ways to organize American science. They came back to America with energy for their work and grandiose plans for American science.

In the back rooms of American education, another important process in its development was taking place. Textbook authors in all areas of science were translating, adapting, and improving the European (mostly French) books for the inexperienced American students. Examples and exercises were inserted into textbooks and more thorough explanations were written to supplement existing presentations. With the excellent work of writers like **Charles Davies (USMA 1815)**, **William Bartlett (USMA 1826)**, **Edward Courtenay (USMA 1818)**, and Elias Loomis of Yale, American students began to have the resources needed to advance and learn.

The nation began to see the value of professionally trained technologists and scientists, as opposed to dilettantes who dabbled in the fields of invention, arts, and crafts. As early as 1835, people were beginning to value science for its utility. John Draper opined, "Mere literacy acumen is becoming utterly powerless against profound scientific attainment."[11] Many of the early efforts involved studying the lands that America was exploring and developing, as geological surveys were conducted throughout the nation. The Sheffield Scientific School at Yale was established in 1846, as was the Smithsonian Institute. In the same year, Louis Agassiz arrived from Europe and became the champion grantsman of American science. Joining with Bache and Henry, Agassiz, along with young European-connected New Englanders Wolcott Gibbs and Benjamin Gould, formed an American science protective and promotion society called the *Lazzaroni*. The Lazzaroni, with Bache as their "chief," became a symbol of professionalism and specialization in the pursuit of scientific knowledge. While only Gould obtained his doctorate (Göttingen 1848), all were accomplished, well-connected scientists. They promoted American science and influenced the progress and success of American science in the middle half of the 19th century. This group, along with several other early American scientists both native born and imported from Europe, found centers of learning in Boston, Albany, and New York; government support in Washington; and bright, scientific minds coming from the Sheffield School of Science at Yale, the Lawrence School of Science at Harvard, the Chandler School of Science at Dartmouth, the Thayer School of Engineering at Dartmouth, and USMA. At Yale, **William Norton (USMA 1831)** became the Professor of Engineering. At Harvard, **Henry Eustis (USMA 1842)** assumed the Engineering professor position, but **Henry Halleck**

---

[11] Guralnick, *Science and the American College, 1828-1860*, p. 288.

(USMA 1839) turned down Sheffield's offer in order to remain in Army service. At Dartmouth, **Robert Fletcher (USMA 1868)** headed the Thayer Engineering School. At first, the American science efforts were concentrated in astronomy, topography, geology, chemistry, applied mathematics, and engineering, but eventually physics, biology, botany, hydrology, meteorology, and all the sciences captured America's interest. The involvement of the Army's finest scientific minds (West Point educated) in topography, astronomy, geology, and engineering gave an added boost to the advancement. The resources that the United States did not have within its borders were found in Europe, as American science first raided Britain, then France, and finally Germany for their scientists and their education systems. Many of the brightest American students went to Europe to train and returned with credentials, knowledge, and new ideas. When the government, first through the Coast Survey and Bache, and then through Henry and the National Academy of Sciences, opened the public purse to support science, America's scientific movement charged forward.

It was one thing to sell science to Congress, which Bache and Henry had accomplished, but another to convince the American public. Fortunately, the scientific community found several popular spokesmen. Benjamin Silliman started the effort in the early part of the century. Later, Louis Agassiz was spellbinding in explaining and promoting natural history. **Ormsby Mitchel (USMA 1829)** was the master at public charm and fascination as he presented the rudiments of astronomy to crowds of thousands as he traveled around the country. These men transformed the public into political supporters and financial donators for science. All the elements of success for Bache and Henry's plan were in place.

However, the next challenge for American science was to adjust to war. The American Civil War hit the foundation of the nation hard, and all parts of society had to adapt. American science had to find its way as it contributed to the technology of the world's first modern war. The competition of both Armies to maintain the technological edge kept the science community working full-time. Railroad locomotives became better and more powerful. Telegraphs became more reliable and ubiquitous. Rifles became breech-loading and repeating. Warships were made of iron. Cannons fired projectiles for miles, and many more technological advances entered the battlefield. Since West Pointers had the technological background to work in this environment, the Army endorsed and aided their efforts in science. While many West Point-educated scientists entered field command positions and the Union Army's first Chief of Ordnance during the war and **James Ripley (USMA 1814)** sought to restrict the new technologies in order to streamline his operations, other West Point graduates made tremendous contributions in the area of battlefield technologies and ordnance. Some of the major contributors for the Union Army were: **Robert Parrot (USMA 1824), Herman Haupt (USMA 1835), John Barnard (USMA 1833), Alexander Dyer (USMA 1837), Thomas Rodman (USMA 1841),** and **William Trowbridge (USMA 1848)**. On the Confederate side, the technological leaders were **Joseph Anderson (USMA 1836), Josiah Gorgas (USMA 1841)** and **George W. Rains (USMA 1842)**.

After the war, graduate programs in science, the activities of the American Association for the Advancement of Science, the expertise of disciplinary science organizations like the American Chemical Society and the American Society of Civil Engineers, and Alexander

Bell's telephone became symbols of "The Age of Enterprise." America was growing in population, area, wealth, power, and science. The nation needed both expert, professional scientists and the services of technically trained citizens to advance the cause for the good of the nation. The American technical education community provided both. Borrowing methodology in funding, research, and organization from its European mentors, the American nation embraced the establishment of higher education for the purposes of advancing scientific discovery. United States citizenry became a proponent for both the advancement of pure science by its educators and researchers and the advancement of applied science for economic prosperity and technical progression.

In 1862, Justin Smith Morrill, through the protracted urgings and pleas of his friend and neighbor **Alden Partridge (USMA 1806)** and the opportunities brought on by the Civil War, did much to promote this cause by authoring a bill in Congress to establish public lands by means of land grants, to be set aside for the building of agricultural and mechanical arts colleges, not to exclude areas concerning science, mathematics, and the tactical, military arts. Evidence of the immense influence of the Morrill Act stands today in the institutions of the state universities of California, Illinois, Maine, Minnesota, Nebraska, Ohio, Pennsylvania, West Virginia, Wisconsin, and Wyoming, and in schools like Purdue and Cornell. This act strengthened and expanded science programs throughout the country.

The new education system had finally found the resources to build universities with the educational expertise, talented faculty, and specialized programs of elective courses to offer quality graduate degrees in science. No longer would America's brightest students travel to Europe to obtain doctorates. Schools like the University of Pennsylvania, Yale, and Harvard began to award Ph.D. degrees in the early 1870s, and by 1876, 25 American institutions had awarded 44 Ph.D. degrees. The standards were set high in 1876 as Johns Hopkins University endorsed research for its faculty and graduate students as their primary task. Hopkins made one last assault on Europe as famous British mathematician J. J. Sylvester brought his reputation to America to insure success at the very highest levels of scholarship. Native-born astronomer Simon Newcomb and other Ph.D. scientists filled leading roles in this final advancement. Adequate fellowships for potential in performing scientific work kept students in America for their graduate work. On the applied side, Lehigh University, Rensselaer Polytechnic Institute, Worcester Polytechnic Institute, Massachusetts Institute of Technology, Stevens Institute of Technology, and several other technical schools, all began advanced, specialized programs to produce engineers and applied scientists, capable of building products and improving industrial methodology. Thriving industries hired these graduates and clamored for more. What remained were liberal arts colleges that still embraced science at the undergraduate level, producing managers, business executives, and government officials that supported and collaborated with their technological colleagues. The American educational system had come of age by the end of the century. It was flexible, efficient, effective, and successful. While America's first Nobel Laureate waited until 1907, American science education had completed a century of amazing progress, which was accurately summarized by author and historian Robert Bruce in the following:
"During the mid-nineteenth century, American science responded . . . . Science came to see itself, and society came to see it, as an established profession. Scientific education was

lengthened and specialized by means of scientific schools, graduate education, and the modern university. These institutions in turn gave scientists a livelihood." [12]

References:

Albree, J., Arney, D.C., and Rickey, F., *A Station Favorable to the Pursuits of Science: Primary Material in the History of Mathematics at the United States Military Academy*, American Mathematical Society, Providence, 2000.

Bruce, R.V., *The Launching of Modern American Science 1846-1876.*, Cornell University Press, Ithaca, NY, 1987.

Cajori, F., *The Teaching and History of Mathematics in the United States*, Government Printing Office, Washington, 1890.

Daniels, G.H., *American Science in the Age of Jackson*, Columbia University Press, New York, 1968.

Daniels, G.H. (Editor), *Nineteenth Century American Science*, Northwestern University Press, Evanston, 1972.

Davidson, D.W., "America's first school of engineering," *Cobblestone, 3,*(10), (1982), pp. 31-33.

Greene, J.C., *American Science in the Age of Jefferson*, The Iowa University Press, Ames, Iowa, 1984.

Guralnick, Stanley, *Science and the American College, 1828-1860*, Ph.D. Dissertation, University of Pennsylvania, Philadelphia, 1975.

Guralnick, Stanley, *Science and the Ante-Bellum American College*, American Philosophical Society, Philadelphia, 1975.

Reingold, N., editor, *Science in America since 1820*, Science History Publications, New York 1976.

Struik, D.J., *Yankee Science in the Making*, Collier Books, New York, 1962.

USMA's Mathematics-Science-Engineering (MSE) Program

West Point has a rich history of educating cadets as confident, competent, technological problem solvers, as every graduating cadet has studied bountiful measures of mathematics, science, and engineering. The story of technological education at West Point is teeming with impacts and influences on the scientific and technical developments of the nation and the educational system of America. Many of the Academy's advances in these areas were exported by its graduates and utilized by other educational institutions and scientific organizations. The Academy itself blossomed into a science-based school of high standards

---

[12] Bruce, *Launching of Modern American Science*, 1987, p. 4.

and effective programs making significant contributions to the development and prosperity of the United States.

The Beginning

Technological teaching at West Point dates from even before the Academy was established. In 1801, George Baron taught a few cadets of the Artillery and Engineers the fundamentals and applications of algebra. Then on March 16th, 1802, the U. S. Military Academy at West Point was instituted by act of Congress and signed into law by President Thomas Jefferson. The first professors were Jared Mansfield and William Barron (see **Honorable Mentions**). They taught the first few cadets algebra, geometry, and surveying. As an institute established to teach military engineers to construct fortifications and to build the infrastructure of the nation, USMA needed instructors to teach mathematics, science, and engineering, and fortunately, it found the best the nation had to offer. Ferdinand Hassler and Andrew Ellicott (see **Honorable Mentions**) soon assumed professorships and expanded the instruction beyond applied mathematics into applied science. Ellicott was a distinguished scientist and surveyor, and he added instruction in trigonometry and fluxions (the rudiments of calculus). Hassler was also a surveyor and astronomer. Although the Academy was immature and stark compared to its European counterparts, the first few West Point cadets were learning from the best scientific minds in the nation.

Contributions to the Nation's Educational System

Since the Academy was the first scientific and technical school in America, the early professors had the opportunity to make significant contributions not only to the Academy, but also to other American colleges. Perhaps the most prominent contributors in this respect were the early 19th century Superintendents **Alden Partridge (USMA 1806)** and **Sylvanus Thayer (USMA 1808),** and mathematics professors **Charles Davies (USMA 1815)** and **Edward Courtenay (USMA 1821)**. The work of these educators had a significant impact on elementary schools, high schools, and colleges across the country. Partridge had a challenging time at the Academy, both in establishing a creditable engineering program (he was the nation's first Professor of Engineering) and in leading his faculty as the Acting Superintendent. His vision for USMA focused on science, with less attention paid to the general technical education of cadets. Partridge's faculty did not share this vision, which made for a troublesome time. However, after Partridge left the Academy in 1817, he found faculty to support his vision as he established other military colleges and schools, such as Norwich University, VT. Thayer replaced Partridge as Superintendent and built a shared vision with his faculty for a four-year, rigorous, mathematics- and science-based engineering program. Using the model of the École polytechnique in Paris, West Point became a quality engineering and technical college.

Science section room (from Howitzer)

Under the leadership and effective teaching of

Ellicott and the French military engineer Claudius Crozet (see **Honorable Mentions**), USMA's program combined French theory, British practicality, and American ingenuity to establish a new model for undergraduate education. Thayer created a rigorous, disciplined, academic culture that included sections based on ability, cadets graded daily in every subject, competitive class rank system, blackboards used for drill and practice, and cadets reciting on their work in every class. The program required cadets to spend over three hours per day on mathematics during their first two years, three hours per day on science in the third year, and three hours per day of engineering during their last year. The remaining time was spent on other academic topics, as well as conducting practical military exercises and training. It was the first program of its kind in America, but soon West Point graduates were exporting Thayer's academic system to many other schools.

One mechanism for exporting these initiatives was the textbook. Charles Davies was the most prolific textbook author of his day, writing over 35 books from elementary arithmetic to advanced college mathematics. His books were used in schools throughout the country from grade schools to colleges. He had tremendous influence on the educational system of America throughout the 19th century and his books were tremendous promotional instruments for the Academy. After studying from Davies' mathematics textbooks throughout their elementary and secondary school years, many of the brightest boys of the country aspired to attend the Academy. After leaving USMA, Davies became Professor of Mathematics at Columbia College. Edward Courtenay, while not as prolific a writer, produced a high mark of quality in his mathematics and science. His mechanics and calculus textbooks were among the finest in the world. After teaching at West Point, he was recruited by the University of Virginia to replace the distinguished European mathematician J. J. Sylvester. America had produced its own distinguished scientist-mathematician in West Point educated Courtenay.

Building and Maintaining the Thayer Method

Academic Boardroom, showing the carvings of the nine great warriors (from the West Point Howitzer)

"Perhaps the most singular characteristic of the Thayer System was the emphasis on mathematics, science and engineering ... using École polytechnique as a pattern." [13]

Three professors dominated the middle half of the 19th century at the Academy. As a group, they were more powerful than the other professors and superintendents that usually served for short periods. They dominated the decisions of the Academy's governing body of department heads called the Academic Board. All three were products and devotees of the Thayer system. All three saw mathematics, science, and engineering (MSE) as the essence of the Academy and the life of an Army officer. The three were the MSE department heads, **Albert Church (USMA 1828)** in mathematics, **William Bartlett (USMA 1826)** in science (Department of

---

[13] Morrison, *The Best School in the World*, 1986, p. 23.

Natural and Experimental Philosophy), and **Dennis Mahan (USMA 1824)** in engineering. Together they served at the Academy for over 132 years and were heads of their respective departments for a total of 119 years. They promoted the system and insured its stability and well-being. They refined the pedagogy of the Thayer Method (textbooks with exercises, drill problems to work at blackboards, and rigorous written examinations). The external board of examiners was both a motivational and promotional tool that kept the standards high and the program focused. These three professors carefully developed the technical curriculum to match the talents of the students with the needs of the Army and inspired nearly half of the *SCIENTIFIC 200* to pursue careers in science.

Others were equally convinced for the need for a very technical education for West Point educated officers. As indicated in this endorsement from a *Report* in 1834, mathematics laid the foundation, science and engineered capped off the experience: "Mathematics is the study which forms the foundation of the course at the U. S. Military Academy. This is necessary, both to impart to the mind that combined strength and versatility, that peculiar vigour (sic) and rapidity of comparison necessary for military action, and to pave the way for progress in higher military sciences."[14]

Attracting Quality Cadets

For many years, West Point was the only national educational institution and the only place where bright, talented males, who were not wealthy, could afford to go to school. The United States Naval Academy joined this category with its founding in 1845. Since attendance at the Academy was free and cadets received a stipend, West Point was able to attract many of the brightest young men in the country. Congressional support was required for the candidates, which further increased the selectivity of the cadets. Many, especially those from the rural East and frontier West, found the program too difficult and were dismissed for academic failure or resigned on their own volition, suffering from an overdose of technical subjects. Those that did survive the rigors of their educational excursion were the finest students in America. These bright, practical, hard-working educational pioneers helped establish the culture of the Academy, while receiving the finest technical education in the country. For all 200 years of USMA's existence, it has been blessed with quality students, who were not only talented, but also hard-working and dedicated.

The Academy, however, shared in the nation's deficiency by not seeking diversity. The first African-American graduate was **Henry O. Flipper (USMA 1877)**, and there were very few black graduates until the latter half of the 20th century. Similarly, women were not part of the Corps of Cadets until 1976.

Producing Technological Leaders

West Point graduates became leaders in many technical areas and organizations. The U.S. needed engineers and scientists who could lead its development in the Industrial Age. Early graduates like **William McNeill (USMA 1817)**, railroad engineer; **George Washington**

---

[14] *Report of the Committee on Military Affairs*, 1834, found in the *Annual Report of the Superintendent*, 1896, p. 47.

Whistler (USMA 1819), railroad engineer; **George Sears Greene (USMA 1823)**, engineer for the Croton Aqueduct; **Andrew Humphreys (USMA 1831)**, engineer for canals and rivers; and **John Barnard (USMA 1833)**, Cumberland Road engineer; were among the many graduates who built America's infrastructure and led the way for the development of the American continent. The accomplishments of West Point graduates were found in many areas of applied science and engineering. Some fields where West Pointers excelled were surveying borders, coasts, and the geological characteristics of the country; constructing buildings, roads, fortifications, harbors, canals, bridges, and railroads; and designing transportation systems, weapons systems, and manufacturing systems. These types of technological contributions have continued over the decades. As President Theodore Roosevelt indicated at the Centennial of USMA in 1902, "West Pointers have risen to the first rank in all the occupations of civil life."[15]

USMA's Influence in Mathematics, Science, and Engineering

West Point-educated officers were not required to serve in the Army during the first half of the 19th century. Many of the most scholarly graduates taught at West Point immediately after graduation and then resigned from the Army to teach at other schools. Several had opportunities to start new MSE programs. Others became presidents or deans of schools. Most brought as much of West Point's program as they could with them, in terms of textbooks, courses, programs, standards, and academic culture. Many were on a crusade to spread the education that they had received at West Point to the new schools of America (especially the land-grant colleges established by the Morrill Act of 1862). Many were hired with that expressed purpose. West Point's influential role is demonstrated in the following chronology:

1802: U. S. had 22 colleges (all in liberal arts) when USMA becomes the nation's first engineering school.

1830: U. S. had 56 colleges (all except 2 – USMA and Rensselaer Polytechnic Institute – are in liberal arts). 9 USMA graduates are Professors of Mathematics at other schools. The spread of practical mathematics, applied science, and productive engineering had begun in earnest by 1830.

1832: USMA's Board of Visitors expresses concern about the effects of losing its graduates: "As soon as an officer renders himself useful and respectable at West Point, he is taken away by a higher inducement offered by some literary institution."[16]

1840: U. S. had 79 colleges (several are engineering schools). 29 USMA graduates are MSE professors.

1850: 6 of the 36 mathematicians listed in the *Dictionary of American Biography* (DAB) are from West Point; 21 of the DAB scientists were educated at West Point.[17]

Old West Point Library (from Howitzer)

---

[15] *Centennial*, p. 23.
[16] *Board of Visitors Report*, 1832.

1860: U.S. had 203 colleges, and 86 USMA graduates are MSE professors.

1900: U.S. technical programs had expanded to 45 colleges that taught engineering.

USMA's Library

Before Thayer became Superintendent in 1817, he toured several technical and military institutions in Europe to assess what features USMA could use to advantage. One of Thayer's accomplishments on that trip was procuring numerous MSE books from Europe. Thayer's procurement included over 1000 of the finest books available at that time. These books provided a solid foundation in the technical subjects for the USMA library to build upon. The volumes ranged from encyclopedias to mathematics texts, from works of military arts to engineering. During his years as Superintendent, Thayer continued his commitment to the development of the scientific library. When he left the Academy in 1833, the West Point Library was well supplied to support the technological studies of the most advanced technical program in America.

Science demonstration (from Howitzer)

Facilities and Laboratories

While the academic buildings and science facilities did not always reach the level of outstanding, they were more than adequate during the past 200 years. This gave USMA and its cadets a tremendous advantage. Beginning with the first science instruments brought by Jared Mansfield in 1813 to the establishment of the West Point Observatory in 1842, the Academy, with support of the Army and Congress, supported the educational needs of the cadets and faculty. Laboratory rooms with complete sets of demonstration and experimentation apparatus were the norm. Supplies were maintained, and the equipment kept in working order. Science was an obvious, visible, high-priority component of the Academy's academic culture.

Curricular Development

After Thayer studied the educational systems of Europe, he reorganized the Academy with elements of the École polytechnique, which had been established by Napoleon and ably systematized by scientist Gaspard Monge. Thayer's USMA MSE program was initially restricted only by the quality of students and the limited experience and credentials of the faculty. America did not have the

West Point Observatory in 1922

[17] DAB analysis. In addition, considerable data on the characteristics of American scientists are provided in Bruce, "Statistical Profile," pp. 63-94 in Daniels, *Nineteenth-Century American Science*, 1972.

pool of scientists that the French had available, so Thayer was forced to create his own capable scientific faculty. Each class and each generation of graduates had to be better and more advanced than the previous ones. The best graduates stayed at West Point to teach and bootstrap their replacements. From 1818 to 1827, some upperclass cadets taught cadets in their first two years (primarily mathematics). Among **The 200** who did this were: **Richard Delafield (USMA 1818), Edward Ross (USMA 1821), Alfred Mordecai (USMA 1823), George Green (USMA 1823), Dennis Mahan (USMA 1824), Robert Parrot (USMA 1824), Alexander Bache (USMA 1825), Alexander Bowman (USMA 1825), William Bartlett (USMA 1826), Thomas Cram (USMA 1826), Robert E. Lee (USMA 1829),** and **Catharinus Buckingham (USMA 1829).**[18]

From the necessity to bridge the enormous knowledge gap of incoming cadets to the fundamentals of engineering, USMA's curriculum was very heavy in applied mathematics. From Thayer's time until the late 1800's, cadets took the equivalent of 54 credit hours of mathematics.   The mathematical topics covered were algebra, trigonometry, geometry, descriptive geometry (engineering drawing), analytic geometry, and calculus. The science courses were mechanics, electricity, magnetism, optics, astronomy, chemistry, geology, and mineralogy. In engineering, the course content included fortifications, mines, architecture, civil engineering, stone cutting, machines (beginnings of mechanical engineering), and military strategy.   Over the years, the entering cadets became better prepared and fewer of the elementary mathematics and science subjects were needed to be covered at the Academy.

The following chronology highlights the events that affected the USMA's MSE curriculum and summarizes the courses in the MSE program at the time.

1802-1816: Hutton's *Course of Mathematics* covered algebra, geometry, and surveying. Flexible time was allowed to present some additional engineering and problem-based topics.

1817: Thayer became Superintendent and began his curricular reform. The following summarizes the Thayer approach: "Perhaps the most singular characteristic of the Thayer System was the emphasis on mathematics, science and engineering ... using École polytechnique as a pattern." [19]

1817-1820: Descriptive geometry and spherical trigonometry were added to the program. 1st year courses: algebra, geometry. 2nd year courses: trigonometry, surveying, conic sections, descriptive geometry, fluxions/calculus.   3rd year courses: Natural and Experimental Philosophy (mechanics, optics, and astronomy), chemistry, and topography. 4th year courses: Engineering and Science of War (mines, fortification, machines, stonecutting, and architecture). While Enfield's *Institutes of Natural Philosophy* was the primary science textbook, most of the other textbooks were in French, since textbooks in English were not sufficient. Cadets studied French in the afternoons in order to help them read their technical books.

---

[18] Rickey's website: http://dean.usma.edu/math/people/rickey/dms/Math-Teachers.html
[19] Morrison, *Best School in the World*, 1986, p. 23.

1823-1837: 1ˢᵗ year courses: algebra, geometry, trigonometry. 2ⁿᵈ year courses: descriptive geometry; conics; perspectives, shades and shadows; analytical geometry; calculus; surveying. **Charles Davies (USMA 1815)** and **Edward Courtenay (USMA 1821)** began translating MSE books into English and writing their own textbooks. This *Americanization* of the textbook made them influential authors. In the sciences, electricity and magnetism entered the 3ʳᵈ year program, and mineralogy and geology were added to the 4ᵗʰ year program. The science program temporarily added Gregory's *Mechanics* as a textbook, before moving to higher-level French books as texts during Courtenay's tenure.

1835: President Andrew Jackson ordered four academically dismissed cadets to return to USMA, then called West Point "the best school in the world" and states "the Military Academy has exercised the happiest influence upon the moral and intellectual character of our army."[20] Jackson and the Academy continued to argue over standards for admission and retention. Over 78% of all academic dismissals in the 19ᵗʰ century came from failures in mathematics courses. Without proper preparation, which was practically not existent in the rural and frontier schools of America, the West Point curriculum was too challenging for even the brightest frontier students.

1854-1861: A 5-year program was established by Superintendent **Robert E. Lee (USMA 1829)** to add the study of humanities and military subjects. This had no effects on the MSE courses, which still dominated the curriculum (71% of cadet time was still devoted to MSE study). Chemistry was taught in the 3ʳᵈ year. All the textbooks in mechanics and science were authored by Bartlett, and all the engineering texts were authored by Mahan. Ordnance and Gunnery were added to the curriculum, including a course on pyrotechny. The Practical and Military Engineering program included signal telegraphy.

1881-1902: 1ˢᵗ year courses: algebra, geometry, trigonometry, surveying, analytical geometry. 2ⁿᵈ year courses: descriptive geometry; calculus; determinants; least squares; shades, shadows, and perspectives, and topography. **Edgar Bass (USMA 1868)** became the Mathematics Department Head, replacing Church. Most of the books in mathematics were authored by Church, and Bass's calculus books eventually replaced Church's books. In total, there were 660 classroom hours of mathematics. **Junius Wheeler's (USMA 1855)** books began replacing Mahan's in 1878, and **Peter Michie's (USMA 1863)** books replaced the science books of Bartlett beginning in 1887. The program in Chemistry, Mineralogy, and Geology was expanded.

**Robert E. Lee
(USMA 1829)**

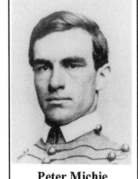

**Peter Michie
(USMA 1863)**

---

[20] Morrison, *The Best School in the World*, 1986, p. 23.

Samuel Tillman's (USMA 1869) chemistry books began appearing in the 1880s, and **James Mercur's (USMA 1866)** engineering series began at the same time.

1902: Surveying and descriptive geometry were dropped. 180 hours of mathematics were lost to modern languages, resulting in 480 classroom hours of mathematics and classes being reduced to 80 minutes.

Outside influences (political and military based) periodically affected the Academy's program. The following executive inquiry in 1908 (despite the curricular change in 1902) demonstrated President Roosevelt's concerns, which are similar to the earlier ones of Andrew Jackson, with an additional military perspective:

"To the Secretary of War: It seems to me a very great misfortune to lay so much stress

Olivier String Models used in Mathematics Department

upon mathematics in the curriculum at West Point and fail to have languages taught in accordance with the best modern conversational methods. I should like to have this matter taken up seriously. I have several times called attention to it, but nothing has been done. Mathematical training is a necessary thing for an engineer or an artilleryman, doubtless; but I esteem it of literally no importance for the cavalryman or infantryman. If tomorrow I had to choose officers from the regular army for important positions in the event of war, I would care no more for their mathematical training than for their knowledge of whist or chess. A man who learns a language by studying a book, but cannot speak it, loses at least half the benefit obtainable. I would like a full report on this matter."[21]

1912: 110 classroom hours returned to mathematics (despite the presidential decree), resulting in 590 classroom hours of mathematics. The science program in the 3rd year included new, modern topics in sound, light, and mechanics, along with classic topics in

Mathematics class recitation (from Howitzer)

physics and astronomy. The Chemistry Department's science program included heat, geology, minerals, rocks, electricity, magnetism, and chemistry. Surveying was taught by the Practical and Military Engineering Department. The courses in the Engineering Department included civil engineering, field fortifications, permanent fortifications, siege works, elements of strategy, and the campaigns of Gettysburg. Books by **Gustav Fiebeger (USMA 1879**) began replacing those of Mercur.

---

[21] President Theodore Roosevelt [letter in the Mathematics Department at USMA]

1920s: Overall cadet class time in the MSE program was cut by a third. The topics stayed the same, only the time in class on each subject was reduced. This was referred to as Superintendent **Douglas MacArthur's (USMA 1903)** liberalization of the program. More responsibility was placed on learning outside of class, and more demanding and longer homework assignments were instituted.

1947-1955: The old riding stable was converted into the Thayer Hall academic building, with modern classrooms equipped with overhead projectors. All faculty

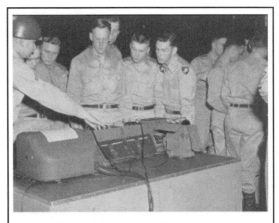

Cadets working on early government computer (from Howitzer)

members were educated with advanced degrees from civilian universities and a computer center was established at West Point in the 1950s. **Charles Nicholas (USMA 1925)** becomes Head of the Mathematics Department. His compre-hensive and challenging textbook was used for the entire core mathematics program.

Scientific Textbooks

USMA underwent several changes in its use of academic textbooks. In the first era (1802-1832), the European (British and French) influence was predominant. In the second era (1832-1900), the internal USMA authors dominated the program, becoming the textbooks writers that influenced academic programs around the country. In the last era (1900-present), external authors gave the academic program a more modern and diverse perspective. MSE textbooks used at the Academy and written by West Point graduates and faculty, generally during the second era, are listed in the following table:

Author	Textbook	Dates of Use
Crozet	Descriptive Geometry (American)	1825-1832
Crozet	Perspectives, Shades, & Shadows	1825-1832
Davies	Descriptive Geometry	1832-1864
Davies	Perspectives, Shades, & Shadows	1832-1866
Davies	Mensuration	1832-1839
Courtenay	Mechanics	1833-1850
Mahan	Treatise on Field Fortifications	1836-1879
Mahan	Civil Engineering	1837-1875
Davies	Bourdon's Algebra	1839-1900
Davies	Legendre's Geometry	1839-1905
Davies	Legendre's Trigonometry	1839-1881
Davies	Surveying	1839-1900
Davies	Calculus	1839-1843
Davies	Analytic Geometry	1839-1852
Bartlett	Acoustics and Optics	1839-1887
Mahan	Descriptive Geometry for Fortifications	1841-1900
Bartlett	Synthetic Mechanics	1850-1853

Mahan	Permanent Fortifications	1850-1879
Church	Analytic Geometry	1852-1899
Bartlett	Analytic Mechanics	1853-1887
Bartlett	Spherical Astronomy	1855-1888
Church	Descriptive Geometry	1864-1920
Church	Shades, Shadows & Perspective	1866-1929
Mahan	Industrial Drawing	1870-1880
Wheeler	Permanent Fortification	1876-1887
Wheeler	Civil Engineering	1876-1896
Wheeler	Elements of the Art and Science of War	1880-1889
Church	Plane Spherical Trigonometry	1881-1888
Knight	Determinants (Pamphlet)	1881-1887
Tillman	Heat	1887-1920
Tillman	Chemistry	1886-1920
Peck	Determinants	1887-1900
Michie	Analytic Mechanics	1887-1914
Michie	Wave Motion Relating to Sound and Light	1884-1905
Mercur	Permanent Fortification	1887-1900
Mercur	Elements of the Art of War	1889-1900
Ludlow	Trigonometry	1888-1908
Bass	Differential Calculus	1889-1908
Michie & Harlow	Astronomy	1895-1905
Tillman	Minerals and Rocks	1895-1920
Ludlow	Logarithm Tables	1892-1906
Fiebeger	Civil Engineering	1901-1922
Fiebeger	Field Fortifications	1899-1922
Fiebeger	Permanent Fortifications	1900-1918
Fiebeger	Military Engineering	1920-1922
Pillsbury	Linear Perspective	1911-1920
Gordon	Mechanics	1914-1920
Yates	Differential Equations (preprint of 1952 version)	1950-1962
Nicholas	Calculus	1962-1972

Introduction of Pedagogy and Technology

West Point's philosophy of active teaching and practical problem solving lent itself to the utilization of various educational reforms and technologies over the years. Sometimes West Point was on the leading edge of these initiatives. The following list includes some of the new educational technologies implemented in the Academy's classrooms and provides the dates when they were first used: chalk and blackboard (1801), drawing portfolios (1813), Thayer's interactive daily teaching methods (1817), American textbooks with numerous examples and exercises (1832), notebooks and engineering projects (1820-1835), demonstration apparatus in mechanics, hydrostatics, and optics (1829), Olivier string models (1830-1870), spectrometers and compound microscopes (1850), slide rule (1944), overhead projectors (1947), mechanical computers (1947), main-frame computer (1958), personal calculators (1975), personal computers (1985), and portable personal computers (laptops) (2002).

Academic Standards and Competitions

While West Point made its mark in the early 19th century as a rigorous, demanding academic institution, that reputation did not endure into the 20th century. Criticisms over a stagnant, military-application dominated program with an inbred faculty became common from academe. West Point's reaction at various times was to insulate itself even further from its critics. Through all this, successful outcomes in the form of productive and competent graduates, as evidenced by the people biographed in this volume, never wavered.

West Point Library in 1950s (from Howitzer)

When an opportunity presented itself to test the quality of USMA's system, the Academy's leaders took advantage. In the spring of 1933, West Point entered a competition in mathematics. After USMA had defeated Harvard in football the previous fall, a remark from President Lowell of Harvard to Superintendent William Connor (USMA 1897) led the two schools to arrange a mathematics challenge match with competing teams composed of 10 second-year students. Army was the home team, so the Harvard competitors traveled by train to West Point. The competitors took a test written by the President of the Mathematical Association of America. This academic competition was reported in the sports section of the *New York Times*. The subtitle of the "Sports of the Times," column by John Kieran on 18 May 1933 read "The Coordinate Clash, or Block that Abscissa!" The article was a humorous analogy of the mathematics competition with a football game. The *New York Times* later reported the results in sports headlines: "Army Mathletes defeat Harvard." Connor reflected the Academy's pride in this victory with his letter to Mathematics Department Head **Harris Jones (USMA April 1917)** and team coach **Charles Nicholas (USMA 1925):** "I congratulate you very sincerely upon the results which for the first time give me concrete backing to the belief that I have always held, that is, that our instruction methods at West Point were up to date and on a par with those of other similar institutions." Echoing in this same vein was the Army Chief of Staff who had recently reformed the program at the Academy, **Douglas MacArthur (USMA 1903)**. West Point had proven its standards were still high and its product, scientifically educated cadets capable of solving technical problems, was a valuable natural resource.

The Genius of West Point

While West Point claimed a unique place as America's leading undergraduate technical school during the 19th century, much of the same special traits continued into the 20th century. Professor Charles Larned (USMA 1870) explained these traits exactly 100 years ago: "The genesis of a great school is a gradual process depending mainly upon principle, personnel, and environment. In all of these the Military Academy has been fortunate. The basic principle of its purpose and methods; the personality of the men guiding its formation and early operation; its ideal location for its special functions -- all have been remarkable and admirable."[22]

References:

Albree, J., Arney, D. C., and Rickey, F., *A Station Favorable to the Pursuits of Science: Primary Material in the History of Mathematics at the United States Military Academy*, American Mathematical Society, Providence, 2000.

Ambrose, Stephen, *Duty, Honor, Country; a History of West Point*, Johns Hopkins Press, Baltimore, 1966.

Annual Report of the Superintendent of the United States Military Academy, Government Printing Office, Washington, DC, 1896.

Arney, D. C., "Army Beats Harvard Twice," *Math Horizons*, Sep 1994, pp. 14-17

Bartlett, B. W., "Physics at the United States Military Academy," *American Journal of Physics*, vol. 12, 1944, pp. 78-91.

Bruce, R., "A Statistical Profile of American Scientists" *Nineteenth-Century American Science: A Reappraisal*, Northwestern University Press, Evanston, 1972.

Cajori, F., *The Teaching and History of Mathematics in the United States*, Government Printing Office, Washington, 1890.

Centennial of the United States Military Academy at West Point, New York, Government Printing Office, Washington, 1904.

Cullum, George W., *The Official Register of the Officers & Cadets of the US Military Academy*, West Point, NY 1841-1870, 1911-1915.

Daniels, George, *Nineteenth-Century American Science: A Reappraisal*, Northwestern University Press, Evanston, 1972.

---

[22] *Centennial*, p. 467.

Dupuy, Ernest, *Where They Have Trod; the West Point Tradition in American Life*, Fredrick A. Stokes Co., New York, 1940.

Dupuy, Ernest, *Sylvanus Thayer: Father of Technology in the United States*, USMA, 1958.

Elliott, Clark, *The American Scientist, 1800-1863, his Origin, Career, and Interests*, Ph.D. Dissertation, Case Western Reserve, Cleveland, 1970.

Endler, James R., *Other Leaders, Other Heroes*, Prager, Westport, CT, 1998.

Forman, Sidney, *West Point; a History of the United States Military Academy*, Columbia University Press, New York, 1950.

Hoskins, Keith, "Textbooks and the mathematisation of American reality: the role of Charles Davies and the US Military Academy at West Point," *Paradigm*, May 1994 (11-41).

McMaster, Richard K., "West Point's Contributions to Education, 1802-1952," McMath Printing Co, El Paso, 1951.

Molloy, P., *Technical education and the young republic: West Point as America's Ecole Polytechnique, 1802-1833*, Ph.D. Dissertation, Brown University, 1976.

Morrison, J. L., *The Best School in the World,; West Point, the Pre-Civil War Years, 1833-1866*, Kent State University Press, Kent, OH, 1986.

Morrison, J. L., "Educating the Civil War Generals: West Point, 1833-1861," *Military Affairs*, September 1974, pp. 108-111.

Official Register of the Officers and Cadets of the United States Military Academy, 1818-1899, United States Military Academy Printing Office, West Point, NY, 1818-1899.

Register of Graduates, Association of Graduates, United States Military Academy, West Point, 2000.

Ross, William L., "Early Influences of the US Military Academy on Engineering , Technology and Engineering Graphics Education in the US" *ASEE Annual Conference Proceedings*, 1991, pp. 1603–1606.

Sesquicentennial of the United States Military Academy, Government Printing Office, West Point, 1952

Streett, W.B., "The Military Influence on American Engineering Education" *Cornell Quarterly*, Winter 1993.

Streett, W.B., "West Point and the Rise of American Science in the 19th Century," *Assembly*, Nov/Dec 1996.

Army Corps of Engineers

The United States Army engineers began work in 1775, serving on General George Washington's staff during the Revolutionary War. In 1779, Congress created a separate Corps of Engineers in the Army. In 1794, Congress combined the two most technical branches by establishing the Corps of Artillerists and Engineers, and then in 1802 separated the two, re-forming the Corps of Engineers. This action was concurrent with the establishment of the United States Military Academy at West Point, NY, by the order of President Thomas Jefferson. Jefferson foresaw the engineer officers produced at the Academy as valuable resources to build the country's infrastructure. Because of the engineering focus at the Academy, the Superintendent of the Military Academy was an engineer officer until 1866. The first Superintendent of the Academy, Jonathan Williams (see **Honorable Mentions**), was also the Chief of Army Engineers.

From its beginning, the Corps of Engineers contributed to both military construction and public works. Army engineers supervised construction of coastal fortifications, mapped the American frontier, and built the nation's transportation system. For 25 years, the Corps of Topographical Engineers (see the next section for its history) were a separate branch, but generally topographic work has been performed by the Corps of Engineers. The Corps of Engineers have also been involved in constructing lighthouses, canals, harbor facilities, and navigation channels. The Corps' fortifications duties grew considerably during and after the War of 1812. Williams and **Joseph Swift (USMA 1802)** expanded and improved the fortifications protecting New York Harbor. Seeing the success of fortification defenses during the War of 1812, the United States developed large masonry fortifications at strategic locations to provide defense against attack from enemy ships and land forces. After the war, the rest of the Army shrank, but the size of the Engineer Corps remained large to perform all the constructions duties needed by the Army and the public. Congress doubled the size of the Corps in 1838 to keep up with the need to build more infrastructure and push civilization west. The fortifications built by Army engineers securely defended the nation until the latter part of the 19th century when rifled artillery ended the utility of these massive defensive structures.

The early engineer officers provided America with a solid infrastructure of buildings, roads, canals, rivers, and aqueducts. Since travel was so difficult through the forests, rivers and canals provided the primary routes for commercial and passenger travel. In 1824, the Supreme Court ruled that federal interest involved interstate commerce, including river and canal travel; therefore, Army engineers were able to work on the nation's transportation system. Army engineers removed sandbars and obstacles to improve navigation on the Ohio and Mississippi Rivers. Similar projects on other rivers soon followed. This work was important for America to develop commerce. The Board of Internal Improvements, run by the Corps of Engineers, coordinated surveys and the building of canals, roads, and railroads. Innovative work to deepen the nation's rivers continued after the Civil War as **Quincy Gillmore (USMA 1849)** converted a steamer for suction dredging, which was the first hydraulic dredge. **William Merrill (USMA 1859)** developed a system of dams on the Ohio River to allow passage of coal barges. Congress approved Merrill's plan, and the Corps of

Engineers constructed the world's largest locks and dams. These locks were some of the first in the country to use concrete instead of stone. This type of navigation improvement work on many of the nation's major rivers continued throughout the 19th century. Army engineers were also involved in the construction and maintenance of several valuable canals. Several prominent Army engineers worked on the Muscle Shoals Canal after the Civil War. This part of the Tennessee River in AL was restricted by a series of rapids, shoals, and shallow water. An earlier canal had been attempted, but a new canal was needed. **William King (USMA 1863), William Marshall (USMA 1868), and George Goethals (USMA 1880)** were involved in this effort. Goethals designed a lock with a lift of 26 feet, the largest in the United States at that time. This success further built Goethals' reputation, which later led to his assignment to build the Panama Canal.

George Goethals (USMA 1880)

The Corps of Engineers worked on flood control after the Civil War, particularly on the Mississippi. In 1879, Congress created the Mississippi River Commission to improve navigation and flood control of the great river. The commission decided to use levees to protect the lower Mississippi Valley and oversaw their construction. The work on the Mississippi River was a substantial part of the Corps effort. The great river that drains nearly one half of the United States needed constant watch to protect the residents in its flood zone and to control its fertile, but sometimes dangerous, waters.

Army engineers performed survey and charting work. Two significant survey projects were located on the Great Lakes and the Mississippi Delta. The charting of the Great Lakes was critical to improve navigation. Topographers began the survey in 1823. **William G. Williams (USMA 1824)**, who had constructed harbor improvements on Lake Erie, later headed the survey from his office in Buffalo. The survey was challenging, with over 6,000 miles of shoreline on America's side of the lakes. The surveyors charted the shoreline; measured the discharge of rivers; located shoals; developed detailed navigation charts and maps; and marked points of danger. The Mississippi Delta survey was also a challenge. In addition to the charting and construction, engineer officers performed research in hydraulic engineering. Congress supported a proposal for a 20-foot deep navigation channel to the Gulf, and Army engineers **Andrew Humphreys (USMA 1831)** and **Henry Abbot (USMA 1854)** went to work on this project. Their 1861 report contained data on river flow, channel cross sections, and geological features. They developed a formula to measure the flow of water in rivers. Their work was a starting point for other engineers. Further research led to many important discoveries about hydrology and water flow in large rivers. Their report gained the attention of engineers around the world.

Congress also tasked the Army engineers to construct roadways for commercial traffic. The most famous and challenging project was the Cumberland Road that was built between 1811 and 1841. It went from Cumberland, MD all the way to Vandalia, IL, crossing the Appalachian Mountains. In constructing the Cumberland Road, the Corps performed innovative tunneling, substantial digging, and superb bridge building. In Pennsylvania, **Richard Delafield (USMA 1818)** built the first bridge in America with an iron superstructure.

Engineer officers also performed considerable railroad construction work. Liberal policies on leaves of absences were in effect so that Army officers could work on the railroads. They surveyed railroad routes and constructed the bridges and railways. In 1828, **William McNeill (USMA 1817)** supervised the construction of Baltimore and Ohio Railroad line. In 1829, **George Whistler (USMA 1819)** joined this work. By 1830, several more officers worked on railroads. In the 1850s, the quest for a rail link to the Pacific involved several Army engineers as they selected and evaluated the four possible routes. This effort was so substantial that it led to the gathering a great deal of scientific information.

During the middle of the 19th century, engineer officers were employed in building lighthouses. Work on the ocean shores often involved substantial challenges. In 1852, Congress instituted the Lighthouse Board to coordinate lighthouse construction, and engineer officers supervised the construction of dozens of lighthouses along the nation's coasts and on the shores of the Great Lakes. The Corps of Engineers also constructed public buildings and monuments in Washington, DC. In 1853, the responsibility for building the water supply system for Washington, DC was given to **Montgomery Meigs (USMA 1836)**. His work included two large aqueducts and many miles of piping. During the last half of the 19th century, the Corps completed the Washington Monument and numerous structures including the Executive Office Building, the Lincoln Memorial, the Library of Congress, and the Government Printing Office. **Thomas Casey (USMA 1852)** was able to rescue the Washington Monument from collapse by placing a sturdier foundation under the partially completed monument.

Cadets building pontoon bridge in Practical Military Engineering class

Army engineers played significant combat service roles in the Mexican and Civil Wars. Several engineers gained renown for their combat service. **Joseph Totten (USMA 1805)** directed the siege of Veracruz, and **William G. Williams (USMA 1824)**, who had earlier directed the Great Lakes survey, served as chief engineer for General Zachary Taylor until Williams' death in the battle of Monterey. During the Civil War, engineers built numerous bridges (many were portable pontoon bridges), constructed fortifications, and destroyed enemy supply routes. The 2,170-foot pontoon bridge, built across the James River in 1864 under the supervision of **James Duane (USMA 1848)**, was the longest floating bridge erected before World War II. Drawn from the top of their West Point classes, the engineer officers included several successful military leaders.

Among the famous combat leaders were John McClellan (USMA 1826), **Henry Halleck (USMA 1839)**, George Meade (USMA 1835), **Robert E. Lee (USMA 1829)**, Joseph Johnston (USMA 1829), and **Pierre G. T. Beauregard (USMA 1838)**.

Effective leadership of the Corps of Engineers was important for its growth and mission accomplishment. From 1812 to 1992, there were 41 Chiefs of Army Engineers and all but two were West Point graduates. Most were at the very top of their graduating class and some also served as Superintendent of the Academy. A few examples of the special people in *THE SCIENTIFIC 200* involved in the technical leadership of the Corps of Engineers are highlighted here. **Joseph Totten (USMA 1805)** was a regent for the Smithsonian Institution and a founding member of the National Academy of Sciences. **Richard Delafield (USMA 1818)** was the observer of combat engineering operations during the Crimean War and served as Superintendent of the Academy. **John Newton (USMA 1842)** was famous for blowing up rocks at Hell Gate in New York Harbor with many tons of dynamite. **Henry Robert (USMA 1857)** was Chief of Engineers in 1901 and oversaw the planning and construction of the Galveston Seawall after its destruction due to a hurricane. **John Wilson (USMA 1860)** and **George Gillespie (USMA 1862)** won the Medal of Honor for their combat service. **William Bixby (USMA 1873)** was Chief of Engineers from 1910 to 1913 and oversaw the raising of the battleship Maine. **Hiram Chittenden (USMA 1884)** supervised the construction of roads, bridges, and aqueducts in Yellowstone National Park and became an expert on flood control. **William Gribble (USMA 1941)** was Chief of Engineers from 1973 to 1976 and constructed nuclear power plants.

The Army Corps of Engineers built the nation's infrastructure, the foundation of America's prosperity. In addition to helping fight wars and building splendid facilities, the Corps contributed greatly to the advancement of the world's science and technology. West Point's role in providing highly qualified engineers and effective leaders for this effort was essential to the Corps' success.

References:

Goetzmann, William, *Army Exploration in the American West, 1803 1863*, Yale University Press, New Haven, 1959.

Hill, Forest. *Roads, Rails & Waterways: The Army Engineers and Early Transportation*, University of Oklahoma Press, Norman, 1957.

Leyson, Burr, *The Army Engineers in Review*, E. P. Dutton, New York, 1943.

Maass, Arthur, *Muddy Waters: the Army Engineers and the Nation's Rivers*, Harvard University Press, Cambridge, 1951.

Moore, Jamie and Moore, Dorothy. *The Army Corps of Engineers and the Evolution of Federal Flood Plain Management Policy*, University of Colorado Institute of Behavioral Science, Boulder, 1989.

Reuss, Martin and Hendricks, Charles, "U.S. Army Corps of Engineers Brief History," http://wwww.hq.usace.army.mil/history.

Schubert, Frank, editor, *The Nation Builders: A Sesquicentennial History of the Corps of Topographical Engineers, 1838 1863*, Office of History, U. S. Army Corps of Engineers, Fort Belvoir, VA, 1988.

Shallat, Todd, *Structures in the Stream: Water, Science, and the Rise of the U. S. Army Corps of Engineers*, University of Texas Press, Austin, 1994.

Corps of Topographical Engineers

Topographical engineers began in 1813 to conduct surveys for military purposes and to explore routes westward across the continent. The Topographical Bureau was established in 1818 under the Office of the Chief Engineer, with Isaac Roberdeau designated as the Topographical Engineer. He had a small cadre of officers to perform the assigned duties. In 1831, the Topographical Bureau was given responsibility for civil works projects in addition to their military functions. In 1838, the Army instituted a separate Corps of Topographical Engineers for civil works projects, under the new position of Chief of the Topographical Engineers. This structure remained in place for 25 years until, in 1863, the Corps of Topographical Engineers consolidated back with the Corps of Engineers. During the 25-year existence of the Corps of Topographical Engineers, it contributed greatly to the development of America. Its duties included public works, exploration, Coast Survey and lake survey assistance, and lighthouse construction. In performing these duties, the Topographical Engineers developed a force of bright, capable, scientific-minded officers, who were leaders of American engineering and scientific efforts.

As prescribed in 1813, the duties of the topographical engineers were "to make such surveys and exhibit such delineations as the commanding generals shall direct; to make plans of all military positions which the army may occupy and of their respective vicinities, indicating the various roads, rivers, creeks, ravines, hills, woods, and villages to be found therein; to accompany all reconnoitering parties sent out to obtain intelligence of the movements of the enemy or of his positions; to make sketches of their routes, accompanied by written notices of everything worthy of observation therein; to keep a journal of every day's movement when the army is in march, noticing the variety of ground, of buildings, of culture, and distances, and state of roads between common points throughout the march of the day; and lastly, to exhibit the positions of contending armies on the fields of battle, and the dispositions made, either for attack or defense."[23] In short, the *topo engineers* or in their own jargon *topogs* were designated the surveyors, mathematicians, scientists, and engineers of their units.

A Board of Engineers for Fortifications organized in 1816 to select sites for forts, and the Topographical Engineers performed the surveys. Roberdeau, **John Abert (USMA 1811)**, and **Hartman Bache (USMA 1818)** were detailed to the Board as surveyors. In 1816, topographic engineer Stephen Long began a series of explorations in the West. His earliest surveys were of the Illinois, Fox, Wisconsin, Mississippi, and Minnesota Rivers in connection with the establishment of forts. During 1819 to 1820, he conducted an expedition

[23] Beers, "A History of the U.S. Topographical Engineers, 1818-1863".

to the Rocky Mountains. The Corps was limited to just ten officers, which made for busy times and many unfulfilled missions. As topo engineers retired, new officers were appointed to this competitive branch. All the new topo engineers were graduates of West Point.

The Board for Internal Improvements formed to provide surveys, plans, and estimates for roads and canals. This resulted in even more duties for the overworked Topographical Engineers. In 1824, several survey parties were engaged on these types of internal improvements. There were so many requests for topographic services that the 10 officers, along with supplements of officers from other branches and civilian engineers, were still unable to meet the demands. This demand resulted in recommendations for expansion or for formation of an organization similar to the Corps of Engineers. Abert urged the Secretary of War to establish a separate Corps of Topographical Engineers. The changes sought by Abert were soon accomplished. In 1831, the Topographical Bureau became an independent office directly responsible to the Secretary of War. In addition to the 10 Topographical Engineers, 12 civilian engineers were hired and 30 officers were formerly detailed from the artillery and infantry to the Topographic Bureau.

Cadets in surveying class on The Plain

This group of topographical engineers became engaged in numerous civil works projects. Surveys were made of rivers, roads, canals, railroads, and harbors in all parts of the country. After these surveys were completed, the Corps of Engineers carried out construction projects for the improvement of rivers and the construction of roads. In Washington, a cadre of Topographical Engineers built an aqueduct over the Potomac River. **William Turnbull (USMA 1819)** was in charge of the project from 1832 to 1843. Topographical Engineers assisted the Coast Survey with its work. **William H. Swift (USMA 1819)** directly assisted the Survey's Superintendent Ferdinand Hassler. Other officers who served on the Survey over the years were: Joseph Johnston (USMA 1829), **Andrew Humphreys (USMA 1831)**, and **Thomas Cram (USMA 1826)**. **Hartman Bache (USMA 1818)** conducted numerous surveys and designed lighthouses for Delaware Bay.

Several Topographical Engineers saw combat support service in the Seminole War. In 1837, Washington Hood compiled a map from data on hand in the Topographical Bureau. Throughout the war, more topographical information of the area was obtained and new maps were produced. After several years, a topographical map of FL was prepared by John Mackay and Jacob Blake. Another map was compiled by John McClellan and Humphreys in 1843. In 1845, **William Franklin (USMA 1843)** improved on that map. During 1845 to 1847, Hartman Bache and others surveyed the reefs of FL, which added considerably to the geographical knowledge of the area.

Abert continued to lobby for a separate Corps of Topographical Engineers, and it finally was accomplished through a law in 1838 to increase the size of the Army and create a separate Corps of Topographical Engineers. The law gave the branch one colonel, one lieutenant colonel, four majors, ten captains, ten first lieutenants, and ten second lieutenants. Most of the new appointments were graduates of USMA who had already performed topographic duties. The new Corps was responsible for all civil works. Appropriations by Congress enabled public works to increase in 1852. The Corps of Engineers were in charge of improvements on the Atlantic and Gulf coasts, while the Corps of Topographical Engineers controlled those on the Great Lakes and western rivers. The Topographical Engineers maintained several field offices. Stephen Long, who remained in charge of improvements on the western rivers, was located in St. Louis. The Office of the Tennessee River Improvements was in Knoxville. The office for works on Lakes Michigan and St. Clair was in Chicago. The projects on Lakes Erie, Ontario, and Champlain were supervised by William Turnbull from his office in Oswego, NY. Numerous important surveys of the Great Lakes were performed. The development of commerce on the lakes compelled the government to provide charts for safe navigation. Systematic surveying began in 1841 by Williams and Franklin. The survey progressed in later years under **E. Parker Scammon (USMA 1837)**.

Several Topographical Engineers participated in the Mexican War. Cram performed surveys of rivers and bays in Texas. Williams was mortally wounded at the battle of Monterey in 1846. An important contribution to the topographical literature of the West came from Kearny's expedition from Missouri to California. **William Emory (USMA 1831)** and **William Peck (USMA 1844)** made a survey of Kearny's route. Emory's *Notes of a Military Reconnaissance from Fort Leavenworth to San Diego* became an important guidebook of the route to California. Topographical engineers also accompanied John E. Wool on his march from Texas to Mexico. Franklin reconnoitered the route for Wool's army and prepared scientific notes and sketches.

The acquisition of more land by the United States increased the topo engineers duties. The Topographical Bureau set up new Departments in Oregon, California, New Mexico, and Texas. Engineers in these departments improved harbors and rivers, built roads and bridges, and constructed lighthouses. Surveys were made in Kansas and Nebraska Territories by **Gouverneur Warren (USMA 1850)**. In Oregon and Washington, Hartman Bache surveyed the road system. For several years, the topos were heavily engaged in surveys of routes for railroads. Humphreys was in charge of this work, while Warren and **Henry Abbot (USMA 1854)** assisted.

Boundary surveying became an important duty for the Topographical Engineers. The long, difficult Texas boundary took several topographic engineers. The survey of the Mexican boundary began in 1849 and continued until 1856. Emory was astronomer for this work and the running of the line of the Gadsden Treaty of 1853. **Robert E. Lee (USMA 1829)** under the direction of **Andrew Talcott (USMA 1818)**, set the Ohio-Michigan line and surveyed the western boundary of Missouri. During 1843 to 1846, McClellan, Cram, and Williams surveyed the Michigan and Wisconsin Territory boundary. In 1854, **Thomas Jefferson Lee (USMA 1830)** established the northern boundary of the Kansas Territory. Many other topos performed similar boundary surveying.

As they mapped America, the Topographical Engineers created detailed reports. Many of the pioneer explorers and land agents pictured the West as a land of opportunity and paradise. However, this was not representative of the entire West. The topo engineers were scientists and reported their findings objectively. One such objective report by Emory caused great controversy. He used scientific data to argue that his report of Texas, which differed from that of others, was the most accurate.

The beginning of Civil War brought an end to the Corps of Topographical Engineers. The officers in the branch transferred to combat duty. Hartman Bache took charge of the Topographical Bureau in 1861, but two years later the Corps of Topographical Engineers was abolished and its officers entered the Corps of Engineers.

References:

Beers, Henry, "A History of the U. S. Topographical Engineers, 1818-1863", *The Military Engineer*, 2 parts, June 1942, pp. 287-291 and July, 1942, pp. 348-352 (publication of Society of American Military Engineers).

Dawson, Joseph, *Army Generals and Reconstruction: Louisiana, 1862-1877*, Louisiana State University Press, Baton Rouge, 1982.

Goetzmann, William, *Army Exploration in the American West, 1803-1863*, Yale University Press, New Haven, 1959.

Hill, Forest, *Roads, Rails & Waterways: The Army Engineers and Early Transportation*, University of Oklahoma Press, Norman, 1957.

Norris, L. David; Milligan, James; and Faulk, Odie, *William H. Emory: Soldier-Scientist*, University of Arizona Press, Tucson, 1998.

Reinhartz, Dennis and Colley, C. C., editors, *The Mapping of the American Southwest*, Texas A&M University Press, College Station, 1987.

Ryan, Garry D. "War Department Topographical Bureau, 1831-1863." Ph.D. Dissertation, American University, 1968.

Schubert, Frank (Editor), *The Nation Builders: A Sesquicentennial History of the Corps of Topographical Engineers, 1838-- 1863*, Office of History, U. S. Army Corps of Engineers, Fort Belvoir, VA, 1988.

Shallat, Todd, *Structures in the Stream: Water, Science, and the Rise of the U. S. Army Corps of Engineers*, University of Texas Press, Austin, 1994.

Traas, Adrian, *From the Golden Gate to Mexico City - The U. S. Army Topographical Engineers in the Mexican War, 1846 - 1848*, Government Printing Office, Washington, DC, 1992.

Ordnance Corps

The Ordnance Corps dates back to the American Revolution. In 1776, the U.S. Army created a Board of War and Ordnance with the responsibility of issuing supplies and weapons. In 1777, the first ordnance powder magazine was built at Carlisle, PA, and the first arsenal and armory at Springfield, MA. Other arsenals and armories were soon established at Harper's Ferry, Philadelphia, PA and Watertown, MA. In 1812, Congress established the Ordnance Department with responsibility for arms and ammunition production, distribution, and storage. In 1813, the Army purchased 12 acres of land, which became Watervliet Arsenal in NY. In 1815, the Army gave specific duties to Colonel of Ordnance to "direct the inspection and proving of all pieces of ordnance, cannon balls, shot, shells, small arms and side arms, and equipment procured for use by the armies of the United States, and to direct the construction of all cannon and carriages and every implement and apparatus for ordnance, and all ammunition wagons, travelling forges and artificers' wagons, the inspection and proving of powder and the preparation of all kinds of ammunition and ordnance stores."[24] In 1832, the Ordnance Department assumed the new responsibilities of research and development of new weapons and systems. During the Civil War, the Ordnance Corps took on a great importance for both sides. Ordnance officers for both Armies successfully developed and procured advanced weapons and provided field support for their fast moving forces. During World War I, the Ordnance Department mobilized America's industrial base, developed many new weapons systems, built new facilities, and established overseas depots. Similar activities occurred during World War II.

The accomplishments of the Ordnance Corps are demonstrated through its development of weapons and equipment. Throughout the War of 1812, soldiers performed their work at the arsenals. Among the items produced were fuses, rockets, percussion caps, and gun carriages. In 1822, Thomas Blanchard at the Springfield Armory introduced a lathe for turning irregular-shaped wood and through this breakthrough, gunstocks were made by machine instead of by hand. In 1844, **Thomas Rodman (USMA 1841)** began experiments to improve the casting of cannons. **Alfred Mordecai (USMA 1823)** applied scientific methods to armament research and published a foundational report entitled *Artillery for the United States Land Service* in 1849. By 1860, the Army had 24 arsenals.

During the Civil War, ordnance advancement was a major component of the war effort on both sides. Several types of breechloader small arms were available to the Union Army by 1861, including the Springfields. The Spencer weapon also achieved considerable success. It used a brass cartridge case in a magazine that loaded from a hole in the butt plate, so it could be fired rapidly. This weapon gave the Union Army a temporary advantage. At the beginning of the war, the Springfield Armory made 800 rifles in a month and by October 1861 production increased to 6,900 per month. In 1862, Richard Gatling demonstrated the first successful machine gun, firing at a rate of 250-300 shots a minute. During the Civil War, the Union Army used more than 90 million pounds of lead, 13 million pounds of artillery

[24] *History of Ordnance Corps*, 1998, p. 7.

projectiles, and more than 26 million pounds of powder – all provided by the Ordnance Corps.

After the war, the interest in ordnance development continued. In 1874, the Army established its first proving grounds at Sandy Hook, NJ, and in 1879, the Army bought land for a powder depot, which became Picatinny Arsenal, NJ. The Army implemented smokeless powder in 1892. In 1896, the Army began construction of big guns with disappearing mounts for protection. Watervliet Arsenal produced the first 16-inch seacoast cannon in 1897. In 1902, the Ordnance School of Application was established at Sandy Hook Proving Ground, NJ.

When the United States declared war on Germany in April 1917, the Army had only 97 Ordnance officers. By war's end, the Ordnance branch's strength reached nearly 6,000 officers and over 60,000 enlisted soldiers. The Aberdeen Proving Ground, MD was built in 1917 to expand and improve the Army's test facilities.

A reorganization in 1921 assigned arsenals specific roles. Among them were small arms at Springfield Armory; small-arms ammunition at Frankford Arsenal; cannon production at Watervliet Arsenal; artillery carriages at Rock Island and Watertown Arsenals; artillery ammunitions at Picatinny and Frankford Arsenals; and tanks at Rock Island Arsenal. In 1936, the Garand rifle became the soldiers' standard weapon, designated as the M1 rifle.

The following West Point graduates in *THE SCIENTIFIC 200* were among those who served as Chief of Ordnance: **George Bomford (USMA 1805), James W. Ripley (USMA 1814), Alexander B. Dyer (USMA 1837), Stephen Benet (USMA 1849), and William Crozier (USMA 1876).** Several others of *THE 200* spent their careers in the Ordnance Corps. Given the broad technical nature of ordnance duties, most of them could be classified in any of the four discipline categories. Some were mathematicians, doing theoretical studies of ballistics or other weapon characteristics. Others were primarily scientists, studying metallurgy or the chemical processes in explosions. Others were engineers, building weapons, transport systems, or weapons platforms (e.g., gun carriages or structures for coastal artillery). Still others were technologists, inventing new weapons or manufacturing systems, running arsenals and foundry operations, or developing new production methods and equipment.

Some of the ordnance officers in *THE 200* with their disciplinary classification are **Alfred Mordecai (USMA 1823)**, scientist; **Robert Parrot (USMA 1824)**, scientist; **Gabriel Rains (USMA 1827)**, scientist; **Josiah Gorgas (USMA 1841)**, technologist; **George Rains (USMA 1842)**, scientist; **Alfred Mordecai (USMA June 1861)**, mathematician; **Henry Metcalf (USMA 1868)**, scientist; **John Thompson (USMA 1882)**, technologist; and **Colden Ruggles (USMA 1890)**, scientist.

References:
Davis, Carl, *Arming the Union; Small Arms in the Civil War,* Kennikat Press, Port Washington, NY, 1973.

History of the Ordnance Corps, U.S. Army Ordnance Center and School, Aberdeen Proving Ground, MD, Feb 1998.

Melton, Jack and Pawl, Lawrence, *Introduction to Field Artillery Ordnance, 1861-1865,* Kennesaw Mountain Press, Kennesaw, 1994.

Murray, James and Swantek, John, *1813-1997, The Watervliet Arsenal: A Chronology of the Nation's Oldest Arsenal,* Watervliet Arsenal Public Affairs Office, Watervliet, NY, 1997.

Ripley, Warren, *Artillery and Ammunition of the Civil War,* Van Nostrand Reinhold, New York, 1970.

"United States Army Ordnance Corps: A Brief History," http://www.goordnance.apg.army.mil/Corpshis

U.S. Coast Survey*

Ferdinand Hassler (see **Honorable Mentions**) was the first Superintendent of the Coast Survey, and following his death in 1843, there was competition to become his successor. The Coast Survey was a small organization by today's standards, but it was one of the largest and most powerful organizations of science and engineering in America in 1843. The Army Corps of Engineers was larger, but more restricted in its mission. Some of the principal candidates for the new Superintendent were Hassler's assistant James Ferguson, Army engineer and surveyor **Andrew Talcott (USMA 1818)**, and Professor **Alexander Bache (USMA 1825)**. Bache with the aid of his scientist friends mounted a letter writing campaign. John Kane, Secretary of the American Philosophical Society, and scientist Joseph Henry lobbied in Bache's behalf, along with many other prominent scientists and military officers. They sent endorsements of Bache directly to President John Tyler. Tyler had almost no choice given the impact of the campaign and selected Bache as Superintendent. As was demonstrated, Bache already had developed an ability to garner the support of the American scientific community. He would continue over many years to use his political influence on behalf of himself, the Coast Survey, and American science. He would also support America's most capable scientists, since "under Bache's direction, the Coast Survey became the largest and most important institution supporting science in antebellum America."[25]

The Swiss-born mathematician Hassler had laid a good foundation for the Coast Survey, but it was on Bache's shoulders to build the rest of the structure. Fortunately, Bache inherited an organization that had resources, instruments, people, and effective methods. Bache was replacing a forceful man and a fine scientist in Hassler. Bache had those same attributes as well as the advantages of being native-born and associated with a powerful political family. In the 1840s, the United States was seeking its own identity and needed assurance that an American was capable of directing such a large scientific endeavor. American science had

---

* The major reference for this section is the extensive history of the Coast Survey written by Albert Theberge (see References and the website: http://www.lib.noaa.gov/edocs).

[25] Slotten, *Patronage*, p. 1.

improved dramatically since Hassler had first started the survey in 1807. Much of the progress was from the jumpstart in engineering provided by the program that **Sylvanus Thayer (USMA 1808)** had established at USMA. Bache, having gone through West Point's rigorous science and engineering program, understood better than anyone the strengths and needs of the growing scientific infrastructure of the nation. He knew many West Point-educated scientists and engineers who could step in and help, and he was well-connected with other academic organizations. Despite these advantages, his task was not easy. As an outsider to the Survey, some of the senior assistants challenged his authority. In particular, Ferguson resented Bache's selection. Bache countered this by hiring people who were loyal to him for the key positions in the organization.

Shortly after his appointment, Bache revised the regulations and formalized them in a document. This document, much like a military order, set the chain of command and gave directions for communications, promotions, disbursements, and pay. These regulations strengthened Bache's position. However, he still had to deal with Ferguson's resentment. Bache gave Ferguson an important survey to perform to close out Hassler's previous work. Ferguson completed the survey with apparently good results. However, when the results were checked by **Andrew Humphreys (USMA 1831)**, irregularities in the computations were discovered, mostly from using faulty equipment. Bache confronted Ferguson, and a board of investigation convened to determine Ferguson's fate. The board was comprised of mathematician Benjamin Peirce of Harvard, **Andrew Talcott (USMA 1818)**, and the Professor of Mathematics at West Point **Charles Davies (USMA 1815)**. The board reported findings directly to Secretary of the Treasury that went against Ferguson – there were numerous errors and false results. Because of these discrepancies, the board recommended that Ferguson's work be rejected. Bache dismissed Ferguson from the Survey. Bache no longer had an internal rival, but he had created a strong external enemy. Ferguson went to work for the Naval Observatory and became a source of problems for Bache. However, in just a short time, Bache had realigned the Coast Survey into the structure that he wanted. Bache's energy and leadership were outstanding. He effectively guided the Coast Survey as the scope of its work expanded. Aiding Bache were his uncle George Dallas, Vice President of the United States; his brother-in-law Robert Walker, Secretary of the Treasury; another brother-in-law William Wilkins, Secretary of War; and his close friend Mississippi Senator Jefferson Davis (USMA 1828).

By 1845, the Survey had parties working on every part of the coastline of the country. Bache divided the coast into sections and gave teams responsibilities for sections. Results were tied together later. He obtained from Congress budget increases to purchase more equipment and hire more personnel. The office operations were set up to handle the large influx of data from the survey crews operating in the widely dispersed areas. The Coast Survey grew in size, scope, and influence in nearly every year of Bache's 20-year tenure.

Bache spent considerable time in the field surveying, both because he enjoyed the work and to eliminate the idea that he was only an administrator. Bache was an excellent scientist and mathematician, and his fieldwork and research were valuable contributions to the Survey and to science. His work set a high standard for others to follow. However, spending time away from the office required that he had a trustworthy assistant. He selected bright, dedicated Army officers as his assistants. They were responsible for all day–to–day the office functions in Bache's absence. Bache improved communications and insured that he was kept informed of developments when he was in the field. A computing division was established with office computers (the job title for those performing computations to check the field surveys).

By 1847, the Survey was operating in 17 states with several crews on the Pacific Coast. Besides expanding the geographical scope of the Survey, Bache also expanded its role in science. Several prominent scientists were either hired or worked under contract. Among this group were Benjamin Peirce, naturalist Louis Agassiz, meteorologist Elias Loomis, microscopist **Jacob Bailey (USMA 1832)**, astronomer Maria Mitchell, and astronomer **Ormsby Mitchel (USMA 1829)** of the Cincinnati Observatory. The Coast Survey was

**Ormsby Mitchel
(USMA 1829)**

providing direction and support to the top echelon of the American scientists. Bache also had strong ties with two influential scientists, Joseph Henry, who later became the Secretary of the Smithsonian, and Charles H. Davis of the Navy. These and many other scientists, who recognized Bache as the leader of organized science in America, started calling him "chief." This group of scientific colleagues referred to themselves as the Lazzaroni, and whenever a Lazzaroni came to Washington, he stayed with Bache.

Bache acquired a number of very capable Army officers, mostly West Point graduates, to help with the surveying, mapping, and administration. His relations with the Navy were not as strong, because there was an element within the Navy that coveted the Coast Survey as a Navy function.

The outward flow of information increased dramatically as Bache's annual reports were expanded. They not only reported on the Survey's progress but also requested funds for the following year. Dangers to navigation were quickly reported to ships. In addition to Bache's role in publicizing the work and accomplishments of the Survey, his colleagues were effective advocates of the Coast Survey. Many scientists actively supported the Survey, and politicians like Jefferson Davis promoted the Coast Survey. American science was beginning to flex its muscle, and Bache was the leader of this effort. His motivations were to raise American science to a higher level and to make science an important contributor to American society. This required a strong spokesman who could deal with both the world's scientific community and the American politicians. Bache was well suited for both these activities.

An important project during the early years of Bache's tenure was to determine the longitude of locations in the United States. During the period of 1845 to 1850, the Survey made great progress in this effort. Through new technologies that the Survey developed, Bache was able to declare in 1848 that the determination of longitude by the telegraphic method had become a regular method of the Survey. This was called the American method. Through support by Bache, Saxton's chronograph and Mitchel's instrument had removed the human element of striking the telegraph key and listening to a key click. The new system was much more precise. The longitude of the Cincinnati Observatory was accomplished through the cooperation of its director Mitchel as the second location precisely set by the Coast Survey in the interior. Earlier, the longitude of the Hudson Observatory in Cleveland had been determined using this American method.

The determination of latitude was also of interest, and the Talcott method of latitude observation was adopted by the Coast Survey. This method of observation was devised by Andrew Talcott and involved precise star observation. **Thomas Jefferson Lee (USMA 1830)** used this method in 1846, but discovered a problem in the accuracy of the method. To resolve the problem, Lee went to West Point and with the cooperation of Professor of Natural and Experimental Philosophy **William Bartlett (USMA 1826)** used the equipment at the West Point Observatory to determine the needed corrections.

In 1849, Senator Thomas Benton of Missouri attempted to place the Coast Survey under the Navy's control. The head of this movement was Matthew Maury, the head of the Naval Observatory. The reality of this conflict was a clash of egos vying for control of American science – Maury verses Bache. This issue was just the opening volley of a continuing battle between these two men. Bache came out the winner when the proposal to eliminate the Survey received only two votes in the Senate. Over the years, Maury and Bache argued over whether the Survey should be involved in deep sea soundings, be the nation's time-keeper, and be the first to determine telegraphically the longitude of a point in the United States from signals sent through the trans-Atlantic cable. Bache realized that conflicts were part of the consequence of aggressively advancing Army science.

The Coast Survey continued its progress in conducting surveys, topographic studies, and hydrologic studies along the American coastline. Office work expanded to meet the demands of the increased fieldwork with a growing group of computers, draftsmen, and engravers. New techniques were developed to expedite the printing and distribution of nautical charts to meet the increasing demand for products. New products such as tidal tables were developed, although the primary product remained the nautical chart. The Survey processed and distributed geographic, oceanographic, and technical information. To produce more charts and reports, the office in Washington was expanded to over 120 employees by 1860 to meet the needs of over 100 field surveyors.

Bache selected mathematically talented Army officers to perform the duties of his assistant and office manager. The first was **Andrew Humphreys (USMA 1831)**, who was the perfect person for the job. He was both an effective manager and a strong enough leader to keep the momentum going during Bache's absences. In 1849, **Isaac Stevens (USMA 1839)** replaced Humphreys. Stevens was an ambitious and aggressive manager. He took on the task of increasing efficiency in all facets of the office functions of computing, drafting, engraving, printing, publishing, and distributing finished products. Stevens put the office operations on an assembly-line basis. However, Stevens was interested in new, higher-level challenges, and in 1853, resigned from the Army and the Survey to become the first governor of the Washington Territory. Upon Stevens departure, **Henry Benham (USMA 1837)** became assistant. Benham faced the problem of losing engravers, who were in demand for bank note production and book illustrations. Without sufficient engravers to produce quality plates for the maps, the Survey would fail in its mission. Benham and fellow Army officer **Edward Hunt (USMA 1845)** came up with what they thought was a solution. Hunt realized that the

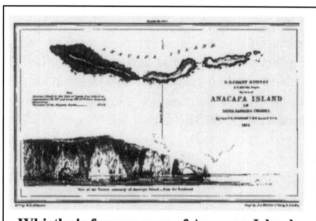

Whistler's famous map of Anacapa Island

assembly-line environment for engravers was detrimental to their artistic spirit, so a compromise system was devised. However, this did not solve the problem. As a last resort, Bache sent Benham to Europe in 1856 to recruit first-class topographic engravers. This trip was successful and a number of immigrant engravers signed on with the Survey and stayed. The Survey finally had enough skilled engravers to accomplish its mission.

One American who showed great promise for this type of work was James McNeill Whistler. Whistler had dropped out of West Point and came to the Survey as a potential draftsman. Whistler's father, **George Washington Whistler (USMA 1819)** was a well-known Army engineer. It was hoped that the son had the same talents. However, young Whistler's artistic talents would not be restricted by the exactness required in topographic drafting. When things did not work out in the Drawing Division, he transferred to the understaffed Engraving Division to see if he could learn topographic engraving. He learned quickly and produced a view of the Boston Harbor, along with other items, as a test product to learn this new skill. This first copper-plate etching by Whistler later became known as his Coast Survey Plate. After his initial practice plate, he produced two production plates. The first has been lost, but the second plate was a map of Anacapa Island (see the figure with the map). This plate is unique in having sea gulls on the map. Whistler either resigned or was fired shortly after making the Anacapa plate. Given that the Coast Survey needed skilled engravers, it was a blow to their staffing situation; however, Whistler's later accomplishments as an artist in Europe more than made up for this set back.

In spite of Benham's success in obtaining engravers, the Coast Survey never would have met the demand for charts if it had not been a leader in breakthrough in two technical fields, electrotyping and photography. Neither of these technologies were invented by the Coast Survey. However, because of the skills of George Mathiot, these methods were refined and utilized to produce charts and maps more efficiently and accurately. Mathiot made major contributions to cartographic methods by using photography to convert hand-drawn sheets to the scales required for charts.

Bache's annual reports included examples of the advances in scientific methods developed by the Coast Survey. For example, Mitchel's important astronomical work on north polar distances and Mathiot's work on electrotyping appear in annual reports. The reports also served to advance Bache's political agenda by making the point that the work of the Survey was solving problems in commerce and defense. Mitchel's report also showed the robustness of American science. At the Cincinnati Observatory, Mitchel had taken more observations and accomplished more studies and results than the premier European observatories.

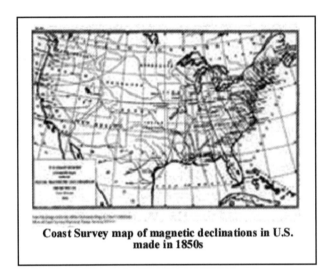

Coast Survey map of magnetic declinations in U.S. made in 1850s

So great was the demand for the Survey's annual reports that there was a mailing list of over 4,000 individuals and institutions including over 300 colleges, many Army and Navy organizations, all Navy ships, lighthouses, and government land offices. Commercial organizations also bought copies. In 1858, Congress ordered over 11,000 reports as complimentary copies to pass out to constituents. This helped the Survey's public image. Bache developed another promotional product to educate influential people as to the capabilities of the Survey. The *Congress Map* demonstrated to Congress and other supporters the extent of Coast Survey's capabilities. The map was almost 9 feet on a side, perfect to hang on walls of large offices and buildings.

The Survey's research involved many fields of science – geology, oceanography, biology, hydrography, and meteorology. Examples of scientific discoveries made by the Survey include local gravitational anomalies, the extent of the continental shelf, the nature of tides, mapping canyons on the ocean floor, and locating cold-water bands in the Gulf Stream. The nature of Coast Survey work forced it to perform very precise measurements and to conduct very refined mathematical analysis. Therefore, design and construction of precise instruments and development of sophisticated mathematical methods were also part of the Survey's accomplishments. A special class of problems attacked by the Coast Survey was that of predicting the future conditions of changing phenomena such as tides, currents, weather, and climates. Bache utilized the concept of interdisciplinary teamwork to solve these difficult problems. He formed teams with mathematicians to do the theoretical and computational work, physicists to investigate the science, and engineers to implement the results. This represented a new way of tackling complex problems. This concept was a manifestation of the increasing specialization of the American scientific community as well as a realization that a talented team working toward the solution of a problem was more apt to produce a solution. In particular, he had his teams follow a systematic approach: 1) conduct observations of the phenomena, 2) generate a scientific theory to explain the phenomena, 3) develop mathematical formulas to describe the data, 4) use the formulas to predict the future of the phenomena, 5) test the prediction against real world observations, and 6) if the model does not agree with the real world data, start over again. With the nation's best mathematicians wrestling with the large data sets collected by the field crews, important breakthroughs in mathematical analysis and modeling and science were discovered. People like **William Trowbridge (USMA 1848)** became world leaders in dynamical modeling and data analysis through their opportunities to work on these problems for the Coast Survey. By aggressively communicating Coast Survey methodology and philosophy to the American scientific community, Bache drove American science into the modern world.

Bache was one of the most accomplished administrators in the government. He was able to establish merit as the over-riding principle of his personnel management system. There were no pay tables, since increases in pay were negotiated directly between the employee and Bache. Bache's progressive policies led to the Survey being the first government agency to hire women for professional work. Astronomer Maria Mitchell was hired by Bache to assist in observations. In 1848, Mitchell joined Bache's field crew for observations at Mount Independence, ME. By the mid 1850's, several women were in professional positions, such as computers and engravers. Bache ran the Survey as an extended family. Bache's greatest strength as a leader was his ability to attract people with tremendous talents. An example was the quality of Army officer who served in the organization. Although there were less than 50 Army officers who served on the Survey during Bache's tenure, 25 of them became Generals. Among these were several members of *THE SCIENTIFIC 200*: **Andrew Humphreys (USMA 1831), Isaac Stevens (USMA 1839), Thomas Cram (USMA 1826)**, and **Henry Benham (USMA 1837)**.

There were several more attempts to reduce the Survey's funding or turn over functions to the Navy. However, Bache always prevailed in Congress. Budgets continued at high levels and additional functions were taken on, including locating and surveying sites for lighthouses. The Coast Survey's budget was more than 1% of the total federal budget. Bache anticipated controversy about the Survey's appropriation in 1858, so he took preemptive action. At the meeting of the American Association for the Advancement of Science and at Bache's request, a committee formed to investigate the Coast Survey's operations. It was known as the Committee of Twenty. This committee consisted primarily of scientists who were sympathetic to Bache. John Kane, President of the American Philosophical Society, headed the group. Members included Benjamin Peirce, Joseph Henry, **Joseph Totten (USMA 1804)**, John Frazer of the University of Pennsylvania, William Chauvenet of the Naval Academy, and other associates of Bache. The committee worked for a year. Not surprisingly, its report was highly complimentary of the Coast Survey. The report detailed the Survey operations, presented comparisons between the costs of America's operations and costs of similar European organizations, and made 12 recommendations for the future operations of the Survey. The major recommendations were that the Coast Survey expand its operations into the interior of the United States and the structure of the Survey remain the same (separate from the Navy). The most significant part of the report was its evidence for the increasing level of American science and its recognition that the prosperity of America was linked to advancement in science. The report insured its validity by including praise from the most famous European scientists and a description of Bache's most recent triumph, the attainment of the prestigious Victoria Medal of the Royal Geographical Society.

The years before the Civil War saw even further improvements in the operations of the Survey. Bache revealed in 1858 that the Survey was not a temporary organization, but he was in a dilemma concerning his political allegiances. He received tremendous support from Southern politicians, and, therefore, tried to remain politically neutral in the squabbles over secession and slavery. Given the charged political atmosphere, Bache somehow salvaged his budget. The years 1850 through 1860 were the most productive and successful years of the Coast Survey. The budget would never again approach 1% of the federal budget. Never again would the Survey have such influence on American science. During the Civil War, the Coast Survey was relegated to a minor position, and it never returned to its pre-war prominence. Other science and engineering agencies evolved and became more prominent, such as the Smithsonian Institution and the National Academy of Sciences. The Coast Survey changed its name to the Coast and Geodetic Survey. Although few West Point graduates worked in the organization after the Civil War, the impact of the early graduates was significant.

Alexander Bache (USMA 1825)

One of Bache's major contributions to American science was the building of a sense of identity. Bache and the Lazzaroni were the leaders in this movement. Bache's West Point background gave him the motivation and skills to lead, and there was little doubt, American science in the middle of the 19th century needed a leader. Bache had been concerned with the development of professional standards in American science. When Bache had traveled to Europe in 1836 for the purpose of studying European educational methods, he and Henry, who had traveled with him, created a plan to bring American science out of the colonial period and into the forefront of the world. They wanted to eliminate bad science, develop means for policing the publication of scientific information, develop scientific organizations to guide the American science community, and develop means to judge the worth of proposals in order to fund the worthy investigators. Bache as Superintendent of the Coast Survey was in the perfect place to implement their plan. Henry, as head of the Smithsonian Institution, was also perfectly placed to support Bache. Although these two men occasionally had differences of opinion, they usually worked together and with other Lazzaroni to implement their plan. First, they set up and controlled the newly formed American Association for the Advancement of Science (AAAS) and established it according to Henry's view of the British Association. (See a separate essay on the AAAS.) They gained control of the leadership positions of the Association and placed Lazzaroni as chairs of the committees of the Association. Meteorologist William Redfield, sympathetic to the Lazzaroni, was elected the first president in 1848. In 1849, Henry was President and followed successively by other Lazzaroni, Bache, Agassiz, and Peirce. Bache delivered the most influential address of the first decade of the AAAS as the outgoing President at the Albany meeting in 1851. He suggested additional support for science and laid the foundation for the National Academy of Sciences. It was 12 years later that Bache would have the opportunity to build from this foundation and complete his task of building the image of American science. His other idea of establishing a national scientific college in Albany in association with Dudley Observatory never came to realization.

During the Civil War, in January 1863, Bache and Henry discussed the possibility of forming a national scientific organization through an Act of Congress. They felt the time was right for instituting an advisory organization composed of top scientists to help the Government formulate policy and allocate funds for scientific projects, especially related to the issues of warfare. Henry became the driving force in establishing the Navy's Permanent Commission composed of himself, Davis (of the Navy), Bache, and **John Barnard (USMA 1833)**. The commission served for the duration of the Civil War investigating opportunities and evaluating scientific proposals. By war's end, it had produced over 250 reports. In 1864, the Lazzaroni enlisted the aid of Senator Henry Wilson of Massachusetts, and asked him to introduce a bill to form the National Academy of Science. He introduced a bill that named fifty scientists to the National Academy of Sciences. (See the essay on the National Academy of Sciences.) The bill passed, and Bache became its first President. However, he had become seriously ill. With his incapacitation in 1864 and death in 1867, Henry was the one that kept the Academy together. Bache willed his estate to the National Academy.

The scientific world had experienced both great growth and chaos during the lifetime of Bache. Science and technology in America had expanded considerably. Following the Civil War, the growth of many branches of science and engineering precluded the control of American science by any one individual like Bache or organization like the Coast Survey. The establishment of land grant colleges and the opportunity to conduct basic research at major universities necessitated the decentralization of science, but by then, Bache's work was done. American science was mature enough to decentralize and still prosper. There was no need for another dominant leader to follow Bache. Bache's role and influence in these formative years was a success. That there is a National Academy of Sciences able to assist the government in making decisions in a technically complex world is a result of Bache's leadership. He was much more than the Superintendent of the Coast Survey, President of the American Association for the Advancement of Science, Chief of the Lazzaroni, and first President of the National Academy of Sciences. He was in many ways the "Father of American Science." The legacy of his life's work as a science administrator, national-level organizer, politician, and leader is still felt by the American science community. It was because of the leadership of Alexander Dallas Bache that American science began to change the world.

References:
Kohlstedt, Sally; Sokal, Michael; and Lewenstein, Bruce, *The Establishment of Science in America: 150 Years of the American Association for the Advancement of Science*, Rutgers University Press, New Brunswick, NJ, 1999.

Slotten, Hugh R., *Patronage, Practice, and the Culture of American Science: Alexander Dallas Bache and the U. S. Coast Survey*, Cambridge University Press, Cambridge, MA, 1994.

Theberge, Albert E., "The Coast Survey 1807-1867: Volume I of the History of the Commissioned Corps of the National Oceanic and Atmospheric Administration," http://www.lib.noaa.gov/edocs

True, Frederick (Editor), *A History of the First Half-Century of the National Academy of Sciences, 1863-1913*, National Academy of Sciences, Washington, 1913.

Wraight, A. Joseph and Roberts, Elliot, *The Coast and Geodetic Survey, 1807-1957; 150 Years of History*, U. S. Coast and Geodetic Survey, Washington, 1957.

National Academy of Sciences

The law establishing the National Academy of Sciences (NAS) was signed by President Abraham Lincoln on March 3, 1863. The NAS's role is to "investigate, examine, experiment, and report upon any subject of science or art"[26] whenever called upon by any department of the government. Following in the footsteps of private organizations like the American Philosophical Society (1743), the American Academy of Arts and Sciences (1780), the National Institute for the Promotion of Science and the Useful Arts (1840), the Smithsonian Institution (1846), and the American Academy for the Advancement of Science (AAAS) (1848), the NAS was the government's own assemblage of scientific advisors.

The roots of the NAS started in the 1850s with a group of scientists, which called themselves the Lazzaroni. Among the Lazzaroni were scientist **Alexander Dallas Bache (USMA 1825)**, naturalist Louis Agassiz, Harvard Professor of Mathematics Benjamin Peirce, astronomer Benjamin Gould, Harvard Professor Cornelius Felton, and the foremost American scientist Joseph Henry. Bache gave the most explicit endorsement to the idea of forming a national scientific academy in his speech as outgoing president of the AAAS in 1851. He recommended that the federal government establish a body for the promotion of science and outlined the benefits of such an organization. The primary benefit was a trusted advisory group for any matters involving science and technology. By 1858, the Lazzaroni had outlined the structure of an academy of sciences.

Alexander Dallas Bache (USMA 1825)

The technical military needs of the government during the Civil War were instrumental to the formation of such a scientific consulting group. Many people contributed to the war effort by submitting inventions and ideas to the government and military. In order to evaluate these suggestions, Henry proposed that the Navy form an agency to test new military equipment and weapons. In 1863, the Secretary of the Navy approved Henry's plan, and the Permanent Commission, made up of Henry, Bache, and Rear Admiral Charles H. Davis, was established. At the same time, Agassiz had obtained support from Massachusetts Senator Henry Wilson. With Wilson's help, the Lazzaroni proposed a bill for the establishment of the National Academy of

---

[26] Section 3 of Act of Incorporation, signed by Abraham Lincoln on 3 May 1863

Sciences. Wilson brought the bill to the Senate, and it was passed. Later that same day, the House of Representatives passed the bill and Lincoln signed the bill into law. The National Academy of Sciences was established.

It didn't take long for the organization to begin operations. There were 50 scientists who were corporators (charter members) of the NAS, among them were the following six West Point graduates: **Alexander Dallas Bache (USMA 1825), John Gross Barnard (USMA 1833), William Holmes Chambers Bartlett (USMA 1826), Andrew Atkinson Humphreys (USMA 1831), Dennis Hart Mahan (USMA 1824),** and **Joseph Gilbert Totten (USMA 1805)**. Bache was elected President of the Academy. There was plenty of controversy over these first appointments since many were members of the Lazzaroni or their friends. However, with Bache's failing health and Joseph Henry's influence, cooler heads prevailed and the Academy was ready to work.

After the organizational meeting in April 1863, the NAS received its first request for scientific advice. Although the Academy was founded during the Civil War, its first study was not war related. The Secretary of the Treasury requested a study on matters related to commerce. The NAS set up a Committee on Weights, Measures, and Coinage, and after holding several meetings, the committee submitted its report in January 1864. It recommended that a thorough survey of other systems and requested more time to conduct the survey. The committee also felt that the United States should adopt the metric system, which was studied again later but never implemented.

The Committee on Weights, Measures, and Coinage was exemplary of NAS activities. It established a model for many of the later NAS committees. It offered its recommendations in the form of a written report. Requests for advice on matters of warfare soon followed. The Navy requested three studies, two related to the capabilities of the Union fleet. One request asked the Academy to find ways for the Navy to protect the bottoms of its iron-hulled ships from corrosion. A Committee on Protecting the Bottoms of Iron Vessels was appointed. This committee failed to devise an effective way to protect iron ships because of the limitations of available technologies and the lack of understanding of this science. The Navy also requested the Academy to investigate magnetic deviation in iron ships. The Academy's Compass Committee formed. The large amounts of iron in ships was causing compasses to deviate, making navigation difficult. In 1864, this committee issued its recommendations and directly oversaw the correction of compasses on 27 ships.

Government agencies continued to request studies during the Civil War. The NAS was off to a good start in its first few years of existence. After the war, the government continued to find needs for the NAS. The aftermath of the war brought numerous problems in need of technical solutions. In 1868, Joseph Henry, who was the first Secretary of the Smithsonian Institution, was elected President of the NAS, replacing Bache who had died a year earlier. Henry held both of these leadership positions until his death in 1878. Under Henry's direction, the NAS grew and prospered. During the later part of the nineteenth century, the Academy was called on to advise on a diverse set of subjects. There were committees on Proving and Gauging Distilled Spirits (1866); on Metric Standards (1866); on

Distinguishing Calf's Hair from Woolen Goods (1875); and on the Restoration of the Declaration of Independence (1880). The Academy also recommended the establishment of the U. S. Geological Survey. This was the first time a NAS committee helped establish a government agency. In 1895, the Academy recommended that in the near term, the Army should protect public areas from fires, and in the long term, a national forest service was needed to oversee public forests. In 1905, the Forest Service was established.

Like the NAS, its off-shoot, the National Research Council (NRC), was organized in a time of war. The NRC was founded in 1916 as the country began its preparations for World War I. As the NAS tried to generate interest in coordinating scientific and technological research and development, it appointed a Committee for the Organization of the Scientific Resources of the Country for National Service. The NRC was a result of this committee. The Research Council was not restricted to NAS members so it had a broader membership and scope of activity. Initially, the NRC members were drawn from the government, military, universities, and private research laboratories. In 1964, the National Academy of Engineering was founded to focus on subjects related directly to engineering.

Over the years other West Point graduates were inducted into the National Academy of Sciences, among them were: **Edward Hunt (USMA 1845), Henry Abbot (USMA 1854), Thomas Casey (USMA 1852), Edward Holden (USMA 1870), William Kaula (USMA 1948), Montgomery Meigs (USMA 1836), John Newton (USMA 1842), William Norton (USMA 1831), William Trowbidge (USMA 1848),** and **Gouverneur Warren (USMA 1850)**. In addition to this group, **Kenneth Nichols (USMA 1929)** was elected to the NAS sister organization, the National Academy of Engineering.

References:

Calvin, Melvin et. al., *The Scientific Endeavor*, Rockefeller Institute Press, New York, 1965.

Cochrane, Rexmond, *The National Academy of Sciences: the first hundred years, 1863-1963*, The Academy, Washington, 1978.

True, Frederick (Editor), *A History of the First Half-Century of the National Academy of Sciences, 1863-1913*, National Academy of Sciences, Washington, 1913.

National Academy of Sciences website: http://nationalacademies.org/about/

American Association for the Advancement of Science

The formation of the American Association for the Advancement of Science (AAAS) gave life to the scientific community in America. The AAAS was the first organization in the United States formed to promote the development of science and engineering at the national level and to represent the interests of all scientific and technological disciplines. In 1848, at the Academy of Natural Sciences in Philadelphia, members of the Association of American Geologists and Naturalists re-formed their society into the AAAS. Eighty-seven American scientists took part in the first AAAS meeting. William Redfield, meteorologist and geologist, was elected president. They followed their organizational meeting with five days of scientific sessions. The aims of the AAAS were "to promote intercourse between those who are cultivating science in different parts of the United States, to give a stronger and more general impulse, and a more systematic direction to scientific research; and to procure for the labours (sic) of scientific men, increased facilities and a wider usefulness."[27] The British Association for the Advancement of Science, which had formed in 1831, provided a model for the AAAS. In its early years, AAAS sought to build a cohesive organization under the dynamic leadership of its second President, **Alexander Bache (USMA 1825)**.

Participants in AAAS meetings, which were held in cities around the country, represented the best of American science. Because the meetings were covered widely by newspapers, science was given a positive and creditable public image. Despite this strong start, the Association came close to disbanding several times in its history. Fortunately, an alliance with *Science* magazine, rejuvenated both the magazine and AAAS. During the early years, AAAS was a popular and growing organization with over 2000 people joining during 1848 to 1860. Most were scientists or engineers, but others were ordinary citizens with an interest in science. The first woman member was astronomer Maria Mitchell in 1850. AAAS meetings were major events for the cities where they met. Science leaders used the meetings to leverage support for their own organizations and institutions. The 1856 meeting in Albany, NY, involved the dedication of two major scientific facilities: the state geological museum and the Dudley Observatory. The Civil War threatened the continuance of the organization, and the AAAS did not meet or elect officers during the war. Fortunately, the Association was revived under the leadership of Frederick A. P. Barnard, President of Columbia University and brother of **John G. Barnard (USMA 1833)**. The AAAS met again in Buffalo, NY, in 1866. Brought back to life, AAAS quickly grew and assumed an important role in American science. By then, the AAAS was no longer the only national science organization. It shared the science stage with the National Academy of Sciences (begun in 1863) and several disciplinary societies.

The 1869 meeting, held in Salem, MA, featured a session on microscopy. Prominent scientists brought their microscopes and gave demonstrations. In the 1870s, a new constitution created the more prestigious category of *fellows* for members who had greater accomplishments in science. In 1884, the AAAS meeting returned to Philadelphia for the first time since its founding. The meeting was arranged so members of the British Association, meeting in Montreal, could attend. The meeting was a tremendous success. The Association developed into a stabilizing and supporting force for the scientific community in the midst of a chaotic time in science. The Association discovered a role for itself – environmental conservation. Ever since botanist Asa Gray gave his presidential address in 1872 on "The Sequoia and Its History," there had been substantial interest in environmental conservation. Soon the AAAS was deeply involved in conservation issues, which continued as its major focus into the 20th century. This interest led to the establishment of an AAAS Committee on the Preservation of the Forests in 1874.

---

[27] "Rules and Objects" of the American Association for the Advancement of Science, 1848.

The AAAS link with *Science* magazine helped both organizations. *Science* was originally independent of the Association. Thomas Edison was the magazine's early benefactor and invested nearly $10,000 in its operation in 1880, but there were never enough subscribers to pay the bills, and Edison eventually withdrew his support. *Science* ceased publication for a year and was reborn in February 1883, under a new editor. However, the magazine was soon in financial trouble again. In November 1894, James Cattell, professor at Columbia University, bought the magazine. He worked out an exclusive agreement with AAAS and turned *Science* into America's premier scientific journal. Cattell edited the magazine for nearly 50 years.

As scientific disciplines grew more specialized, many disciplinary groups of the AAAS formed independent societies. The AAAS again faced stagnating membership and difficult times, but somehow it managed to sustain itself. In 1873, a gift of $1,000 prompted the AAAS to establish a fund to provide research grants. One of the first grants went to Albert Michelson and Edward Morley, recipients of the first Nobel Prize in physics in 1907, for research on optical precision instruments. Michelson and Morley both later served as presidents of AAAS and reported some of their experiments at the 1887 meeting. They also published their work in *Science* magazine.

AAAS grew and changed during the 20th century as the American scientific community took on its modern shape. Disciplinary societies, many of them spawned by AAAS, performed many of the functions AAAS had formerly provided. The Association still had an integrating position in science. Some of the most interdisciplinary of American scientists, people like Thomas Hunt Morgan, Albert Einstein, and Edwin Hubble published in *Science,* presented their work at annual AAAS meetings, and received grants or prizes from the AAAS. The Association acquired a home in the Smithsonian Institution, and initiated its first programs in education and public understanding of science. It also sought to assert influence on national science policy and to steer science toward greater social responsibility.

The AAAS entered science education in a substantial way in 1955, when it received a grant from the Carnegie Corporation to develop the "Science Teaching Improvement Program." For 20 years, the AAAS held conferences and workshops for teacher preparation in science. Another AAAS initiative was the creation of a traveling library of science books for schools under a program supported by the National Science Foundation (NSF). AAAS had played a role in the debates leading up to the establishment of the NSF in 1949. Since then the AAAS has been involved in sponsoring several important initiatives in science and science education.

Some of the West Point graduates who were members (mostly Fellows) of the AAAS include: **Joseph Totten (USMA 1805), John Abert (USMA 1811), Charles Davies (USMA 1815), Edward Courtenay (USMA 1821), Alexander Bache (USMA 1825), Albert Church (USMA 1828), Ormsby Mitchel (USMA 1829), Charles Hackley (USMA 1829), William Norton (USMA 1831), Charles Whittlesey (USMA 1831), Jacob Bailey (USMA 1832), Francis H. Smith (USMA 1833), Benjamin Alvord (USMA 1833), Henry Eustis (USMA 1842), Edward Hunt (USMA 1845), William Trowbridge**

(USMA 1848), Lewis Haupt (USMA 1867), David Lyle (USMA 1869), Arthur Hardy (USMA 1869), William Holden (USMA 1870), William Bixby (USMA 1873), John Thompson (USMA 1882), Charles Pettis (USMA 1904), and **Boyd Bartlett (USMA 1919)**.

References:

American Association for the Advancement of Science, *Centennial,* American Association for the Advancement of Science, Washington, 1950.

American Association for the Advancement of Science website: http://www.aaas.org/exhibit

Kohlstedt, Sally; Sokal, Michael; and Lewenstein, Bruce, *The Establishment of Science in America: 150 Years of the American Association for the Advancement of Science*, Rutgers University Press, New Brunswick, NJ, 1999.

Kohlstedt, Sally, *The Formation of the American Scientific Community: the American Association for the Advancement of Science, 1848-60*, University of Illinois Press, Urbana, 1976.

Reingold, Nathan, editor, *The Sciences in the American Context: New Perspectives*, Smithsonian Institution Press, Washington, 1979.

American Philosophical Society

The American Philosophical Society (APS), America's first learned society, was founded in 1743 in Philadelphia, PA. Benjamin Franklin's influence and the technical needs of American colonies led the Society to pursue many interesting undertakings. Early members included doctors, lawyers, clergymen, merchants, and scientists. Famous Americans like Franklin, George Washington, John Adams, Thomas Jefferson, Alexander Hamilton, Benjamin Rush, James Madison, and John Marshall were members, along with many distinguished foreigners like Lafayette, von Steuben, and Thadeus Kosciusko. In the eighteenth century, natural philosophy was the study of nature, and therefore was scientific and technological. This was the type of science that the Society sought to pursue, although it was not until West Point was established some 60 years later that America's education system included natural philosophy as an applied science. The members of the APS were primarily interested in improving agriculture, manufacturing, and transportation and gaining understanding in the sciences of astronomy, geology, and climate. An introductory page in the first *Transactions of the American Philosophical Society* stated the Society's goals, "The Promoting of useful Knowledge in general, ... being the express purpose for which the American Philosophical Society was instituted; the publication of such curious and useful Papers as may, from time to time, be communicated to them, becomes of course, one material part of their design."

The Society withstood the tough times of the Revolutionary War and even grew stronger. In 1780, Pennsylvania granted the APS a charter and deeded to the Society a portion of

Independence Square, on which it erected Philosophical Hall in 1789. Philadelphia was the first capital of the United States, and it was fortunate that APS was collocated with the seat of government. Through the influence of the Society, the new nation linked education and freedom, each supporting the other. For many years, the Society fulfilled many of the functions of a national academy of science -- keeping a national technical library, scientific museum, and patent office. Members of the Society were involved in helping Lewis and Clark in the scientific, linguistic, and anthropological aspects of their *Corps of Discovery.* Over the years, the APS has spawned other learned societies and technical organizations.

In the latter half of the nineteenth century, the Society's primary interests were in paleontology, geology, astronomy, and American Indian studies. The membership included many notable scientists and citizens -- John J. Audubon, Robert Fulton, Charles Darwin, Thomas Edison, and Albert Einstein. The Society first elected a woman in 1789, and later Elizabeth Cady Agassiz, Marie Curie, and Margaret Mead became members. New interests and needs always provided fresh ideas for research, meeting topics, and publications. A research grant program began, where the APS funded scientific endeavors.

Election to the APS requires extraordinary accomplishments in a person's field. Over the years, membership reached as high as 900 members with over 200 members having received the Nobel Prize. The Society awards prizes and medals for special accomplishments by members. APS also has substantial journal publications. Starting in 1771, the *Transactions* became a monograph series. The quarterly journal, the *Proceedings* began in 1838 by including papers delivered at meetings of the Society. In 1935, the *Memoirs* began for larger studies. The APS Library is a center for research in the history of science and technology and houses over 300,000 volumes, seven million manuscripts, and thousands of maps and prints. It is located in Philosophical Hall, Philadelphia, where the Society still holds it meetings.

Many West Point graduates have been members of the APS, among this group are: **Henry Abott (USMA 1854), Alexander Dallas Bache (USMA 1825), Hartman Bache (USMA 1818), Jacob Bailey (USMA 1832), William H. C. Bartlett (USMA 1826), Edward Courtenay (USMA 1821), George Goethals (USMA 1880), Edward Holden (USMA 1870), Andrew A. Humphries (USMA 1831), Thomas Jefferson Lee (USMA 1830), Montgomery Meigs (USMA 1836), Ormsby McKnight Mitchel (USMA 1829), William Norton (USMA 1831), Andrew Talcott (USMA 1818), Sylvanus Thayer (USMA 1808), Joseph Totten (USMA 1805),** and **William Trowbridge (USMA 1848)**.

References:

American Philosophical Society, *The Early History of Science and Learning in America*, American Philosophical Society, Philadelphia, 1942.

Guralnick, Stanley, *Science and the American College, 1828-1860*, Ph.D. Dissertation, University of Pennsylvania, Philadelphia, 1975.

Guralnick, Stanley, *Science and the Ante-Bellum American College*, American Philosophical Society, Philadelphia, 1975.

Stapleton, Darwin, *The Transfer of Early Industrial Technologies to America*, American Philosophical Society, Philadelphia, 1987.

United States Military Philosophical Society

When President Thomas Jefferson appointed Jonathan Williams (see **Honorable Mentions**) the first Superintendent of USMA in 1802, Williams faced the considerable challenge of building quality programs in both military training and academic technical education. Williams possessed the credentials needed for the position. He was Benjamin Franklin's grandnephew and received his education in London under Franklin's direction. Williams also assisted Franklin in France after the American Revolutionary War. On their voyage back to America in 1785, Williams and Franklin had conducted studies of water temperatures and had located the Gulf Stream. With Franklin's help, Williams became an active member of the American Philosophical Society (APS) and published a book entitled *Thermometrical Navigation* (1799). Williams was always more of a scientist than a military officer, but in his role of Superintendent, the Army required him to be both. The mission of the Academy was to train officers while also educating scientific leaders. George Washington had advocated the military officership model, and Thomas Jefferson had envisioned the science and academic model. Right from the Academy's beginning, there was a tension between scholarly interests and military activities. The first faculty appointments were two of America's finest scholars Jared Mansfield and William A. Barron (see **Honorable Mentions**). The rest of the staff members were military officers who knew training and discipline. Williams' job was to meld the two groups into an effective staff to develop leaders for both America's Army and a corps of engineers and scientists in order to build the infrastructure of the country.

It was a difficult time to start a technical school in America. There were few scientists available for the faculty, and potential students had a poor preparation for high-level science, learning, for the most part, arithmetic in their schooling. During its first decade, the Academy had no standards for admission, no specified academic program, and no standards for graduation. Cadets could enter the Academy at any time and be ordered to other military duties when needed. Whenever the faculty thought a cadet was ready, he graduated and entered commissioned service with Army duties. However, the graduate was not required to serve in the Army, and many were enticed into civilian business or academic duties instead.

To help set a more academic climate at the Academy, Williams organized the United States Military Philosophical Society (USMPS) in 1802. He recruited President Thomas Jefferson as a perpetual patron, and the USMPS elected a *Keeper of the Cabinet* to run the Society's library. All cadets and faculty were members of the USMPS. As the Academy struggled in the early years, the USMPS prospered and by 1807, the Society was a center of scientific activity, especially in areas related to military science (fortifications, ordnance, ballistics). Meetings occurred regularly, and papers were read and studied. The USMPS was off to a fine start, following in the footsteps of the APS, which Benjamin Franklin had established in 1743.

In Williams' view many areas of military science were based on mathematics, mechanics, and science. He saw these underpinnings of military science as the need for West Point to be a technology and engineering school. In reality, Williams' vision was different from both Washington's and Jefferson's. Williams recruited DeWitt Clinton, James Madison, Robert Fulton, Eli Whitney, and other prominent men for membership in the USMPS. The USMPS was designed both to support the study of science and to help promote the Academy. Even though Williams was often absent from West Point to fulfill duties as the Army's chief engineer, he made sure the USMPS kept to its schedule and tried not to miss its meetings. Meetings were mostly held at West Point, but some were held in City Hall in New York City and the War Department in Washington, DC. The USMPS had succeeded while the Academy had struggled. Williams worked to build the Academy's facilities, academic program, and the faculty quality. He fought for more resources from the War Department to enrich and expand the Academy. He set higher standards to obtain a better academic stature. One of his proposals, which he shared with many national leaders, was to move the Academy to Washington, DC and make it into a national university of science and engineering. In 1810, he complained that the Academy was suffering from lack of support from the Army and Congress. In addition, the Secretary of War decided that USMA graduates would not get commissions but rather they would become privates in the Army. Most of the cadets resigned, and in March 1812, the Academy had no faculty. Fortunately, Congress interceded with the "Act Making Further Provision for the Corps of Engineers," which adopted many of William's suggestions, except for the move of the Academy to Washington. The faculty was strengthened and expanded to three full professors: natural and experimental philosophy, mathematics, and the art of engineering; along with appropriate assistants. Money for buildings was also appropriated. However, Williams never saw the fruits of this labor as the War of 1812 intervened. In July, Williams resigned and the USMPS disbanded in November 1813.

Joseph G. Swift (USMA 1802), the Academy's first graduate, succeeded Williams as Superintendent. However, Swift had little vision for the Academy nor much of a basis to build upon. Swift was preoccupied with the war and its aftermath. He spent most of his time in Washington. Fortunately, conscientious faculty kept the Academy on course. Andrew Ellicott (see **Honorable Mentions**) was appointed Professor of Mathematics, and Jared Mansfield (see **Honorable Mentions**) was Professor of Natural and Experimental Philosophy. The acting Superintendent during Swift's absences was Engineering Professor **Alden Partridge (USMA 1806)**. The Academy's academic building, which contained all of the classrooms and the library, was completed in 1815. Despite this progress, the strong personalities of the faculty members and Partridge's view of military education made it a contentious time at the Academy. In 1815, Swift had the idea to send **Sylvanus Thayer (USMA 1808)** and William McRee (USMA 1805) to Europe to examine the military and technical schools in France and England and to collect books, maps, and instruments. Upon their return and Thayer becoming the Superintendent, there would no longer be a need for an external organization like the USMPS to provide the Academy's scholarly example. The superb military and technological school in France, the École polytechnique, would set Thayer's vision and provide the inspiration for quality technical scholarship and teaching.

In 1829, several Academy leaders, along with scientists in the New York area and science professors from Union College, established the American Association for the Promotion of Science, Literature, and the Arts. While there was progress in building membership, this organization only lasted three years.

References:

Albree, J., Arney, D. C., Rickey, V. F., *A Station Favorable to the Pursuits of Science*, American Mathematical Society, Providence, 2000.

Ambrose, Stephen, *Duty, Honor, Country: A History of West Point,* John Hopkins Press, Baltimore, 1966.

Kohlstedt, Sally, *The Formation of the American Scientific Community: the American Association for the Advancement of Science, 1848-60*, University of Illinois Press, Urbana, 1976.

Molloy Peter M., *Technical Education and the Young Republic: West Point as America's Ecole Polytecnique, 1802-1833*, Ph.D. Dissertation, Brown University, Providence, 1975.

Ross, William L, "The United States Military Academy: The Inception, Establishment, and First Thirty Years," 25 April, 1990, Purdue University EDFA 603.

Zuersher, Dorothy, *Benjamin Franklin, Jonathan Williams, and the United States Military Academy*, Ed.D. Dissertation, University of North Carolina at Greensboro, Greensboro, 1974.

Appendix: Tables of Statistics for *THE 200*

Disciplines of *THE 200*

Mathematicians	48
Scientists	45
Engineers	89
Technologists	18

Eras of *The 200* (Graduation dates by quarter century)

1802-1826	32
1827-1851	59
1852-1876	44
1877-1901	14
1902-1926	25
1927-1951	20
1952-1976	6

Combat Service of *THE 200**

War of 1812	7
Indian Wars (Seminole and others)	17
Mexican War	26
Civil War	74
Spanish-American War	9
Philippine War	2
World War I	22
World War II	26
Korean War	5
Vietnam War	4

* Author judged whether service was combat related.

Class Rank of *The 200**

Top Cadet	28
Second Cadet	21
3rd- Top 10%	45
10-20%	34
Bottom 80%	60
No class rank	12

* No class rank was calculated or relevant for the graduating classes before 1818 and for William Swift (USMA 1819).

Organizational Service of *The 200**

Corps of Engineers	103
Corps of Topographical Engineers	19
Ordnance Corps	17
Coast Survey	11
USMA Faculty	106
Other Colleges/University Faculty	70
Railroad Companies	32

* Based on available information. May not be complete.

Honors of *The 200**

Medal of Honor	9
National Academy of Sciences	17
American Philosophical Society	17
American Association for the Advancement of Science	23
General Officer	106#

* Based on available information. May not be complete.

Many of the ranks were brevet promotions earned in wartime and not kept after the war and promotions made at the time of retirement.

References

While bibliographic references appear directly in the essays and in the biographies, the following bibliographic list contains general references and further reading on the subjects related to the history of West Point science.

Albree, Joe; Arney, David; and Rickey, Frederick, *A Station Favorable to the Pursuits of Science: Primary Material in the History of Mathematics at the United States Military Academy*, American Mathematical Society, Providence, 2000.

Ambrose, Stephen, *Duty, Honor, Country; a History of West Point*, Johns Hopkins Press, Baltimore, 1966.

(ANB) American National Biography, John A. Garraty and Mark C. Carnes, editors, 24 vols, Oxford University Press, New York, 1999.

Annual Report of the Association of Graduates of the United States Military Academy, Seamon and Peters, Saginaw, MI, 1917-1941.

Annual Report of the Board of Visitors of the USMA made to the Secretary of War, Government Printing Office, Washington, 1871-1990.

Annual Report of the Superintendent of the United States Military Academy, Government Printing Office, Washington, DC, 1896.

Annual Reunion, Association of Graduates of the United States Military Academy, West Point, 1870-1941.

(ACAB) Appleton's Cyclopaedia of American Biography, James Grant Wilson and John Fiske, editors, D. Appleton and Company, New York, 1888.

Baumer, William Henry, Jr., *Not All Warriors; Portraits of 19th Century West Pointers Who Gained Fame in Other than Military Fields*, Ayer Co. Publications, New York, 1977.

Boynton, Edward C., *History of West Point, and its Military Importance During the American Revolution: and the Origin and Progress of the United States Military Academy,* Books for Libraries Press, Freeport, NY, 1863.

Bruce, Robert, "A Statistical Profile of American Scientists," *Nineteenth Century American Science: A Reappraisal*, Northeastern University Press, Evansville, 1972.

Bruce, Robert, *The Launching of Modern American Science, 1846-1876,* Alfred A. Knopf, New York, 1987.

Cajori, F., *The Teaching and History of Mathematics in the United States*, Government Printing Office, Washington, 1890.

Centennial of the United States Military Academy at West Point, New York, 2 vols. Government Printing Office, Washington, 1904.

Crane, John and Kieley, James, *West Point: The Key to America*, Whittlesey House, McGraw-Hill, New York, 1947.

Cremin, Lawrence A., *American Education: The National Experience, 1783-1876*, Harper & Row, New York, 1980.

Cullum, George, *The Official Register of the Officers & Cadets of the US Military Academy*, West Point, 1841-1870, 1911-1915.

Daniels, George, *American Science in the Age of Jackson,* Columbia University Press, New York, 1968.

Daniels, George, *Science in American Society: A Social History,* Alfred A. Knopf, New York, 1971.

Daniels, George, *Nineteenth--Century American Science: A Reappraisal,* Northwestern University Press, Evanston, IL, 1972.

(DAB) Dictionary of American Biography, Under the auspices of the American Council of Learned Societies, 28 vols, including Supplements, C. Scribner's Sons, New York, 1928-1990.

Dossey, John, editor, *Confronting the Core Curriculum*, Mathematical Association of America, Washington, 1998.

Dupuy, Ernest, *Where They have Trod; the West Point Tradition in American Life,* Frederick Stokes Company, New York, 1940.

Dupuy, Ernest, *The Story of West Point: 1802-1943; the West Point Tradition in American Life,* The Infantry Journal, Washington, 1943.

Dupuy, Ernest, *Men of West Point; the First 150 Years of the United States Military Academy*, Sloane, New York, 1951.

Dupuy, Ernest, *Sylvanus Thayer, Father of Technology in the United States,* The Association of Graduates, United States Military Academy, West Point, 1958.

Dupuy, Trevor, Johnson, Curt, and Bongard, David, *The Harper Encyclopedia of Military Biography*, Harper Collins Publishers, New York, 1992.

(BDAS) Elliott, Clark, *Biographical Dictionary of American Science: The Seventeenth Through the Nineteenth Centuries*, Greenwood Press, Westport, CT, 1979.

Elliott, Clark, *The American Scientist, 1800-1863, his Origin, Career, and Interests*, Ph.D. Dissertation, Case Western Reserve, Cleveland, 1970.

Endler, James, *Other Leaders, Other Heroes*, Prager, Westport, CT, 1998.

Ford, Norman Robert, *Thayer of West Point*, Thayer Book Press, St. Johnsbury, VT, 1953.

Forman, Sidney, *West Point; a History of the United States Military Academy*, Columbia University Press, New York, 1950.

(DSB) Gillespie, Charles Coulston, editor, *Dictionary of Scientific Biography*, 15 vols., plus Supplements. Charles Scribner's Sons, New York, 1972-1980.

Guralnick, Stanley, *Science and the Ante-Bellum American College*, The American Philosophical Society, Philadelphia, 1975.

Hemphill, John and Cumbow, Robert , editors, *West Pointers and Early Washington: The Contributions of U.S. Military Academy Graduates to the Development of the Washington Territory, from the Oregon Trail to the Civil War, 1834-1862,* West Point Society of Puget Sound, Seattle, 1992.

Hoskins, Keith, "Textbooks and the mathematisation of American reality: the role of Charles Davies and the US Military Academy at West Point," *Paradigm*, May 1994 (11-41).

Hutton, Paul Andrews, editor, *Soldier's West: Biographies from the Military Frontier,* University of Nebraska Press, Lincoln, 1987.

Kohlstedt, Sally, *The Formation of the American Scientific Community: the American Association for the Advancement of Science, 1848-60,* University of Illinois Press, Urbana, 1976.

Mathematics at West Point and Annapolis, U. S. Bureau of Education Bulletin, Government Printing Office, Washington, 1912.

McMaster, Richard K., "West Point's Contributions to Education, 1802-1952," McMath Printing Co, El Paso, 1951.

Molloy, P., *Technical Education and the Young Republic: West Point as America's Ecole Polytechnique, 1802-1833,* Ph.D. Dissertation, Brown University, 1976.

Morrison, James L., *The Best School in the World; West Point, the Pre-Civil War Years, 1833-1866,* Kent State University Press, Kent, OH, 1986.

Murray, James and Swantek, John, *1813-1997, The Watervliet Arsenal: A Chronology of the Nation's Oldest Arsenal,* Watervliet Arsenal Public Affairs Office, Watervliet, NY, 1997.

(NCAB) National Cyclopedia of American Biography, James T. White and Company, 1892-1987.

Official Register of the Officers and Cadets of the United States Military Academy, 1818-1899, United States Military Academy Printing Office, West Point, 1818-1899.

Reeder, Red, *Heroes and Leaders of West Point,* Thomas Nelson, New York, 1970.

Register of Graduates, Association of Graduates, United States Military Academy, West Point, 2000.

Rickey, Frederick, website on History of Mathematics Department, USMA: http://www.dean.usma.edu/math/people/rickey/dms/Math-Teachers.html

Sesquicentennial of the United States Military Academy, Government Printing Office, West Point, 1952.

Simmons, John, *The Scientific 100,* Citadel Press, New York, 1996.

Simons, William E., *Liberal Education in the Service Academies.* Published for the Institute of Higher Education, Teachers College, Columbia University, New York, 1965.

Skelton, William B., *An American Profession of Arms: The Army Officer Corps, 1784-1861,* University Press of Kansas, Lawrence, 2001.

Smith, David Eugene and Ginsburg, Jekuthiel, *History of Mathematics in America Before 1900,* The Carus Mathematical Monographs, No. 5, The Mathematical Association of America and Open Court Publishing Co., Chicago, 1934.

Smith, Francis H., "West Point Fifty Years Ago," An address delivered before the Association of Graduates of the U.S. Military Academy, West Point, at the annual reunion, June 12, 1879, D. Van Nostrand, New York, 1879.

Spiller, Roger J., *Dictionary of American Military Biography,* 3 vols. Greenwood Press, Westport, CT, 1984.

(DNB) Stephen, Leslie and Lee, Sidney (Editors), *Dictionary of National Biography*, 22 volumes with Supplements. Smith, Elder, London, 1885.

Streett, William B., "The Military Influence on American Engineering Education," Cornell Engineering Quarterly, Winter, pp. 3-10. 1993

Thrapp, Dan L., *Encyclopedia of Frontier Biography*, 4 vols. Arthur H. Clark Co., Glendale, 1988-1994; University of Nebraska Press, Lincoln, 1995.

Traas, Adrian G., *From Golden Gate to Mexico City: The U.S. Army Topographical Engineers in the Mexican War, 1846-1848*, Office of History, Corps of Engineers, Washington, 1993.

Woodworth, Steven E., *Grant's Lieutenants, volume I: From Cairo to Vicksburg*. University Press of Kansas, Lawrence, 2001.

Who Was Who in America, Marquis Company, Chicago, 1963.

Zuersher, Dorothy, *Benjamin Franklin, Jonathan Williams and the United States Military Academy*, Ed.D. Dissertation, University of North Carolina at Greensboro, Greensboro, 1974.

Index

(names of people in *The 200* are listed in boldface type)

Toftoy, Holger, 206
Topographic Engineers, 16, 24, 28, 46, 50, 52, 56, 62, 66, 70, 256
torpedoes, 42, 67, 106, 141
Totten, Joseph, 10, 45, 268
Tower, Zealous, 98
Tredegar Iron Works, 88-89
Trinity College, 8
Trowbridge William, 24, 268
tunnels, 50, 87, 141, 144
Turnbull, William, 54

Union College, 97, 116, 159
United States Air Force Academy, 224, 225
United States Military Philosophical Society, 26, 232, 278
United States Naval Academy, 64, 86, 90, 91
University of Alabama, 100
University of California (Berkley), 23, 146, 182, 214
University of California (Los Angeles), 223
University of Delaware, 39
University of Göttingen, 182, 235
University of Louisiana, 102
University of Michigan, 186, 216, 225, 226
University of Mississippi, 74, 102, 106, 107, 115, 186
University of New Hampshire, 188
University of New York (NYU), 71, 222
University of Pennsylvania, 2, 10, 75, 89, 204
University of Rochester, 110, 181
University of South Carolina, 129, 134
University of the South, 100, 114, 176
University of Virginia, 10, 74, 219. 220, 225

Vietnam War, 216-219, 223, 227, 229
Virginia Military Institute, 62, 83, 125
Virginia Polytechnic Institute, 122, 123

War Department, 70, 90, 138, 150
War of 1812, 4, 8, 43-49

Warren, Gouverneur, 120, 142
Washington and Lee University, 69, 108, 125
Washington Monument, 121, 143
Washington University at St. Louis, 21, 159
Watertown Arsenal, 49, 101, 260, 261
Watervliet Arsenal, 44, 58, 92, 100, 118, 119, 122, 126, 138, 260
Webb, Alexander, 128
Webster, Horace, 51, 58, 128
West Point Foundry, 44, 61, 119, 138
West Point Library, viii, xxi, 22, 249, 242
West Point Observatory, 24, 37, 243
Weyher, Theodore, 207
Wheeler, Junius, 127
Wheeler, Raymond, 190
Whistler, George W., 54, 56, 231, 254, 266
Whistler, James McNeill, 120, 231, 266
White, Edward H., 226
Whittlesey, Charles, 79
Wilhoyt, Ellis, 213
Willet's Point, 17, 25, 42, 116, 141, 143, 162, 163, 166, 168, 169, 175
William and Mary College, 64, 80, 225, 234
Williams, Jonathan, 232, 279
Williams, William G., 62
Williams, William H., 181
Wilson, John, 135
Wilson, Roscoe, 40-41, 190
Wisser, John, 160
World War I, 13, 165–198
World War II, 182, 186, 189-195, 197-218, 223
WPA, 183, 198
Wright, Orville, 185, 189
Wright, Horatio G., 99

Yale University, 25, 40, 92, 208, 233, 234
Yates, Robert, 233
Yellowstone Park, 28, 137, 172

zoology, 34